Checkbook's 2020 Guide to Health Plans for Federal Employees

41st Edition

By Walton Francis and the Editors of Consumers' Checkbook

For more copies of this book:
Checkbook–Health Insurance Guide
1625 K Street, NW, 8th Floor, Washington, DC 20006
202-347-7283
Send $15.95 per copy (price includes shipping)
Make checks payable to "Checkbook"

This book is a special publication of the Center for the Study of Services, which publishes Washington Consumers' Checkbook magazine and Checkbook.org. The Center is a nonprofit organization dedicated to giving consumers the information they need to find high quality, reasonably priced services. We cannot promise that the health plan you choose using this book will be satisfactory to you. However, we believe that our advice is sound. Employees may want to encourage their agencies to purchase copies in bulk for broad distribution, as many agencies have done with previous editions of the Guide.

 ISBN 1-888-124-33-4

Contents

Chapter 1

Introduction, Basics, and Changes for 2020

What the Guide Does

Checkbook's Guide to Health Plans for Federal Employees gives you vital shopping information that you cannot get from any other source. It tells you how much money you can save by changing—or by staying in—your health insurance plan. It summarizes thousands of facts about the plans to simplify your choice. The *Guide* comes in both print and Internet versions. They are almost identical but the print version is more convenient for many, and the online version allows more depth and details. The online version is particularly useful for Federal agencies that subscribe for all their employees, giving the employees invaluable money-saving advice while saving the agencies money as well, since they pay most of the premium cost. We show employees how to save thousands of dollars in unnecessary costs. Federal agencies also save, over a thousand dollars on average, for every employee who switches to a lower-cost plan using our advice. In both versions:

- Our ratings cover **all** of about 280 health insurance plans available to Federal employees and retirees, including about 20 national plans, and about 260 health maintenance organizations (HMOs) and other local options, including two dozen Consumer-Driven and High Deductible plan options. Wherever you live, we rate all the plans in **your community**.
- Our **ratings** of plan costs take into account premiums, catastrophic limits, and estimates of likely out-of-pocket costs for medical expenses of every kind.
- We compare plans for **insurance value** in dealing with unforeseen medical expenses, not just for the routine costs you can predict.
- We **compare** limits on out-of-pocket costs based on the actual coverage allowed by each plan, not just what the plan seems to say before you read the fine print.
- We rate plans for **each coverage group**—employees in different pay systems, annuitants with or without Medicare, former spouses, families of various sizes, children at age 26, part-time employees, and former employees.
- We rate plans according to how well each covers **low, average, or high medical expenses**, analyzing coverage of all major types of cost.
- We adjust our estimates for the **tax advantages** that reduce the after-tax premium cost to most employees (but not retirees) by about one third.
- We provide information on **coinsurance, copays and other cost sharing**, so you can quickly determine whether a plan pays well for a benefit you need.
- We provide **accurate estimates of potential exposure to catastrophic expense** by adjusting plans' claimed limits on out-of-pocket expenses so they don't omit important categories of cost.
- We give you data on **coverage features** of each plan, including skilled nursing, dental, and hearing aid coverage.
- We address **plan quality**, and provide data on **enrollee satisfaction** with each plan's service. We provide in-depth results from an annual survey in which plan members rate their plans on ease of getting needed care, customer service, claims processing, and other factors.

- We **rate dental and vision** plans as well. We provide dollar estimates of likely dental costs, taking into account both premiums and out-of-pocket expense. We compare dental coverage in all plans, not just standalone plans.
- We provide up-to-date information on changes in the FEHB program, including the **effects of health reform**, of **Medicare premium changes**, and of the **Self plus One option**.
- We provide detailed **consumer advice** on which plan options work best in different situations, on plan advantages you may not have thought about, and on mistakes to avoid.

As a result, the *Guide* gives you a solid basis for selecting the best health or dental plan for you and your family. Hundreds of thousands of employees and annuitants have followed our advice over the years, and many of them have saved thousands of dollars a year by finding better coverage for lower premiums. **There is no other source of plan comparisons or Open Season advice that provides even half of these features.**

The Setting

Every Federal employee and annuitant can choose from twenty plans or more. Choices include well-known national plans, such as three Blue Cross/Blue Shield options; local plans available in many areas, such as the Aetna, Humana, UnitedHealthcare and Kaiser plans; and plans sponsored by unions and employee associations, such as the American Postal Workers Union (APWU) and the Government Employees Health Association (GEHA). You are free to join most union and association plans, regardless of your employing agency and whether you are an employee or annuitant. At most you must pay annual dues, which are generally near $30. However, a few plans restrict enrollment. For example, two plans are open only to those involved in foreign affairs, intelligence, or defense—a pool, however, that is very large and covers many agencies.

You can switch plans for the coming year during the annual Open Season, scheduled from November 11 through December 9, 2019. You are also free to switch among plans at certain other times—for instance, if you marry. You are allowed to switch from plan to plan regardless of preexisting conditions, even if you are in the hospital when the new plan enrollment year begins.

Hundreds of thousands of employees and annuitants are still enrolled in plans that are much more expensive than average, and that give them no needed extra benefits. In Open Season almost all of these persons will be able to reduce premium costs greatly while maintaining or even improving benefits.

> ***Getting "Free" Health Insurance***
>
> Some Consumer-Driven and High Deductible plans provide you a savings account larger than your actual premium cost after taxes. You can end the year with more money than you started if your medical costs are low.

As always, this year's *Guide* reflects changes as plan options have been added or dropped, benefits modified, and premiums gone up in some plans and down in others. For newly hired employees, and those who can change plans after Open Season, the information in the *Guide* applies throughout the year.

The Savings

Whether your family's circumstances are "average" or unusual, some HMOs, some national plans such as Blue Cross Basic and GEHA Standard option, and a number of High-Deductible plans offer big savings compared to other plans. To help decide which is best, we estimate likely, and not so likely, costs to you under each plan, and compare coverage features of the plans and several aspects of customer service. In addition to dollar costs, customer service is an important element of plan choice, particularly for HMOs. We present customer survey data on plan satisfaction, data on which plans are least likely to have claims disputes, and data on accreditation.

Our tables rate each plan on total expenses—including premium and out-of-pocket costs. The tables show what each plan will cost you in an "average" year and in years when your medical costs are much higher or lower than average. As our tables show, **likely savings available to most employees and annuitants range from hundreds to thousands of dollars a year.**

You should not pick a plan on the basis of its premium, benefit coverage, or catastrophic expense guarantee alone. We help you avoid these traps by including all of these complex factors in our ratings.

The information we give you is especially important if you expect a major change in your medical or financial situation. If you plan to have a baby next year, or face heavy dental bills, the plan that was best for you last year may not be best this year. Also, if you will retire, divorce, leave Federal employment, or join Medicare, you should review your choices very carefully.

Even if your plan satisfies you, why not consider switching to another? Those who switch in Open Season save hundreds of millions of dollars every year for themselves and their employing agencies, through migration to lower-cost plans that offer better value. You, too, can share in these savings.

> ***Protect Your Retirement***
>
> It is not expensive to enroll in the FEHBP for the five years before retirement. Several plans have annual self only premiums below $1,500. These plans cost under $1,000 after tax savings. Some plans give you savings accounts higher than the tax advantaged premium cost.

Consider the following examples. If you are a single employee in the Washington, DC area, our estimates show that you are likely to save well over $1,000 next year by joining the Kaiser HMO Standard Option instead of the Blue Cross Standard Option, the most popular plan. If you are unwilling to make such a drastic departure from fee-for-service medicine, you can save almost $1,000 by enrolling in the Blue Cross Basic plan rather than the Standard Option. We rate a half dozen Consumer-Driven (CD) and High Deductible (HD) options as equal to or better than even Blue Cross Basic for most enrollees. All of these estimates include your premium cost, your savings from tax preferences, and your likelihood of a range of expenses up to and including a catastrophically expensive illness.

Perhaps you are a retired couple with Medicare parts A and B. The great majority of such retirees select the Blue Cross Standard option. But we rate the MBHP High Deductible plan, the Aetna Direct plan, the new FEP Blue Focus option, the Blue Cross Basic option, the CareFirst High Deductible plan, and the new Aetna Advantage plan as likely to save you $4,000 or even more. Why? Most of these plans, like Blue Cross Standard Option, allow you to pay nothing for hospital and physician charges when you have Medicare parts A and B. In some of them their prescription drug coverage is not quite as good, but their premiums are far lower. So, you start the year with major savings in hand. The Consumer-Driven plans have "Personal Care Accounts" that you can spend on dental costs and drugs that Medicare doesn't cover to offset the cost of the Medicare premium, and Blue Cross Basic now offers a similar arrangement through a premium rebate. Our ratings even show that enrolling in Part B and several of these plans will reduce your overall costs. In the Consumer-Driven plans, and most High Deductible plans, you have the potential for even larger savings in future years if you build up your account. Our comparisons show that even the most popular plans may not be the best buys.

Using the Guide

We prepared the *Guide* because we know that choosing the right plan can be difficult, even if you have time to read hundreds of pages in plan brochures. The coverage details are hard to understand, and trying to compare multiple benefit details simultaneously is very difficult. As a result, it is often hard to determine which plan is best for you. Many employees depend on advice from their friends, or stick with a "name brand" or the plan sponsored by their own union. However, that choice can waste hundreds or thousands of dollars.

The Office of Personnel Management (OPM), which administers the program, sets standards for plan benefits and for information in plan brochures, and also presents summary plan comparison information on its Web site. The complexity of comparing plans is substantial. We have studied and restudied each plan and have checked many details with plan officials. But we have undoubtedly missed a few limitations or special coverages. So, before making a final choice, you should compare the brochures of several plans.

We structure the *Guide*'s advice and information as follows:

- You are reading the "Introduction, Basics, and Changes for 2020."
- "Comparing Plan Costs" explains how and why some choices can save so much money.
- "Cost Comparisons and Advice" for Employees and Former Employees explains and provides our cost ratings for each plan, organized separately by eligibility group.
- "Cost Comparisons and Advice" for Annuitants provides cost ratings that take into account higher costs for the elderly, and the effects of enrolling in Medicare Part A or Parts A and B.
- "Cost Sharing" provides basic information on plan benefits for hospital, medical, and prescription drug expenses.
- "Coverage Features" addresses features such as skilled nursing and mental health coverage.
- "Dental, Vision, and Hearing" compares standalone plans with each other and with the dental, vision, and hearing aid coverage in the health insurance plans.
- "Plan Types and Flexibility" explains the various types of plans and how they affect your ability to use the provider of your choice and to achieve additional savings.
- "Quality and Service" describes several measures of quality of plan service, and presents quality ratings for all plans.
- "Premiums and Taxes" explains how premiums and out of pocket spending can be tax advantaged and how much employees can save.
- "Key Tips and Final Plan Selection" reminds you of factors vital to you and gives advice on making a final decision among plans.
- "Our Methods and Data Sources" explains the information we use to create our ratings.

Be Sure to Elect a Survivor Annuity for Your Spouse

If you die and your spouse receives no Federal pension, your spouse will lose FEHBP coverage forever. If you die while enrolled as self-only, your spouse will also lose coverage.

We rate health plans by their likely cost to you, taking into account your pay system, employment or retirement status, family size, age, health status, location, and other factors. For example, we present information on premium cost to employees using the "premium conversion" tax-advantaged basis available to employees, but not retirees. Online *Guide* users reach the table applicable to them by answering questions regarding family size, age, retirement status, health status, zip code, pay system, and several other factors. They see a summary ratings table for their area and then have the option to choose whether to look at tables providing detailed cost comparisons, cost sharing, coverage features, plan flexibility, or plan quality for plans in their area. Readers of the print *Guide* turn to applicable cost comparison and other tables within each of the book chapters. Information on the cost, coverage, and features for local plans in all States is available online simply by entering your zip code, and in the print *Guide* provided in summary in a table at the end of the "Key Tips and Final Plan Selection" chapter.

The information contained in our print and online versions is almost identical. Both versions allow users to compare plans based on their pay system, age, family size, and health status. Many people prefer to use paper copies. However, the online *Guide* makes the customization, selection, and presentation of comparative information exceptionally fast and convenient, and you can print out plan comparisons customized to your needs. In the Washington, D.C. area, you can use the online version to see which plan networks include your doctors. Not everyone uses the Internet, so we publish both versions and let individual purchasers decide which they want. In addition, many Federal Departments and agencies provide free access to the online version for all their employees. You can check to see if your agency provides free access, at our Web site at *www.guidetohealthplans.org.*

General FEHB Program Procedures

The Federal Employees Health Benefits (FEHB) program is an unconventional government program. Instead of giving you one "take it or leave it" choice, the government authorizes plans to compete for your premium dollar. It pays most of the premium cost—up to 75 percent for annuitants and most employees—and even more for Postal employees and employees of some other agencies, such as the FDIC and SEC. Taking into account tax advantages, the government pays between 80 and 90 percent of premium costs for most plans for employees (but not retirees). Nationally, about 280 plan options are offered, with almost all employees and retirees eligible to join 20 or more. You decide which plan you want to join. If you are not satisfied, you can switch in the next Open Season.

The FEHB program enrolls about 8 million persons. Enrollees spend over $50 billion a year through their health plans. About five percent of enrollees switch among plans in most Open Seasons. Until the Medicare Advantage program, which was modeled on the FEHB program, it was the largest "managed competition" system for harnessing consumer choices to contain health insurance costs. Studies have shown that it outperforms both Original Medicare and private employer plans in coverage, cost control, and consumer satisfaction.

OPM sets minimum financial, administrative, and benefit terms and conditions for every plan participating in the program. Insurance companies and OPM agree each year on contracts setting forth both benefits and costs. A few key points about FEHB plans are:

- All employees and annuitants can enroll in whatever plan they choose, or not enroll at all.
- Everyone can change plans once per year in Open Season. You also may switch plans or options in circumstances such as marriage, birth of a child, or geographic transfer. If you belong to an HMO and move out of its service area, you may enroll in a new plan.
- A family or self plus one enrollment covers only immediate family members: your spouse and children. Coverage for children now lasts until they reach age 26, unless they are severely handicapped. In that case they may be eligible at any age.
- **Plans cannot exclude coverage for any preexisting conditions or illnesses your family may have when you switch plans.** You may switch to gain the best coverage for your condition, and use the new plan without penalty.
- Plans must publish brochures in a common format that provides a clear explanation of their benefits and your cost for covered services, how you access plan services, how you get approvals, and your rights in disputes.
- Each plan must pay for the medical and related costs as explained in its brochure—no more and no less. If a brochure says that a particular category of service is limited or excluded, believe it.
- Plan brochures may word the same benefits differently. Sometimes the wording used is not clear to a layperson. However, **you can often figure out what specific benefit language really means by comparing two or three brochures to see how they differ.**

Check Your Brochure!

Do not stay in the same plan without reading at least "How We Change" for next year or join a new plan without checking any benefits of particular importance to your health care.

Getting Information

Our website at *www.guidetohealthplans.org* includes a great deal of useful information including not only uniquely informative plan comparisons, but a great deal of advice including Questions and Answers addressing more than one hundred problems. OPM has a website with plan brochures and a great deal of other useful information at *www.opm.gov/insure*. You can access this site at most libraries if you do not use the Internet in your home or office. Unlike many government websites, OPM's are user friendly and easy to navigate. You can also visit plan websites directly. This is especially useful if you want to check how a particular plan covers your medicines.

You change plans by filling out OPM's form SF 2809 or an online equivalent. Personnel offices have copies and will give you form SF 2809 if you decide to change your enrollment. In many agencies, an online service such as "Employee Express" can be used to change plans. Annuitants are mailed only abbreviated information and should use the Internet to get more details. A special OPM procedure provides an easy way for annuitants to order paper copies of plan brochures.

If you have a problem getting information from these normal channels, you can call OPM for help. There is an automated phone system, called "Open Season Express" at 800-332-9798 to help annuitants get brochures, change plans, or get other help. In addition, the retirement information office number is 1-888-767-6738. This office can answer many questions, and help you with enrolling in a Medicare-participating HMO. We caution, however, that these numbers are often overburdened with calls—don't wait until the last minute.

Of course, Checkbook provides information on contacting each plan directly, including its telephone number and website, along with information on enrollment limitations. On our website you can download plan brochures and access the provider list and drug formulary for each plan. You can also purchase online access to the *Guide*, and obtain other consumer information, including national ratings of hospitals and doctors in *Consumers' Guide to Hospitals* and *Consumers' Guide to Top Doctors*, as well as online articles rating physicians, dentists, and other health care providers for quality and price.

Enrollment Limitations

Many plans are open to all employees. However, HMOs require that you live in their service area, and a few plans require that you work for a particular agency or join a specific union. Most of the union plans allow any Federal employee to join. This generally means that you can enroll in the plan no matter what agency you work for, but you may have to pay a small amount for annual dues and become an "associate" member of the union. Some plans are restricted to particular agencies or categories of employees. For example, the Foreign Service and Compass Rose plans enroll employees who serve in foreign affairs, defense, or intelligence functions (both plans interpret these limitations broadly, but they differ in details as explained in their brochures).

Use and Trust Plan Brochures

You can download PDF copies of plan brochures at the Checkbook, OPM, and plan websites, and either use them online or print copies. Plan brochures are necessary to determine what benefits each plan covers, or does not cover. In some cases, a plan does not mention a service at all in its brochure, but has assured us that its claims manual (which is not available to employees) says the service is covered. You cannot fully rely on this, however, since OPM has stated that the brochure "is the only official description of the benefits provided by each plan. Do not rely on statements not contained in the brochure. Study the brochures carefully." We agree, and endorse OPM efforts to assure that brochures are consistently and clearly written. Indeed, compared to most public and private insurance, the FEHB brochures are models of clarity. They are particularly well organized to facilitate comparisons of particular topics, such as surgery or maternity.

Unfortunately, health plan brochures have mushroomed in length. In 1990 the average national plan had a brochure 29 pages in length; by ten years later the average grew to 77 pages. For local plans, brochures grew over the same period from 16 to 65 pages, on average. Some of the increase represents increased clarity through "plain English," some is due to increased complexity in plan benefits, and some is due to unnecessary detail. Nonetheless, downloading brochures is easily accomplished, and vital to final plan selection. Once you have an electronic version, you can easily use "find" to search the brochure for any topic of concern to you.

Why Premiums Differ

The General Schedule (GS) employee and retiree share of the annual premium varies widely among plans. In national plans it ranges from about $1,200 to almost $5,000 for individuals, and from about $2,700 to over $10,000 for self plus one or larger families. What explains these vast premium differences?

Contacting National and D.C. Area Plans

Plan code(s)	Plan name	Plan phone	Website	Enrollment limitations
22, F5, N6, Z2	Aetna HealthFund/Advantage	888-238-6240	aetnafeds.com	None
JN, QQ	Aetna Open Access & Saver	800-537-9384	aetnafeds.com	None
47	APWU	800-222-2798	apwuhp.com	Pay dues
42	Compass Rose	888-438-9135	compassrosebenefits.com	Intel/Foreign Aff/DOD
10, 11, 13	Blue Cross	800-411-2583	fepblue.org	None
2G, B6	Carefirst	888-789-9065	carefirst.com/fedhmo	None
40	Foreign Service	202-833-4910	afspa.org/fsbp	Intel/Foreign Aff/DOD
25, 31, 34	GEHA	800-821-6136	geha.com	None
E3	Kaiser Mid-Atlantic	877-574-3337	kp.org/feds	None
JP	MD-IPA	877-835-9861	uhcfeds.com	None
41, 45	MHBP	800-410-7778	mhbp.com	Pay dues
48	MHBP HDHP	800-694-9901	mhbp.com	Pay dues
32, KM	NALC	888-636-6252	nalchbp.org	Pay dues
38	Rural Carrier	800-638-8432	rcbphealth.com	Rural carrier
44	SAMBA	800-638-6589	sambaplans.com	None
AS, L9, LR, V4, Y8	United	877-835-9861	uhcfeds.com	None

* The DC area number for Blue Cross is 202-484-1650

First, plans vary in the kinds of enrollees they attract. Some plans attract families who expect higher expenses. Some have a disproportionate share of high-cost annuitants who joined when premiums were lower and do not realize that their plan is no longer a good buy. Unfortunately, Federal agencies all too often neglect to encourage sensible Open Season choices, and employees and retirees are all too often dilatory about looking for savings. Despite repeated urging over the years, the Congress has failed to address this problem, which could easily be accomplished by a technique called "risk adjustment" and long used by Medicare. Plans that face higher costs have to cover those costs through higher premiums. Premiums in such plans far exceed the fair value of their benefits.

Second, plans differ in the generosity of benefits they offer. Variations include coverage of different expenses; coinsurance, the percentage of each expense you pay; and deductibles, the amount you have to pay before the plan will reimburse any expenses for a service. Plans with higher cost sharing can charge lower premiums. This is one reason the new Consumer-driven plans have such low premiums.

Third, plans vary in how well they manage costs. A well-run HMO can reduce hospital costs by 25 percent or more compared to traditional insurance through case management. Fee-for-service plans review utilization and use panels of preferred providers. "Disease management" techniques are powerful tools to contain costs.

Fourth, cost sharing creates incentives for doctors and patients to be less wasteful. High deductibles discourage unnecessary visits, while 100 percent reimbursement of psychiatric or laboratory and imaging costs encourages overuse of these "free" services. High Deductible and Consumer-Driven plans' premiums benefit somewhat from slightly younger and healthier enrollees, but mainly from their incentives to reduce unnecessary care. Also, the time and trouble to file claims for expenses slightly above the deductible discourages some enrollees from applying for them.

Fifth, variations in the proportion of enrollees with Medicare Parts A and B has a big effect on plan premiums, since Medicare is "primary" (pays first) for retirees, and covers over four-fifths of hospital and doctor costs. Most HMO benefits are so good that retired enrollees often do not sign up for Part B, which puts these plans at a major disadvantage in keeping premiums low.

Sixth, the formula for sharing premium costs magnifies the differences in what you pay. For GS employees and annuitants, the government pays 75 percent of the overall cost of each plan, up to a maximum amount. This varies each year according to a complex formula. The maximum contribution in 2020 for GS employees and annuitants is about $6,100 for singles, $13,100 for self plus one, and $14,200 for families. There are separate formulas for most postal employees, and for employees of the SEC, FDIC, and several other agencies, with higher government shares. A few types of enrollees, such as former employees, get no government contribution and must pay the full premium.

Employees pay the entire premium amount above the government's share. This employee share is far higher for the more expensive plans because the government contribution is capped by an all-plan average. For example, the total premium cost of the APWU High option for self-only is about $8,700. The government pays the maximum contribution of about $6,100 for GS employees and you pay the

Comparison of Total Cost, Enrollee Cost, and Government Share Under Four Family Plans in 2020 (GS Premiums, Before Tax Savings)

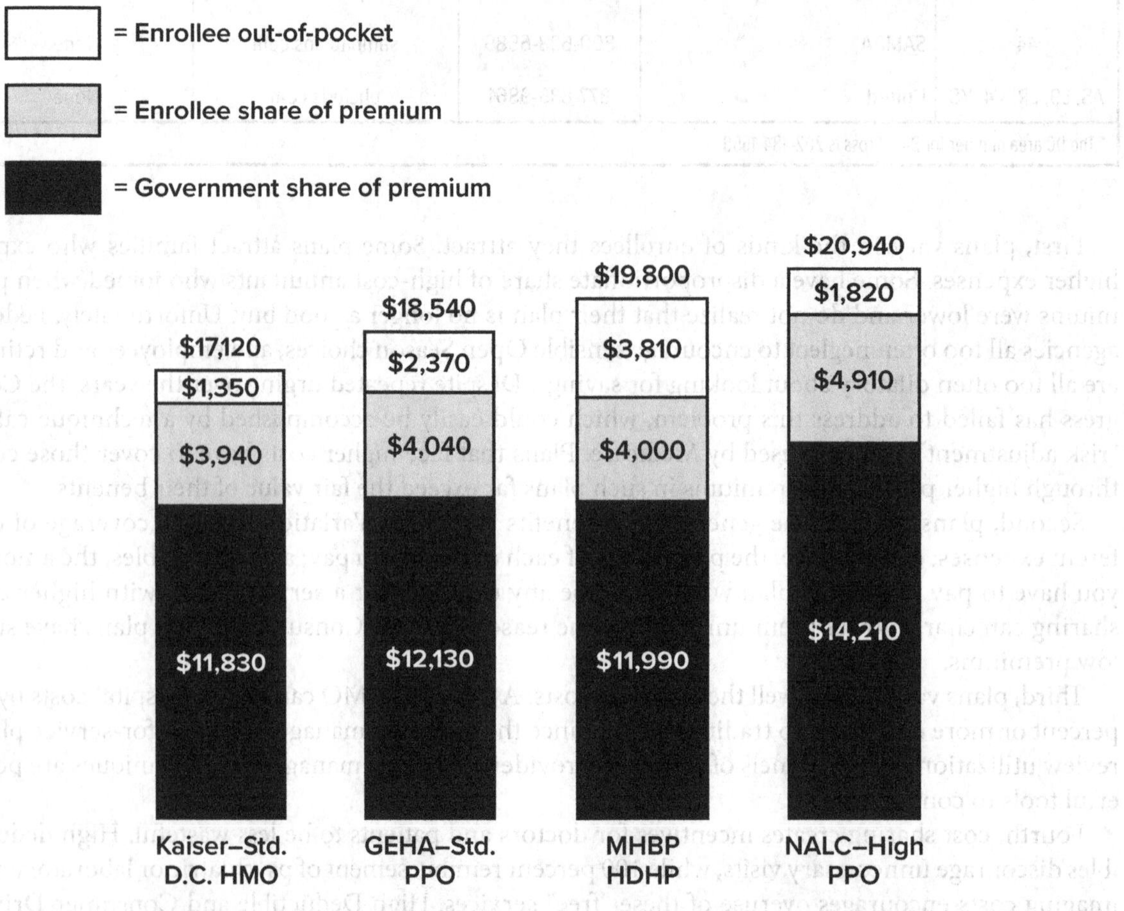

extra $2,600. In contrast, under the APWU Consumer-driven option and some other plans, you pay about $1,800 after the government contribution, a premium saving of almost half.

In summary, you pay modestly for insurance from a well-run plan, but you pay more for a plan's inefficiencies, its unusually generous benefits, or its disproportionate share of high-cost enrollees. Your ability to switch among plans during Open Season gives you a major tool for obtaining the best deal.

The chart "Comparison of Total Cost, Enrollee Cost, and Government Share" shows how the employee's premium, the total premium (employee and government share), and the employee's out-of-pocket costs compare for a family of four under several family plans. All these factors contribute to premium differences, and explain why some plans are such bargains. Of course, some of the differences are offset by what you may have to spend out-of-pocket if you pick a plan with less comprehensive benefits. That is why our ratings tables include both the cost of insurance and the cost of medical bills that are not covered. It would be foolish to select a plan just because it has the lowest premium. It would be equally foolish to pick a plan just because it seems to have the best benefits if you wind up paying more in premiums than those extra benefits are worth to you.

For 2020, most plans' premiums are about the same as this year and a few are lower, but premiums in several plans have risen dramatically. Many plans have changed benefits. As is true every year, opportunities for big savings by switching plans are significant.

Changes for 2020

In recent years, there have been significant program-wide changes to the FEHB program. The recent change that has been probably been the most important to Federal employees was coverage of adult children until age 26.

This year there are three major changes. First, OPM has approved the addition of 18 new plan options for 2020. Seven of these will be available in the DC metro area, either as local or national plans. Our ratings show that some of these are very good values. Second, OPM negotiated with GEHA to give that carrier the important role of being the nation-wide "Indemnity Benefit Plan" as laid out in the FEHB statute. Two of the new offerings this year are the GEHA indemnity plans: Elevate and Elevate Plus. Third, OPM has allowed UnitedHealthcare to offer large Part B premium rebates for enrollees willing to join one of its FEHB plans along with one of its Medicare Advantage plans.

There have been other major changes in recent years, but few as important as these. For example, the FEHB statute now requires each plan to offer separate premiums to families with only two members ("self plus one") and to families with two or more members ("self plus family"). Couples with no dependents and single parents with one dependent can enroll in either variation, depending on which premium is less costly. Plan benefits are usually identical under both and enrollees in most plans can save several hundred dollars in premium costs.

Finally, OPM has asked plans to adopt cost-saving coordination with Medicare, a reform that saves money for the program because Medicare usually pays first, which reduces FEHB premiums, and also offers savings for annuitants because their out-of-pocket costs are reduced. Most national plans already have such "wraparound" benefits. Dozens of local plans have now added them. Most annuitants now can enroll in a wide range of all plan types—PPO, HDHP, CDHP, and HMO—that provide these savings. OPM now also allows plans to reimburse enrollees for part of the cost of Medicare Part B premiums, and use of this technique is growing as shown by the UnitedHealthcare plans that reimburse Part B premium costs if annuitants with Parts A and B join their local Medicare Advantage plan while simultaneously retaining their FEHB enrollment. Other plans are using various techniques to encourage Part B enrollment, and two of the new plans this year, CareFirst Blue Value and Aetna Advantage, are among the better choices. These plan options join such recent innovations as MHBP HDHP, Aetna Direct, and FEP Blue Focus, and such recent reforms as allowing Blue Cross Basic and other plans to reimburse some of the Part B premium costs.

Chapter 2

Comparing Plan Costs

We rate and compare health plans based on their likely cost to you, taking into account your pay system, employment or retirement status, family size, age, health status, location, and other factors. A key element of our ratings are estimates of likely out-of-pocket costs under each plan, based on actuarial estimates of the size and likelihood of low, average, and high spending for families of different sizes and ages. Our ratings also reflect varying premium levels and tax situations faced by different eligibility groups. Full time employees pay lower premiums than annuitants because of tax advantages, and far lower premiums than those who must pay the entire premium. Postal union members and Federal Deposit Insurance Corporation (FDIC) and Securities and Exchange Commission (SEC) employees pay less because the government pays a higher share than for GS employees and annuitants. Neither annuitants nor those who pay full premiums obtain "Premium Conversion" tax advantages. These premium cost differences can reach thousands of dollars a year. We provide separate ratings for each group.

Online *Guide* users see a summary cost comparison table for their group, and then have the option to look at tables providing more detailed cost comparisons. Readers of the printed *Guide* see both summary and detailed cost comparison information for their group in one set of tables for all national plans and local plans available in the DC area, and summary cost comparison information on all local plans in a table covering "Cost and Special Features of All Plans" in all states at the end of *Guide*. The online information is by far more detailed and complete than we can provide in the print version.

Our comparisons take into account not only premiums and potential health care costs, but also plan financial features such as Health Savings Accounts and Wellness benefits that involve cash rewards. We also include dental benefits built into some health plans and, in our separate Chapter on "Dental, Vision, and Hearing," the costs and benefits of standalone dental plans. For annuitants, our estimates and comparisons also take into account both Medicare benefits and Medicare premiums, depending on choices about Medicare enrollment. Online, we also allow for comparisons for those using Flexible Spending Accounts (FSAs). In summary, we provide a comprehensive set of financial comparisons that allow users to make "apple to apple" comparisons of costs for both premiums and likely health care expenses under each plan and across all plans.

Understanding Health Insurance

Individuals and families buy automobile, life, fire, and health insurance policies to protect themselves from catastrophic financial harm from rare events. No one buys "food insurance" because food costs, though large, are unavoidable and predictable. Why pay a middle-man overhead costs to reimburse us for our grocery bills? Nor do we buy rent insurance, or clothes insurance.

We buy life insurance during our working years, because death is very unlikely but financially ruinous to our families if it occurs. For a few hundred dollars a year we can buy support for our families worth hundreds of thousands of dollars if we die. We buy automobile liability insurance because we can protect ourselves from losing huge amounts if we cause an accident.

True health insurance protects our families from ruinous costs of illness. Like most employers, the Federal Government does not offer employees this kind of insurance alone. Instead, it offers various combinations of true insurance and "prepaid" health care. The part of your premium that prepays health care by making advance payment for routine bills will generally equal about what you would have spent by paying the bills directly. However, you wind up paying far less than this because prepaid health care isn't counted as taxable income. Most Federal employees save about one-third of their health care costs because of this exclusion, as explained in our chapter on "Premiums and Taxes."

Unfortunately, prepaid health care creates incentives for enrollees to waste money because the insurance company pays the bill. Prepaid health care may be the single largest cause of wasteful health care spending which, according to some estimates, may be as high as one third of all health care expenditures. There are two major ways to reduce waste. First, health maintenance organizations (HMOs) and other managed care arrangements such as preferred provider organizations (PPOs) use payment incentives for doctors and hospitals to contain costs. Second, high deductible (HDHP) and consumer-driven plans with savings accounts create incentives for enrollees to save costs through prudent shopping decisions. We analyze the advantages and disadvantages of these plans in our analysis of "Plan Types and Flexibility."

How much and what kind of coverage is true insurance? How much is prepaid health care? These questions have no simple answer. A policy protecting against catastrophic medical expense for one family is simply a prepaid health care policy for another family. To a GS-5 with three dependents, $5,000 is a hardship, and $20,000 a heavy burden. To a GS-15 with no dependents, even $20,000 may not be a hardship.

Risk, Premium, and Choice

Since you do not know in advance how high your medical bills will be, there is no way to know which plan will leave you with the lowest total costs. You have to gamble just as you do with any insurance, or indeed with many other choices you make. On sunny mornings you probably won't take an umbrella to work, and sometimes you get wet. In a good year the best policy, in hindsight, would have been no policy, and your total costs would have been zero. In an expensive year, the best policy would have been one that covered every dollar. But we usually don't know whether we'll have a good year or a bad year, which is precisely why we buy insurance. No one but you can decide how much risk you want to bear. Our cost comparisons give you a menu of risk as well as plan choices. They help you think about the level of risk each plan involves, and how much that will cost or save you.

Do not pick a plan either because it has the lowest premium (a seeming best buy) or the highest premium (a seeming set of terrific benefits). As our ratings show, a low premium may hide major coverage gaps, and a high premium may simply reflect expensive enrollees rather than the best benefits. Only some plans have both low premiums and excellent coverage. Pick one of these based on our ratings, which combine both premium and coverage in determining the best buys.

Also, do not pick a plan because it has a lower deductible despite a higher coinsurance amount, or vice versa, and do not try to compare these benefits directly. We use computer programs to perform these calculations, and there are many complexities. For example, whether a plan with a low deductible and a high coinsurance rate is better for you than a plan with the opposites depends on the amount of your expenses, which may not be what you expect. A large body of research shows that very few people are able to juggles cost-sharing variables to pick plans that are the best buys.

Our Ratings

Our cost comparisons cover medical, hospital, dental, and prescription drug costs. They show how you are likely to fare under every national and local plan available to Federal employees. We show how each plan handles various levels of financial risk for you.

Plans are of three main types—combined Preferred Provider Organization (PPO) and Fee-for-Service (FFS) plans, High Deductible (HDHP) and Consumer-Driven (CDHP) plans, and Health Maintenance Organization (HMO) plans, some of which have Point-of-Service (POS) benefits outside the plan network. Most of these options are available in both national and local area plans. Historically, PPO-FFS and HMO plans are distinct approaches. The decision as to which type to join involves service delivery as well as financial factors. The preferred provider or PPO approach now central to most Fee-for-Service plans goes part way toward the HMO model by reducing your cost if you restrict yourself to a network of providers. One national plan, the Blue Cross Basic option, is like most PPOs and HMOs in providing no coverage if you use out-of-network providers. The HDHP plans follow the PPO and FFS model of the national plans, even when they are local. Thus, the differences among plan types are blurring.

Our cost ratings tell you how much you are likely to pay for premiums and out-of-pocket (unreimbursed) medical expenses added together. The tables assume that your bills may be for almost any type or size of expense, including:

- Hospital room and board for surgical or medical care for any illness;
- Other types of hospital services (operating room, anesthesia);
- Surgery, in or out of a hospital;
- Diagnostic tests, X-rays, and lab tests in or out of a hospital;
- Doctor visits in or out of a hospital when you are ill;
- Mental health treatment, outpatient and inpatient;
- Mammograms, Pap smears, and routine immunizations;
- Maternity, even if you are in a self-only plan;
- Emergency care in or out of a hospital;
- Prescription drugs, including insulin and syringes for diabetics;
- Nursing care after an illness;
- Chemotherapy and radiation therapy;
- Physical and rehabilitation therapy;
- Cosmetic ("plastic") surgery or oral surgery—only after an accident;
- Dental care;
- Preventive care including physical examinations and vaccines; and
- **All of these expenses are covered even if you have a preexisting condition or are hospitalized on the date when your enrollment begins.**

With rare exceptions, no plan will pay for any of the following expenses and we do not cover them in our comparisons (however, some of these expenses are covered by Flexible Spending Accounts and Health Savings Accounts):

- Cosmetic or plastic surgery, except after accidents or a disfiguring illness;
- Custodial nursing home care, or any kind of rest care;
- Personal comfort items such as telephone or television while in the hospital;
- Care that is fully paid by another insurance provider;
- Care that is not medically necessary;
- Experimental care (clinical trials are partly excepted);
- Charges that are higher than the plan "allowance" or what the plan has determined to be "reasonable;" and
- Expenses incurred before joining or after leaving a plan.

All plans cover routine exams without deductibles or copayments. Only some plans cover dental care. And most plans expose you to significant out-of-pocket costs, such as not including all prescription drugs in their formularies. Even among plans that cover all services generously, however, there are always some limitations, such as coinsurance and deductibles. Our tables take the major benefit limitations such as these into account in estimating costs. However, we cannot deal with every single coverage nuance or difference (such as which organs are eligible for transplantation, which models of particular medical devices are covered, or which specific medicines are covered). Nor can we assure that all plans will make identical medical necessity decisions in close cases—and they won't. Nor can we reflect extra benefits the plan may provide if, for example, it can save money by giving you more home nursing than its normal limitation on this benefit.

Hence, all of our calculations should be considered approximations that will be broadly accurate in the great majority of situations but that cannot provide precise predictions that cover every possible situation. What our calculations can do, and you cannot do for yourself even if you try to predict your costs, is take into account the risks of ruinously high health care costs from an unexpected illness or accident.

Using the Cost Comparison Tables

There are many separate sets of comparisons, one for each major group facing different premiums, coverage, or likely medical costs. We generally provide comparisons for self-only, self plus one, and families of sizes two through five. However, we limit certain tables to conserve space and because some situations are very uncommon: for older employees, annuitants, part-time employees, and several small enrollment groups we present only self-only, self plus one, and families of two or three rather than larger family sizes. In all family comparisons, the rankings would not change substantially with an additional child. Comparisons for employees and annuitants include:

- Employees who pay **GS premiums** (e.g., General Schedule, special rate, Congressional, and Foreign Service employees).
- Employees who pay lower premiums, including **postal and FDIC employees**. We present rates for postal Category 1 and Category 2 employees both online and in print.
- **Older employees,** whose costs are much higher on average.
- For **part-time employees**, we cover half-time workers and employees who work four days out of five. In almost all agencies, these employees pay part of the "employer share" as well as the regular employee share.
- Former spouses, children turning age 26 who are not covered by a parental FEHB plan, and other **persons who pay full premiums** (both employer and employee share). These persons are not eligible for tax sheltering, and we do not reduce premiums from the nominal rate.
- **Annuitants without Medicare.** Again, there are no tax savings in premium rates.
- **Annuitants with Medicare Parts A and B**. These tables include not only the FEHB plan premium, but also the Part B Medicare premium. No tax savings are available. We cover situations where enrollees pay more, often far more, than the regular Part B premium.
- Finally, we present tables for **annuitants who have only Part A of Medicare,** the hospital benefit. We also compare these with the preceding ratings to see how much you gain, or in most cases lose, by paying the Part B premium. Of course, there are no tax savings.

There are many comparisons, but **only one cost comparison table applies to your current situation**. Of course, your situation may change if your family changes, if you retire, and if you change your Medicare decisions—and you can compare tables to see those differences. Each cost comparison table presents several columns of cost data. Each column except the one for published premium assumes a different level and mix of medical bills, described in the heading. These columns show what your likely costs will be under each plan, including both premium costs and out-of-pocket costs not paid by the plan.

By looking at the different columns in a table, you can find how you will come out under each plan. The columns display:

- The "Published premium" (including when applicable the Medicare Part B premium) that you will pay biweekly or monthly, expressed as an annual cost;
- The actual premium you will pay when you incur "No costs" for health care. This takes into account savings from premium conversion for employees, offsetting savings from money the plan puts in your Health Savings Account or Health Reimbursement Arrangement, and any dues;
- Your premium and out of pocket costs at "Low costs" usage with bills of about $1,000 (self-only) or $3,000 (families);
- Costs for "Average" usage with medical and dental bills averaged over a wide range of expense taking into account the statistical likelihood of costs at each level;
- Costs for "High" usage with bills of about $30,000; and
- The yearly "Limit to you" showing the maximum you will ever be expected to pay for medical (but not dental) bills, also reflecting both premium and out of pocket costs.

We present two different premium columns to reduce confusion over two issues. First, many employees do not understand Premium Conversion. For almost all employees, this tax preference creates about a one-third saving in premium cost. The dollar amount of this saving is never provided to employees, and only shows up indirectly through a lowered taxable income number in form W-2. Your average tax rate is much lower, but for those "marginal" income dollars most employees pay about 33 percent, including Federal income tax, State income tax, and the employee share of Social Security and Medicare taxes. Annuitants are not eligible for Premium Conversion.

Second, many persons find High Deductible plans hard to understand. We believe that the best way to analyze them is to consider the Health Savings Account (HSA) as the equivalent of a reduction in premium. If you don't spend that account at the end of the year you will have a bank balance in that amount. It is therefore possible for you to have "free" health insurance in some High Deductible or Consumer-Driven plans. If your published premium is about $2,100 you actually pay only about $1,400 after Premium Conversion. However, the plan provides you with a savings account that is in your name. If that account is $1,500 you actually come out ahead if you have no medical expenses. In fact, since these plans all provide a free physical exam and routine vaccinations, you come out ahead this much even after your preventive care. The HSA is your money and can earn interest and grow like any other savings account (in this case, grow tax-free). You can save the HSA as an investment, or you can use it to pay your medical bills now or in old age.

If you join a Consumer-Driven plan with a "personal account" or Health Reimbursement Arrangement (HRA), the account belongs to the plan, and must be spent rather than saved if you incur expense, but still has the effect of reducing your "up front and for sure" premium cost. In cases like these where you come out money ahead, we show this in our tables with a negative number in the "Net Premium" column. All HDHP and CDHP plans offer similar net savings, or greatly reduced premiums paid. Even retirees get an offset from these savings accounts if they join one of these plans.

Therefore, the "No costs" column includes your yearly premium adjusted, as pertinent, for Premium Conversion, HSA or HRA account, and any membership dues. These will be your only out-of-pocket costs if you have no medical bills.

We also indicate the percentage chance that you and your family will have bills that are "Low" or "High"—for instance, how likely you are to have bills of about $3,000 or less, or $30,000 or more.

We rank the plans in order of average cost to emphasize the importance of each plan's treatment of "average" expenses for a family of a particular size and type. Most families fall far below the average in most years, but very expensive cases pull the average up. Because almost all plans reimburse 80 percent or more of average or high expenses, the premium counts for most of this average cost, regardless of medical expenses. Very importantly, the "average" includes costs for the entirely unexpected medical problems that can affect any family, such as a heart attack, automobile accident, or onset of an expensive disease. Moreover, the "High costs" and "Limit to you" columns portray directly the insurance value of these plans. You should not select a plan based primarily on the relatively low costs that most of us can predict. It does not make sense to estimate expected costs by doctor visits you expect to make next year—it is the doctor and hospital and drug costs after some major health problem that you do not expect that need to be taken into account in a plan comparison.

You begin by making profile choices to find the one table that relates to families of your age, premium category, and size. Assuming that you don't know something to the contrary, you should expect average expenses in the coming year. The plans that are likely to cost families the least have the lowest dollar figures in this column. **Our cost comparisons assume that you use preferred, network providers exclusively.** You should select a plan primarily based on using network providers, and plan to use non-network providers only in rare instances. You can see some of the financial consequences of using non-network providers in the online *Guide*, but plans' cost-sharing for non-network providers do not include any payment for charges that may be double or triple or even higher multiples of the plan "allowance," except in some emergencies.

But do not choose the highest-ranked plan until you consider whether there is some reason the average column does not apply to you or your family.

First, **consider your particular health situation**. Medical problems are mostly a matter of good or bad luck. However, some people are much more likely than others to have high expenses. In these cases, you should compare plans using the "High cost" or "Limit to you" column. A hip replacement is a large expense. A diabetic may have several expensive ailments. A history of cancer or heart disease worsens your odds. You can use the $30,000 ("High") cost comparisons if you have information that suggests you are much likely to face much higher health expenses than others of your age and family size.

Second, **consider your attitude about risk.** If you are willing to spend a few hundred dollars extra to be sure you will not have heavy out-of-pocket expenses, you may want to pick one of the plans that is lowest cost for a person with high medical bills. However, **all plans have such good coverage that you are well protected from most catastrophic expenses**. Most have a dollar limit on the annual hospital, doctor, and prescription drug expenses you must pay—as noted under the heading "Limit to you." Even where there is a gap, the effect of the generous benefit structure is to create a *de facto* limit.

In your cost table you will notice that differences among closely ranked plans are often very small. Differences of $100 or less are not important. A different mix of bills from those we use to compare plans could overcome these. Differences of several hundred dollars, however, reflect significant variations in how expensively the plans handle most cases as well as the "for sure" premium expense.

Notice that most of the higher-ranked plans will save you money in every year—whether your expenses are high or low—compared to the plans ranked lower. Again, this is because you have to pay the premium whether your medical expenses are high or low.

Bargain with Out of Network Providers

Most plans have very low payments for non-preferred providers. You MUST negotiate with these doctors before any expensive procedure in order to protect yourself. One good tactic is to ask for either their "preferred" or Medicare rate.

Using Preferred Providers

We rate plan costs based on the assumption that you will always or almost always want to use preferred providers, also known as "staying in the network". Your cost is always lower, usually far lower, when you do. However, all but one of the national PPO plans and all CDHP and HDHP plans allow you to obtain care out of network. This can sometimes be a valuable flexibility. But you face not only a higher copayment, but also an additional risk. The plans set limits on the fee they will recognize. For example, the plan may charge a flat amount of $20 to PPO users. For doctors outside the PPO, the plan may pay 70 percent of the cost up to $80 for a particular procedure, but if the physician charges $100 you will pay $30 plus the extra $20, or half the total bill compared to only $20 if you use the preferred provider. You can sometimes negotiate fees down, and we urge this strategy for non-preferred providers. This problem often goes away if you have Medicare Parts A and B, since most of the national plans and some local plans waive most doctor and hospital cost-sharing whether you obtain care in or out of the network. Even in HMOs that don't waive these costs, you can use Medicare to go out of network. Therefore, **for retirees who participate in Medicare Parts A and B preferred provider restrictions largely disappear when enrolled in most plans.** You can go to any hospital and almost any doctor without penalty. Moreover, persons over age 65 who are in any plan are by law guaranteed a Medicare rate and can use all doctors who have not opted out of Medicare with substantial protection, even if cost sharing is not eliminated.

Catastrophic Coverage

The most important reason for buying health insurance is to protect you against financial catastrophe. You may, therefore, wish to approach plan selection by comparing plans on the basis of potential financial risk, rather than average cost. To facilitate this, our cost comparisons include a "Limit to you" column. Our "Limit" calculation includes both the annual premium and the claimed guarantee provided by each plan for hospital, medical, and prescription drug expenses. We combine these two types of expenses because you are sure to incur premium costs and there is little point in picking a plan with $1,000 less in claimed limit if its premium is $2,000 higher. However, no plan includes dental expenses in its guarantee. The "Limits" column, therefore, cannot include these costs. Our figures use a 33 percent premium reduction for tax savings for employees under Premium Conversion (but not for retirees or those paying full premiums, who are ineligible). We also take account of the ability of enrollees in High Deductible plans to reduce costs by using their HSA or HRA accounts. We have not, however, included estimates for additional tax savings from funding high expenses through additional contributions to HSA accounts (see Cost and Taxes). Therefore, these are conservative estimates for High Deductible plans.

Because some plans present catastrophic limits in confusing ways, we attempt to make our limit calculations comparable among plans. For example, we take account of deductibles if these are not included in the claimed limit. A few plans put prescription drug payments under separate limits and we adjust for this difference. Plans calculate limits differently and the dollar numbers published in a plan's "Summary of Benefits" do not necessarily reflect the loopholes and exclusions listed under "Your cost for covered services"). The adjustments we make are necessary to make comparisons that are not inaccurate "apples to oranges."

How We Adjust Catastrophic Limits to Make Them Comparable Across Plans

Illustrative plans	Brand X HDHP	Brand Y High Option Plan
Limit stated in plan's summary of benefits	$5,000	$3,000
Excluded amounts:		
Deductibles	None	None
Hospital copays*	None	$900
Prescription copays*	None	$1,000
Specialty drug limit	None	None
Physician copays*	None	$1,500
Subtotal	$5,000	$6,400
Premium	$1,000	$1,600
Health savings account	–$1,000	None
Total "limit" to you	$5,000	$6,400

* We assume three hospital stays at $300, 50 prescriptions at $20, and 50 physician visits at $30; typical values in many plans.

Although we included dental costs in most columns, we had to leave dental costs out of the "Limits" column because no plan includes dental costs in its guarantee. Most HMOs have a limit and cover nearly all hospital, medical, and prescription drug expenses.

The cost tables can be used to find those plans with the lowest limits. From this group, you can select plans with lower average costs. Or you might wish to select one of the plans with the very best catastrophic coverage and accept somewhat higher out-of-pocket costs as the price of that guarantee. Importantly, because we include premiums in the calculation of the most you can pay, we help you avoid the mistake of paying many thousands in higher premiums for a saving of fewer thousands in catastrophic limits.

If You Have Other Insurance

You cannot use our cost rankings directly if you have health insurance coverage from another source. The best FEHB plan for you depends on the cost and benefit structure of the other plan, though your best choice will almost always be a low premium plan to minimize unnecessary premium payments. But do not assume that you need not enroll in an FEHB plan just because you have other coverage.

If your spouse has a low-cost health plan through a private employer, or you have a health plan from prior employment, check to be sure that it covers you and your children, and has a benefit package as good as the Federal plans. Even if your spouse's plan is every bit as good as any of the Federal plans, consider the cost of this coverage compared to some of the lower-premium Federal plans. Remember that you must be covered under an FEHB plan continuously for the five years preceding retirement to continue enrollment after retirement (there are some very rare exceptions, such as certain agency downsizing situations). You don't have to be in the same plan in each year, but you must be covered continuously by some FEHB plan or, in the special case of former military, TRICARE.

Most importantly, if you should die while you are not enrolled in an FEHB family plan, your spouse will lose eligibility for the program. Since most employers do not continue coverage past retirement, or cannot be counted on to do so, your only guarantee that your spouse can keep this entitlement is to be continuously enrolled. There is an excellent strategy for doing so at minimum cost. All of the plans showing a very low or negative number in the "No Costs" column are Consumer-Driven or High Deductible plans that give you a savings account as large or larger than the premium. With double coverage, you will probably not ever reach the high deductible and will realize this saving in most circumstances. In other words, these plans really are almost "free" if they supplement other coverage from your spouse.

Chapter 3

Cost Comparisons and Advice for Employees and Former Employees

As explained in Chapter 2 on "Comparing Plan Costs," we rate and compare health plans based on their likely cost to you, taking into account your pay system, employment or retirement status, family size, age, health status, location, and other factors. A key element of our ratings are estimates of likely out-of-pocket costs under each plan, based on actuarial estimates of the size and likelihood of low, average, and high spending for families of different sizes and ages.

Readers of the printed *Guide* see both summary and detailed cost comparison information for their group in one set of tables for all national plans and local plans available in the DC area, and summary cost comparison information on all local plans in a table covering "Cost and Special Features of All Plans" in all states at the end of *Guide*.

All of these comparisons take into account not only premiums and potential health care costs, but also plan features such as Health Savings Accounts, personal accounts, and Wellness benefits that involve cash rewards. We also include dental benefits and premiums, both for dental benefits built into some health plans and for the costs and benefits of standalone dental plans. For annuitants, our estimates and comparisons also take into account both Medicare benefits and Medicare premiums (and any Medicare premium rebates), depending on choices about Medicare enrollment. In summary, we provide a comprehensive set of financial comparisons that allow users to make "apple to apple" comparisons of costs for both premiums and likely health care expenses under each plan and across all plans for which they are eligible.

Very importantly, our comparisons take into account that a few plans provide both a Medicare "wraparound" and a fund that will pay part of the Medicare Part B premium. The three national plans that provide a complete wraparound for hospital and doctor costs and also fund Part B costs are Aetna Direct ($900 towards Part B premium), Blue Cross Basic Option ($800 towards Part B premium), and GEHA High option ($600 towards Part B premium). Several Kaiser Plans on the West Coast offer even greater premium rebates if you join their Medicare Advantage plans, as do most of the UnitedHealthcare plans around the country.

All of our calculations should be considered approximations that will be broadly accurate in the great majority of situations but that cannot provide precise predictions that cover every possible situation. What our calculations also do, therefore, is take into account the risks of ruinously high health care costs from an unexpected illness or accident, and compare the maximum out-of-pocket and premium costs under each plan.

Using the Cost Comparison Tables for Employees and Former Employees

There are many separate sets of comparisons, one for each major group facing different premiums, coverage, or likely medical costs. We generally provide comparisons for self-only, self plus one, and families of sizes two through five. However, in the print version of the *Guide* we limit certain tables to conserve space and because some situations are very uncommon: for older employees, annuitants, part-time employees, and several small enrollment groups we present only self-only, self plus one, and families of two or three rather than larger family sizes. In all family comparisons the rankings would not change substantially with an additional child. Comparisons for employees include:

- Employees who pay **GS premiums** (e.g., General Schedule, special rate, Congressional, and Foreign Service employees).
- Employees who pay lower premiums, including **postal, FDIC, and SEC employees**. We present plan comparisons for postal Category 1 and 2 employees (bargaining unit union members) in our print Guide as well as online (most postal management employees have the same premiums as GS employees and these rates are also shown both in print and online). FDIC and SEC results are shown only online.
- **Older employees,** whose costs are much higher on average.
- For **part-time employees**, we cover half-time workers and employees who work four days out of five. In almost all agencies, these employees pay part of the "employer share" as well as the regular employee share.
- Former spouses, children turning age 26 who are not covered by a parental FEHBP plan, and other **persons who pay full premiums** (both employer and employee share). These persons are not eligible for tax sheltering, and we do not reduce premiums from the nominal rate.

There are many comparisons, but **only one cost comparison table applies to your current situation**. Of course, your situation may change if your family changes, or if you retire—and you can compare tables to see those differences. Each plan cost comparison table presents several columns of cost data. Each column except the one for published premium assumes a different level and mix of medical bills, described in the heading. These columns show what your likely costs will be under each plan, including both premium costs and out-of-pocket costs not paid by the plan.

By looking at the different columns in a table, you can find how you will come out under each plan if your expenses range from none to the maximum you could pay in a year. The details are explained in our chapter on "Comparing Plan Costs." Very importantly, the columns other than "Published premium" all include the tax savings you get from Premium Conversion for employees. These columns also credit you with the savings you gain from a Health Savings Account (HSA) or personal care account or Health Reimbursement Arrangement (HRA) in plans that give you these benefits. HSAs and HRAs are the equivalent of a reduction in premium. If you don't spend that account at the end of the year you will have a bank balance in that amount that carries over to the next year. Therefore, the "No costs" column includes your yearly premium adjusted, as pertinent, for Premium Conversion, HSA or personal care account or HRA, and any membership dues. These will be your only out-of-pocket costs if you have no medical bills. We rank the plans in order of average cost to emphasize the importance of each plan's treatment of "average" expenses for a family of a particular size and type.

You begin by making profile choices to find the table that relates to families of your age, premium category, and size. Assuming that you don't know something to the contrary, you should expect average expenses in the coming year. The plans that are likely to cost families the least have the lowest dollar figures in this column. But do not choose the highest-ranked plan until you consider whether there is some reason the average column does not apply to you or your family.

In your cost table you will notice that differences among closely ranked plans are often very small. Differences of $100 or less are not important. A different mix of bills from those we use to compare plans could overcome these.

Avoid a Big Risk

Many people who are covered by their spouse's insurance drop FEHBP. This saves premium costs. However, if you are not enrolled and die suddenly, your spouse cannot ever enroll again. Your best option is to carry a family policy and drop the spousal insurance.

Differences of several hundred dollars or more, however, reflect significant variations in how expensively the plans handle most cases.

Notice that most of the higher-ranked plans will save you money in every situation—whether your expenses are high or low—compared to the plans ranked lower. You can also see that most but not all HMO, CDHP, and HDHP plans will save you hundreds of dollars compared to most national PPO plans.

Savings for Couples Using Self Only Enrollments

For a husband and wife who are **both** employed by the Federal Government and who have no dependent children, it is possible to save on premium costs by enrolling separately as self only rather than together as a self plus one. The premiums for two self only enrollments are usually less than the self plus one premium. This option can be particularly valuable in cases where each spouse prefers a different plan, perhaps because no one plan covers both family physicians in its network.

Be cautious, however, because each person will have to meet a separate catastrophic limit rather than the single limit that applies to self plus one. Most plans do not increase your risk because they include individual limits of about half the amount of the overall self plus one or family limit. Moreover, while you are still technically subject to meeting two catastrophic limits if you both enroll self-only, the fee structure of most HMOs makes it almost impossible to reach those limits. For these reasons you are usually safe with two self only enrollments. But do check the plan brochure's catastrophic limits carefully before making this decision.

Is Self Plus One for You?

In most cases the self plus one premium is lower than the family premium by one or two hundred dollars a year. So check your plan to be sure it gives you this saving and, while you are at it, check our ratings to see if you can't save even more by changing plans.

Savings for Couples or Single Parents with One Child Under Self Plus One

Married couples with no children to cover, and single parents with one child to cover, can enroll as self plus one rather than as a family and, depending on the plan chosen, usually save two or three hundred dollars a year in premium costs, and often more. Since the benefits of the plan are the same regardless of which enrollment type is chosen, this is a clear saving. You should use our comparison table for self plus one with adults of your age to make your initial plan comparison.

If You or Your Spouse Has Other Employer Insurance

If your spouse has a low-cost health plan through a private employer, or you have a health plan from prior employment, check to be sure that it covers you and your children, and has a benefit package as good as the Federal plans. Even if your spouse's plan is every bit as good as any of the Federal plans, consider the cost of this coverage compared to some of the lower-premium Federal plans. Remember that you must be covered under the FEHBP continuously for the five years preceding retirement to be eligible for enrollment after retirement (there are some very rare exceptions, such as certain agency downsizing situations). You don't have to be in the same plan in each year, but you must be covered continuously by some FEHBP plan or, in the special case of military dependents, TRICARE.

If you should die while you are not enrolled in the FEHBP in a family plan, your spouse will lose eligibility for the program. Since most other employers do not continue coverage past retirement, or cannot be counted on to do so, your only guarantee that your spouse can keep this entitlement is to be continuously enrolled. There is an excellent strategy for doing so at minimum cost. All of the plans showing a very low or negative number in the "No Costs" column are Consumer-Driven or High Deductible plans that give you a savings account as large or larger than the premium. With double coverage you will probably not ever reach the high deductible and will realize this saving in most circumstances. In other words, these plans really are almost "free" if they supplement other coverage from your spouse.

Part-Time Employees

Many career Federal employees work part-time schedules. In these cases, most government agencies do not pay the regular share of the premium. Instead, employees receive a *pro rata* amount based on their work schedules. For example, an employee scheduled to work 40 hours per biweekly pay period receives only one half of the regular government contribution and must pay the regular employee contribution plus the extra one half, or about two thirds of the total premium cost for the plan. There are many possible part-time schedules. We present comparisons on the basis of 50 percent and 80 percent of the regular work schedule. Almost all part-time employees are reasonably close to one of these scenarios. (A few agencies, including the Postal Service and the FDIC, give part-time employees the same rates as full-time employees.)

Persons Who Pay Full Premiums

The FEHBP also provides coverage for former spouses, former employees, children turning age 26, and others, but the enrollee must pay the full premium without government contribution. This often results, nonetheless, in a better price than is available for non-group insurance purchased individually, which is the only other insurance available to some. In most cases, however, a marketplace exchange option is worth considering and for those eligible for premium tax subsidies is often a better buy.

Persons eligible for continuing coverage for as long as needed include:

- Those **former spouses** who have a qualifying court order and meet other conditions. They may enroll in any plan on the same basis as employees and annuitants, except for premiums.
- **Temporary employees** who have worked for one full year also may enroll on the same basis as employees, except for premium cost. (Such employees should switch to permanent employment if at all possible to reduce premium costs by three-fourths.)

Time-limited coverage is also available for several categories of persons. They pay a small surcharge—two percent of the premium—and are eligible only for a limited time:

- **Employees separating from Federal service** for any reason may continue their coverage for 18 months.
- **Children reaching age 26** are, unless severely handicapped, no longer eligible for coverage under their parents' family plan. They may obtain coverage in their own name for 36 months.
- **Former spouses without a qualifying court order** also may enroll for 36 months.

For all purposes except premium contribution, tax shelter, and time limit, a temporary enrollee is treated like a regular enrollee. For example, there is no disqualification for preexisting conditions. There is a 60-day time limit for applying after the qualifying event, but once enrolled a person may switch plans in the next Open Season just like any employee or annuitant. At the end of the temporary period, these persons may switch to a "conversion" plan that is not part of the FEHB program and is sold at individual rather than group rates. However, the costs and coverages of these conversion plans are generally far worse than one can get by shopping on the private market. Some young adults will not have a parent with a family plan, or will become ineligible for family coverage upon reaching age 26. **You can usually (but not always) get better deals from marketplace exchange plans than you would from paying full premiums for the regular FEHBP plans, but must pay careful attention because bronze and silver plans have much higher deductibles and other cost-sharing than FEHBP plans.**

For persons who pay full premiums, we compare plans based on paying both the government and employee share. Although some of these persons must pay a two percent surcharge, we have omitted this factor to avoid the need for extra tables. Under any of the less-costly plans, the surcharge would be under $100 per year for singles and $200 per year for families. These tables do not include premium tax savings because persons who are not current employees are not eligible for this benefit. Of particular importance to former spouses turning age 65, joining Medicare Parts A and B, suspending FEHB enrollment, and enrolling in a Medicare Advantage plan will reduce premium costs by two thirds or more, and provide benefits very nearly as good as those in FEHB plans.

Persons Under 55: GS Premiums		Self Only						
				Estimated yearly out-of-pocket costs, including premium and typical hospital, medical, drug, and dental bills near:				
Plan code	Plan name	Plan type	Published premium	No costs*	Low use: $1,000 or less	Average cost	High use: $30,000 or more	Limit to you
D.C. Area Plans When You Use Preferred Providers								
B61	CareFirst HDHP	HDHP	1710	240	780	1710	5140	5140
T71	Kaiser Basic	HMO	1260	840	1060	1740	4840	4840
E34	Kaiser-Std	HMO	1710	1140	1210	1770	4640	4640
V41	United HDHP	HDHP	1460	220	820	1780	5270	5270
E31	Kaiser-Hi	HMO	2540	1700	1720	2110	3950	3950
L91	United Choice Plus Advanced	PPO-FEE	1560	1040	1570	2140	4040	4040
Y81	United Choice Primary	HMO	1520	1010	1190	2180	8360	8360
AS1	United Choice Plus Primary	PPO-FEE	1580	1050	1230	2220	8400	8400
B64	CareFirst Blue Value Plus	HMO-POS	2340	1560	1730	2430	6560	6560
LR1	United Choice Open Access	HMO	2450	1630	1820	2550	6630	6630
JN4	Aetna Open Access Basic	HMO	2240	1490	1690	2650	7490	7490
QQ4	Aetna Saver	HMO	1790	1190	1890	2970	7690	7690
2G4	CareFirst-Std POS	HMO-POS	4020	2680	2680	3130	5180	5180
F51	Aetna HealthFund CDHP	CDHP	3820	1550	2100	3280	7850	7850
F54	Aetna Value Plan	PPO-FEE	3710	2470	2720	3680	8770	8770
JP1	MD-IPA	HMO	4390	2930	3070	3740	7530	7930
JN1	Aetna Open Access-Hi	HMO	7520	5020	5090	5650	8510	10020
National Plans When You Use Preferred Providers								
341	GEHA HDHP	HDHP	1540	130	630	1460	4900	6030
324	NALC CDHP	CDHP	1420	-220	150	1560	7580	7580
481	MHBP HDHP	HDHP	1720	-10	690	1750	5690	7190
254	GEHA Elevate	PPO-FEE	1230	820	1050	1980	7820	7820
474	APWU CDHP	CDHP	1790	30	700	1990	7730	7730
401	Foreign Service	PPO-FEE	1790	1200	1480	2060	5070	6200
251	GEHA Elevate Plus	PPO-FEE	1890	1260	1380	2120	6580	7260
N61	Aetna Direct CDHP	CDHP	1840	330	1030	2140	7230	7230
131	FEP Blue Focus	PPO	1380	920	1440	2180	7420	7420
314	GEHA-Std	PPO-FEE	1570	1050	1280	2220	7550	7550
111	Blue Cross Basic	PPO	1970	1320	1450	2230	6550	6820
454	MHBP-Std	PPO-FEE	1710	1180	1480	2300	6850	7180
KM1	NALC Value Plan	PPO-FEE	1170	710	1080	2300	7410	7410
421	Compass Rose	PPO-FEE	2640	1760	1970	2480	5400	6760
414	MHBP Value Plan	PPO-FEE	1360	950	1370	2480	7550	7550
321	NALC-Hi	PPO-FEE	2360	1610	1890	2530	5970	8210
444	SAMBA-Std	PPO-FEE	2040	1360	1700	2670	8360	8360
224	Aetna HealthFund HDHP	HDHP	2620	940	1460	2740	8640	8640
311	GEHA-Hi	PPO-FEE	2740	1830	2050	2750	6830	6830
471	APWU-Hi	PPO-FEE	2580	1760	2280	2980	7970	8260
Z24	Aetna Advantage	PPO-FEE	1390	930	1630	3000	8430	8430
381	Rural Carrier	PPO-FEE	3180	2120	2440	3130	7120	7120
104	Blue Cross-Std	PPO-FEE	3040	2030	2460	3190	7030	7030
441	SAMBA-Hi	PPO-FEE	4690	3130	3440	4290	9130	9130

* These are the premiums after tax savings, offset by savings accounts for plans that offer them. If you have no or low health-care costs with these plans, it can result in actual saving to you, which we indicate with a negative number.

Persons Under 55: GS Premiums

Plan code	Plan name	Plan type	Published premium	Self Plus One: Estimated yearly out-of-pocket costs, including premium and typical hospital, medical, drug, and dental bills near:				
				No costs*	Low use: $3,000 or less	Average cost	High use: $30,000 or more	Limit to you
D.C. Area Plans When You Use Preferred Providers								
B63	CareFirst HDHP	HDHP	3420	480	2270	3310	7890	8780
T73	Kaiser Basic	HMO	2800	1870	2650	3560	7300	9870
E36	Kaiser-Std	HMO	3940	2630	3040	3790	6510	9630
V43	United HDHP	HDHP	3140	590	2790	3840	8880	9540
B66	CareFirst Blue Value Plus	HMO-POS	4240	2830	3360	4200	7270	12830
Y83	United Choice Primary	HMO	3270	2180	3070	4210	8670	16880
L93	United Choice Plus Advanced	PPO-FEE	3060	2040	3550	4270	8040	8040
AS3	United Choice Plus Primary	PPO-FEE	3390	2260	3150	4290	8750	16960
JN6	Aetna Open Access Basic	HMO	4470	2980	3860	5020	9420	14980
LR3	United Choice Open Access	HMO	5340	3560	4380	5220	8710	13560
E33	Kaiser-Hi	HMO	6840	4560	4840	5300	7000	9060
2G6	CareFirst-Std POS	HMO-POS	7190	4790	4900	5480	7320	9790
QQ6	Aetna Saver	HMO	3750	2500	4660	5820	12010	15500
JP3	MD-IPA	HMO	7440	4960	5650	6400	9480	14960
F53	Aetna HealthFund CDHP	CDHP	9360	4240	6270	7680	13120	16840
F56	Aetna Value Plan	PPO-FEE	8980	5990	6840	8230	13300	18590
JN3	Aetna Open Access-Hi	HMO	17280	11520	12050	12650	14950	21520
National Plans When You Use Preferred Providers								
343	GEHA HDHP	HDHP	3310	410	2280	3020	6080	12210
326	NALC CDHP	CDHP	3130	-270	1450	3450	10000	15330
483	MHBP HDHP	HDHP	3810	180	2580	3590	7600	14580
256	GEHA Elevate	PPO-FEE	2830	1890	2600	3850	8370	15890
476	APWU CDHP	CDHP	3900	230	2580	3960	8940	15630
316	GEHA-Std	PPO-FEE	3380	2260	3010	4310	8870	15260
N63	Aetna Direct CDHP	CDHP	4030	890	3290	4350	9310	14690
133	FEP Blue Focus	PPO	2970	1980	3370	4360	9120	14980
253	GEHA Elevate Plus	PPO-FEE	4430	2950	3490	4390	7900	14950
403	Foreign Service	PPO-FEE	4470	2980	4050	4520	6990	9980
456	MHBP-Std	PPO-FEE	3940	2670	3940	4570	7760	14670
KM3	NALC Value Plan	PPO-FEE	2570	1550	3270	4660	9920	14950
113	Blue Cross Basic	PPO	4640	3100	3790	4690	8200	14100
416	MHBP Value Plan	PPO-FEE	3220	2190	4090	5020	9940	15390
446	SAMBA-Std	PPO-FEE	4470	2980	4080	5120	9310	16980
383	Rural Carrier	PPO-FEE	5330	3550	4490	5380	8900	13550
423	Compass Rose	PPO-FEE	6190	4130	4960	5400	7770	11130
323	NALC-Hi	PPO-FEE	5680	3820	4680	5420	8400	12820
473	APWU-Hi	PPO-FEE	5190	3500	4790	5510	8840	16500
226	Aetna HealthFund HDHP	HDHP	5810	2270	4320	5700	11050	17670
313	GEHA-Hi	PPO-FEE	6410	4270	4920	5830	9090	14270
Z26	Aetna Advantage	PPO-FEE	3060	2040	4440	6110	13090	17040
106	Blue Cross-Std	PPO-FEE	6950	4630	5960	6730	10240	14630
443	SAMBA-Hi	PPO-FEE	10700	7140	8160	9030	12600	19140

* These are the premiums after tax savings, offset by savings accounts for plans that offer them. If you have no or low health-care costs with these plans, it can result in actual saving to you, which we indicate with a negative number.

Persons Under 55: GS Premiums

Family of Two

Plan code	Plan name	Plan type	Published premium	Estimated yearly out-of-pocket costs, including premium and typical hospital, medical, drug, and dental bills near: No costs*	Low use: $3,000 or less	Average cost	High use: $30,000 or more	Limit to you
D.C. Area Plans When You Use Preferred Providers								
B62	CareFirst HDHP	HDHP	4060	910	2700	3740	8320	9210
T72	Kaiser Basic	HMO	3080	2050	2830	3740	7480	10050
E35	Kaiser-Std	HMO	3960	2640	3050	3800	6520	9640
V42	United HDHP	HDHP	3360	740	2940	3990	9030	9690
Y82	United Choice Primary	HMO	3590	2400	3290	4430	8890	17100
AS2	United Choice Plus Primary	PPO-FEE	3730	2490	3380	4520	8980	17190
E32	Kaiser-Hi	HMO	5740	3830	4110	4570	6270	8330
L92	United Choice Plus Advanced	PPO-FEE	4390	2930	4440	5160	8930	8930
B65	CareFirst Blue Value Plus	HMO-POS	5920	3950	4480	5320	8390	13950
JN5	Aetna Open Access Basic	HMO	4940	3290	4170	5330	9730	15290
LR2	United Choice Open Access	HMO	6120	4080	4900	5740	9230	14080
QQ5	Aetna Saver	HMO	4090	2730	4890	6050	12240	15730
F52	Aetna HealthFund CDHP	CDHP	8480	3660	5690	7100	12540	16260
2G5	CareFirst-Std POS	HMO-POS	9900	6600	6710	7290	9130	11600
F55	Aetna Value Plan	PPO-FEE	8320	5550	6400	7790	12860	18150
JP2	MD-IPA	HMO	15290	10200	10890	11640	14720	20200
JN2	Aetna Open Access-Hi	HMO	16480	10990	11520	12120	14420	20990
National Plans When You Use Preferred Providers								
342	GEHA HDHP	HDHP	3900	800	2670	3410	6470	12600
325	NALC CDHP	CDHP	3270	-180	1540	3540	10090	15420
482	MHBP HDHP	HDHP	4000	310	2710	3720	7730	14710
475	APWU CDHP	CDHP	4250	470	2820	4200	9180	15870
255	GEHA Elevate	PPO-FEE	3450	2300	3010	4260	8780	16300
402	Foreign Service	PPO-FEE	4440	2960	4030	4500	6970	9960
132	FEP Blue Focus	PPO	3270	2180	3570	4560	9320	15180
252	GEHA Elevate Plus	PPO-FEE	4690	3130	3670	4570	8080	15130
455	MHBP-Std	PPO-FEE	3980	2700	3970	4600	7790	14700
KM2	NALC Value Plan	PPO-FEE	2680	1630	3350	4740	10000	15030
N62	Aetna Direct CDHP	CDHP	4640	1290	3690	4750	9710	15090
315	GEHA-Std	PPO-FEE	4040	2700	3450	4750	9310	15700
112	Blue Cross Basic	PPO	4970	3320	4010	4910	8420	14320
322	NALC-Hi	PPO-FEE	4910	3310	4170	4910	7890	12310
415	MHBP Value Plan	PPO-FEE	3290	2230	4130	5060	9980	15430
382	Rural Carrier	PPO-FEE	4880	3250	4190	5080	8600	13250
225	Aetna HealthFund HDHP	HDHP	5080	1790	3840	5220	10570	17190
445	SAMBA-Std	PPO-FEE	4660	3110	4210	5250	9440	17110
422	Compass Rose	PPO-FEE	6850	4570	5400	5840	8210	11570
472	APWU-Hi	PPO-FEE	6710	4510	5800	6520	9850	17510
Z25	Aetna Advantage	PPO-FEE	3690	2460	4860	6530	13510	17460
312	GEHA-Hi	PPO-FEE	7910	5280	5930	6840	10100	15280
105	Blue Cross-Std	PPO-FEE	7460	4970	6300	7070	10580	14970
442	SAMBA-Hi	PPO-FEE	11760	7850	8870	9740	13310	19850

* These are the premiums after tax savings, offset by savings accounts for plans that offer them. If you have no or low health-care costs with these plans, it can result in actual saving to you, which we indicate with a negative number.

Persons Under 55: GS Premiums		Family of Three						
		Plan type	Published premium	Estimated yearly out-of-pocket costs, including premium and typical hospital, medical, drug, and dental bills near:				
Plan code	Plan name			No costs*	Low use: $3,000 or less	Average cost	High use: $30,000 or more	Limit to you
D.C. Area Plans When You Use Preferred Providers								
E35	Kaiser-Std	HMO	3960	2640	3050	3990	6520	9640
T72	Kaiser Basic	HMO	3080	2050	2830	4000	7480	10050
B62	CareFirst HDHP	HDHP	4060	910	2700	4090	8320	9210
V42	United HDHP	HDHP	3360	740	2940	4390	9030	9690
E32	Kaiser-Hi	HMO	5740	3830	4110	4690	6270	8330
Y82	United Choice Primary	HMO	3590	2400	3290	4750	8890	17100
AS2	United Choice Plus Primary	PPO-FEE	3730	2490	3380	4840	8980	17190
L92	United Choice Plus Advanced	PPO-FEE	4390	2930	4440	5430	8930	8930
B65	CareFirst Blue Value Plus	HMO-POS	5920	3950	4480	5520	8390	13950
JN5	Aetna Open Access Basic	HMO	4940	3290	4170	5640	9730	15290
LR2	United Choice Open Access	HMO	6120	4080	4900	5980	9230	14080
QQ5	Aetna Saver	HMO	4090	2730	4890	6470	12240	15730
2G5	CareFirst-Std POS	HMO-POS	9900	6600	6710	7410	9130	11600
F52	Aetna HealthFund CDHP	CDHP	8480	3660	5690	7550	12540	16260
F55	Aetna Value Plan	PPO-FEE	8320	5550	6400	8130	12860	18150
JP2	MD-IPA	HMO	15290	10200	10890	11860	14720	20200
JN2	Aetna Open Access-Hi	HMO	16480	10990	11520	12290	14420	20990
National Plans When You Use Preferred Providers								
342	GEHA HDHP	HDHP	3900	800	2670	3720	6470	12600
325	NALC CDHP	CDHP	3270	-180	1540	4100	10090	15420
482	MHBP HDHP	HDHP	4000	310	2710	4120	7730	14710
255	GEHA Elevate	PPO-FEE	3450	2300	3010	4570	8780	16300
475	APWU CDHP	CDHP	4250	470	2820	4660	9180	15870
402	Foreign Service	PPO-FEE	4440	2960	4030	4700	6970	9960
252	GEHA Elevate Plus	PPO-FEE	4690	3130	3670	4800	8080	15130
455	MHBP-Std	PPO-FEE	3980	2700	3970	4850	7790	14700
132	FEP Blue Focus	PPO	3270	2180	3570	4870	9320	15180
315	GEHA-Std	PPO-FEE	4040	2700	3450	5070	9310	15700
322	NALC-Hi	PPO-FEE	4910	3310	4170	5130	7890	12310
112	Blue Cross Basic	PPO	4970	3320	4010	5160	8420	14320
N62	Aetna Direct CDHP	CDHP	4640	1290	3690	5170	9710	15090
KM2	NALC Value Plan	PPO-FEE	2680	1630	3350	5170	10000	15030
382	Rural Carrier	PPO-FEE	4880	3250	4190	5310	8600	13250
415	MHBP Value Plan	PPO-FEE	3290	2230	4130	5430	9980	15430
445	SAMBA-Std	PPO-FEE	4660	3110	4210	5550	9440	17110
225	Aetna HealthFund HDHP	HDHP	5080	1790	3840	5670	10570	17190
422	Compass Rose	PPO-FEE	6850	4570	5400	6010	8210	11570
472	APWU-Hi	PPO-FEE	6710	4510	5800	6760	9850	17510
Z25	Aetna Advantage	PPO-FEE	3690	2460	4860	7060	13510	17460
312	GEHA-Hi	PPO-FEE	7910	5280	5930	7070	10100	15280
105	Blue Cross-Std	PPO-FEE	7460	4970	6300	7340	10580	14970
442	SAMBA-Hi	PPO-FEE	11760	7850	8870	10010	13310	19850

* These are the premiums after tax savings, offset by savings accounts for plans that offer them. If you have no or low health-care costs with these plans, it can result in actual saving to you, which we indicate with a negative number.

Persons Under 55: GS Premiums		Plan type	Published premium	Family of Four: Estimated yearly out-of-pocket costs, including premium and typical hospital, medical, drug, and dental bills near:				
Plan code	Plan name			No costs*	Low use: $3,000 or less	Average cost	High use: $30,000 or more	Limit to you
D.C. Area Plans When You Use Preferred Providers								
E35	Kaiser-Std	HMO	3960	2640	3050	4180	6520	9640
T72	Kaiser Basic	HMO	3080	2050	2830	4240	7480	10050
B62	CareFirst HDHP	HDHP	4060	910	2700	4410	8320	9210
V42	United HDHP	HDHP	3360	740	2940	4770	9030	9690
E32	Kaiser-Hi	HMO	5740	3830	4110	4810	6270	8330
Y82	United Choice Primary	HMO	3590	2400	3290	5050	8890	17100
AS2	United Choice Plus Primary	PPO-FEE	3730	2490	3380	5140	8980	17190
L92	United Choice Plus Advanced	PPO-FEE	4390	2930	4440	5690	8930	8930
B65	CareFirst Blue Value Plus	HMO-POS	5920	3950	4480	5710	8390	13950
JN5	Aetna Open Access Basic	HMO	4940	3290	4170	5930	9730	15290
LR2	United Choice Open Access	HMO	6120	4080	4900	6220	9230	14080
QQ5	Aetna Saver	HMO	4090	2730	4890	6880	12240	15730
2G5	CareFirst-Std POS	HMO-POS	9900	6600	6710	7530	9130	11600
F52	Aetna HealthFund CDHP	CDHP	8480	3660	5690	7960	12540	16260
F55	Aetna Value Plan	PPO-FEE	8320	5550	6400	8470	12860	18150
JP2	MD-IPA	HMO	15290	10200	10890	12060	14720	20200
JN2	Aetna Open Access-Hi	HMO	16480	10990	11520	12460	14420	20990
National Plans When You Use Preferred Providers								
342	GEHA HDHP	HDHP	3900	800	2670	3990	6470	12600
482	MHBP HDHP	HDHP	4000	310	2710	4470	7730	14710
325	NALC CDHP	CDHP	3270	-180	1540	4640	10090	15420
255	GEHA Elevate	PPO-FEE	3450	2300	3010	4870	8780	16300
402	Foreign Service	PPO-FEE	4440	2960	4030	4880	6970	9960
252	GEHA Elevate Plus	PPO-FEE	4690	3130	3670	5020	8080	15130
475	APWU CDHP	CDHP	4250	470	2820	5080	9180	15870
455	MHBP-Std	PPO-FEE	3980	2700	3970	5090	7790	14700
132	FEP Blue Focus	PPO	3270	2180	3570	5170	9320	15180
322	NALC-Hi	PPO-FEE	4910	3310	4170	5340	7890	12310
315	GEHA-Std	PPO-FEE	4040	2700	3450	5370	9310	15700
112	Blue Cross Basic	PPO	4970	3320	4010	5400	8420	14320
382	Rural Carrier	PPO-FEE	4880	3250	4190	5530	8600	13250
N62	Aetna Direct CDHP	CDHP	4640	1290	3690	5560	9710	15090
KM2	NALC Value Plan	PPO-FEE	2680	1630	3350	5580	10000	15030
415	MHBP Value Plan	PPO-FEE	3290	2230	4130	5790	9980	15430
445	SAMBA-Std	PPO-FEE	4660	3110	4210	5840	9440	17110
225	Aetna HealthFund HDHP	HDHP	5080	1790	3840	6090	10570	17190
422	Compass Rose	PPO-FEE	6850	4570	5400	6170	8210	11570
472	APWU-Hi	PPO-FEE	6710	4510	5800	6990	9850	17510
312	GEHA-Hi	PPO-FEE	7910	5280	5930	7290	10100	15280
Z25	Aetna Advantage	PPO-FEE	3690	2460	4860	7550	13510	17460
105	Blue Cross-Std	PPO-FEE	7460	4970	6300	7600	10580	14970
442	SAMBA-Hi	PPO-FEE	11760	7850	8870	10260	13310	19850

* These are the premiums after tax savings, offset by savings accounts for plans that offer them. If you have no or low health-care costs with these plans, it can result in actual saving to you, which we indicate with a negative number.

Persons Under 55: GS Premiums		Family of Five							
				Estimated yearly out-of-pocket costs, including premium and typical hospital, medical, drug, and dental bills near:					
Plan code	Plan name	Plan type	Published premium	No costs*	Low use: $3,000 or less	Average cost	High use: $30,000 or more	Limit to you
D.C. Area Plans When You Use Preferred Providers								
E35	Kaiser-Std	HMO	3960	2640	3050	4350	6520	9640
T72	Kaiser Basic	HMO	3080	2050	2830	4480	7480	10050
B62	CareFirst HDHP	HDHP	4060	910	2700	4720	8320	9210
E32	Kaiser-Hi	HMO	5740	3830	4110	4920	6270	8330
V42	United HDHP	HDHP	3360	740	2940	5110	9030	9690
Y82	United Choice Primary	HMO	3590	2400	3290	5350	8890	17100
AS2	United Choice Plus Primary	PPO-FEE	3730	2490	3380	5440	8980	17190
B65	CareFirst Blue Value Plus	HMO-POS	5920	3950	4480	5900	8390	13950
L92	United Choice Plus Advanced	PPO-FEE	4390	2930	4440	5920	8930	8930
JN5	Aetna Open Access Basic	HMO	4940	3290	4170	6210	9730	15290
LR2	United Choice Open Access	HMO	6120	4080	4900	6440	9230	14080
QQ5	Aetna Saver	HMO	4090	2730	4890	7260	12240	15730
2G5	CareFirst-Std POS	HMO-POS	9900	6600	6710	7650	9130	11600
F52	Aetna HealthFund CDHP	CDHP	8480	3660	5690	8350	12540	16260
F55	Aetna Value Plan	PPO-FEE	8320	5550	6400	8800	12860	18150
JP2	MD-IPA	HMO	15290	10200	10890	12260	14720	20200
JN2	Aetna Open Access-Hi	HMO	16480	10990	11520	12610	14420	20990
National Plans When You Use Preferred Providers								
342	GEHA HDHP	HDHP	3900	800	2670	4250	6470	12600
482	MHBP HDHP	HDHP	4000	310	2710	4790	7730	14710
402	Foreign Service	PPO-FEE	4440	2960	4030	5050	6970	9960
325	NALC CDHP	CDHP	3270	-180	1540	5140	10090	15420
255	GEHA Elevate	PPO-FEE	3450	2300	3010	5160	8780	16300
252	GEHA Elevate Plus	PPO-FEE	4690	3130	3670	5240	8080	15130
455	MHBP-Std	PPO-FEE	3980	2700	3970	5310	7790	14700
132	FEP Blue Focus	PPO	3270	2180	3570	5460	9320	15180
475	APWU CDHP	CDHP	4250	470	2820	5470	9180	15870
322	NALC-Hi	PPO-FEE	4910	3310	4170	5540	7890	12310
112	Blue Cross Basic	PPO	4970	3320	4010	5620	8420	14320
315	GEHA-Std	PPO-FEE	4040	2700	3450	5670	9310	15700
382	Rural Carrier	PPO-FEE	4880	3250	4190	5750	8600	13250
N62	Aetna Direct CDHP	CDHP	4640	1290	3690	5920	9710	15090
KM2	NALC Value Plan	PPO-FEE	2680	1630	3350	5970	10000	15030
445	SAMBA-Std	PPO-FEE	4660	3110	4210	6110	9440	17110
415	MHBP Value Plan	PPO-FEE	3290	2230	4130	6130	9980	15430
422	Compass Rose	PPO-FEE	6850	4570	5400	6330	8210	11570
225	Aetna HealthFund HDHP	HDHP	5080	1790	3840	6480	10570	17190
472	APWU-Hi	PPO-FEE	6710	4510	5800	7210	9850	17510
312	GEHA-Hi	PPO-FEE	7910	5280	5930	7510	10100	15280
105	Blue Cross-Std	PPO-FEE	7460	4970	6300	7840	10580	14970
Z25	Aetna Advantage	PPO-FEE	3690	2460	4860	8010	13510	17460
442	SAMBA-Hi	PPO-FEE	11760	7850	8870	10490	13310	19850

* These are the premiums after tax savings, offset by savings accounts for plans that offer them. If you have no or low health-care costs with these plans, it can result in actual saving to you, which we indicate with a negative number.

Persons Under 55: Postal Premiums (Category 1)		Self Only						
				Estimated yearly out-of-pocket costs, including premium and typical hospital, medical, drug, and dental bills near:				
Plan code	Plan name	Plan type	Published premium	No costs*	Low use: $1,000 or less	Average cost	High use: $30,000 or more	Limit to you
D.C. Area Plans When You Use Preferred Providers								
B61	CareFirst HDHP	HDHP	1640	200	740	1670	5100	5100
T71	Kaiser Basic	HMO	1210	810	1030	1710	4810	4810
E34	Kaiser-Std	HMO	1650	1100	1170	1730	4600	4600
V41	United HDHP	HDHP	1400	180	780	1740	5230	5230
E31	Kaiser-Hi	HMO	2460	1640	1660	2050	3890	3890
L91	United Choice Plus Advanced	PPO-FEE	1500	1000	1530	2100	4000	4000
Y81	United Choice Primary	HMO	1460	970	1150	2140	8320	8320
AS1	United Choice Plus Primary	PPO-FEE	1510	1010	1190	2180	8360	8360
B64	CareFirst Blue Value Plus	HMO-POS	2260	1510	1680	2380	6510	6510
LR1	United Choice Open Access	HMO	2360	1580	1770	2500	6580	6580
JN4	Aetna Open Access Basic	HMO	2150	1430	1630	2590	7430	7430
QQ4	Aetna Saver	HMO	1710	1140	1840	2920	7640	7640
2G4	CareFirst-Std POS	HMO-POS	3930	2620	2620	3070	5120	5120
F51	Aetna HealthFund CDHP	CDHP	3740	1490	2040	3220	7790	7790
F54	Aetna Value Plan	PPO-FEE	3620	2420	2670	3630	8720	8720
JP1	MD-IPA	HMO	4300	2870	3010	3680	7470	7870
JN1	Aetna Open Access-Hi	HMO	7440	4960	5030	5590	8450	9960
National Plans When You Use Preferred Providers								
341	GEHA HDHP	HDHP	1480	90	590	1420	4860	5990
324	NALC CDHP	CDHP	1360	-250	120	1530	7550	7550
481	MHBP HDHP	HDHP	1650	-60	640	1700	5640	7140
474	APWU CDHP	CDHP	1720	-20	650	1940	7680	7680
254	GEHA Elevate	PPO-FEE	1180	790	1020	1950	7790	7790
401	Foreign Service	PPO-FEE	1720	1150	1430	2010	5020	6150
251	GEHA Elevate Plus	PPO-FEE	1810	1210	1330	2070	6530	7210
N61	Aetna Direct CDHP	CDHP	1760	280	980	2090	7180	7180
131	FEP Blue Focus	PPO	1330	880	1400	2140	7380	7380
111	Blue Cross Basic	PPO	1900	1260	1390	2170	6490	6760
314	GEHA-Std	PPO-FEE	1510	1010	1240	2180	7510	7510
381	Rural Carrier	PPO-FEE	1800	1200	1520	2210	6200	6200
454	MHBP-Std	PPO-FEE	1640	1140	1440	2260	6810	7140
KM1	NALC Value Plan	PPO-FEE	1120	680	1050	2270	7380	7380
421	Compass Rose	PPO-FEE	2560	1710	1920	2430	5350	6710
414	MHBP Value Plan	PPO-FEE	1310	910	1330	2440	7510	7510
321	NALC-Hi	PPO-FEE	2280	1550	1830	2470	5910	8150
444	SAMBA-Std	PPO-FEE	1960	1310	1650	2620	8310	8310
224	Aetna HealthFund HDHP	HDHP	2530	890	1410	2690	8590	8590
311	GEHA-Hi	PPO-FEE	2660	1770	1990	2690	6770	6770
471	APWU-Hi	PPO-FEE	2500	1700	2220	2920	7910	8200
Z24	Aetna Advantage	PPO-FEE	1340	890	1590	2960	8390	8390
104	Blue Cross-Std	PPO-FEE	2950	1970	2400	3130	6970	6970
441	SAMBA-Hi	PPO-FEE	4610	3070	3380	4230	9070	9070

* These are the premiums after tax savings, offset by savings accounts for plans that offer them. If you have no or low health-care costs with these plans, it can result in actual saving to you, which we indicate with a negative number.

Persons Under 55: Postal Premiums (Category 1)		Self Plus One						
		Plan type	Published premium	Estimated yearly out-of-pocket costs, including premium and typical hospital, medical, drug, and dental bills near:				
Plan code	Plan name			No costs*	Low use: $3,000 or less	Average cost	High use: $30,000 or more	Limit to you
D.C. Area Plans When You Use Preferred Providers								
B63	CareFirst HDHP	HDHP	3280	390	2180	3220	7800	8690
T73	Kaiser Basic	HMO	2690	1800	2580	3490	7230	9800
E36	Kaiser-Std	HMO	3790	2530	2940	3690	6410	9530
V43	United HDHP	HDHP	3010	510	2710	3760	8800	9460
B66	CareFirst Blue Value Plus	HMO-POS	4070	2710	3240	4080	7150	12710
Y83	United Choice Primary	HMO	3140	2090	2980	4120	8580	16790
L93	United Choice Plus Advanced	PPO-FEE	2930	1960	3470	4190	7960	7960
AS3	United Choice Plus Primary	PPO-FEE	3260	2170	3060	4200	8660	16870
JN6	Aetna Open Access Basic	HMO	4290	2860	3740	4900	9300	14860
LR3	United Choice Open Access	HMO	5150	3440	4260	5100	8590	13440
E33	Kaiser-Hi	HMO	6660	4440	4720	5180	6880	8940
2G6	CareFirst-Std POS	HMO-POS	7000	4670	4780	5360	7200	9670
QQ6	Aetna Saver	HMO	3600	2400	4560	5720	11910	15400
JP3	MD-IPA	HMO	7260	4840	5530	6280	9360	14840
F53	Aetna HealthFund CDHP	CDHP	9170	4120	6150	7560	13000	16720
F56	Aetna Value Plan	PPO-FEE	8800	5870	6720	8110	13180	18470
JN3	Aetna Open Access-Hi	HMO	17100	11400	11930	12530	14830	21400
National Plans When You Use Preferred Providers								
343	GEHA HDHP	HDHP	3180	320	2190	2930	5990	12120
326	NALC CDHP	CDHP	3010	-360	1360	3360	9910	15240
483	MHBP HDHP	HDHP	3650	80	2480	3490	7500	14480
256	GEHA Elevate	PPO-FEE	2720	1810	2520	3770	8290	15810
476	APWU CDHP	CDHP	3740	130	2480	3860	8840	15530
316	GEHA-Std	PPO-FEE	3250	2170	2920	4220	8780	15170
N63	Aetna Direct CDHP	CDHP	3870	780	3180	4240	9200	14580
253	GEHA Elevate Plus	PPO-FEE	4240	2830	3370	4270	7780	14830
133	FEP Blue Focus	PPO	2850	1900	3290	4280	9040	14900
403	Foreign Service	PPO-FEE	4280	2860	3930	4400	6870	9860
456	MHBP-Std	PPO-FEE	3780	2570	3840	4470	7660	14570
113	Blue Cross Basic	PPO	4460	2980	3670	4570	8080	13980
KM3	NALC Value Plan	PPO-FEE	2470	1480	3200	4590	9850	14880
416	MHBP Value Plan	PPO-FEE	3090	2110	4010	4940	9860	15310
446	SAMBA-Std	PPO-FEE	4290	2860	3960	5000	9190	16860
383	Rural Carrier	PPO-FEE	5140	3430	4370	5260	8780	13430
423	Compass Rose	PPO-FEE	6010	4010	4840	5280	7650	11010
323	NALC-Hi	PPO-FEE	5490	3700	4560	5300	8280	12700
473	APWU-Hi	PPO-FEE	5010	3380	4670	5390	8720	16380
226	Aetna HealthFund HDHP	HDHP	5620	2150	4200	5580	10930	17550
313	GEHA-Hi	PPO-FEE	6230	4150	4800	5710	8970	14150
Z26	Aetna Advantage	PPO-FEE	2940	1960	4360	6030	13010	16960
106	Blue Cross-Std	PPO-FEE	6760	4510	5840	6610	10120	14510
443	SAMBA-Hi	PPO-FEE	10520	7010	8030	8900	12470	19010

* These are the premiums after tax savings, offset by savings accounts for plans that offer them. If you have no or low health-care costs with these plans, it can result in actual saving to you, which we indicate with a negative number.

Persons Under 55: Postal Premiums (Category 1)		Family of Two							
		Plan type	Published premium	Estimated yearly out-of-pocket costs, including premium and typical hospital, medical, drug, and dental bills near:					
Plan code	Plan name			No costs*	Low use: $1,000 or less	Average cost	High use: $30,000 or more	Limit to you
D.C. Area Plans When You Use Preferred Providers								
B62	CareFirst HDHP	HDHP	3900	800	2590	3630	8210	9100
T72	Kaiser Basic	HMO	2960	1970	2750	3660	7400	9970
E35	Kaiser-Std	HMO	3800	2540	2950	3700	6420	9540
V42	United HDHP	HDHP	3220	650	2850	3900	8940	9600
Y82	United Choice Primary	HMO	3450	2300	3190	4330	8790	17000
AS2	United Choice Plus Primary	PPO-FEE	3580	2390	3280	4420	8880	17090
E32	Kaiser-Hi	HMO	5540	3700	3980	4440	6140	8200
L92	United Choice Plus Advanced	PPO-FEE	4210	2810	4320	5040	8810	8810
B65	CareFirst Blue Value Plus	HMO-POS	5720	3820	4350	5190	8260	13820
JN5	Aetna Open Access Basic	HMO	4740	3160	4040	5200	9600	15160
LR2	United Choice Open Access	HMO	5930	3950	4770	5610	9100	13950
QQ5	Aetna Saver	HMO	3920	2620	4780	5940	12130	15620
F52	Aetna HealthFund CDHP	CDHP	8280	3520	5550	6960	12400	16120
2G5	CareFirst-Std POS	HMO-POS	9700	6470	6580	7160	9000	11470
F55	Aetna Value Plan	PPO-FEE	8130	5420	6270	7660	12730	18020
JP2	MD-IPA	HMO	15090	10060	10750	11500	14580	20060
JN2	Aetna Open Access-Hi	HMO	16280	10860	11390	11990	14290	20860
National Plans When You Use Preferred Providers								
342	GEHA HDHP	HDHP	3740	700	2570	3310	6370	12500
325	NALC CDHP	CDHP	3140	-270	1450	3450	10000	15330
482	MHBP HDHP	HDHP	3840	200	2600	3610	7620	14600
475	APWU CDHP	CDHP	4080	360	2710	4090	9070	15760
255	GEHA Elevate	PPO-FEE	3310	2210	2920	4170	8690	16210
402	Foreign Service	PPO-FEE	4260	2840	3910	4380	6850	9840
252	GEHA Elevate Plus	PPO-FEE	4500	3000	3540	4440	7950	15000
132	FEP Blue Focus	PPO	3140	2090	3480	4470	9230	15090
455	MHBP-Std	PPO-FEE	3820	2590	3860	4490	7680	14590
N62	Aetna Direct CDHP	CDHP	4450	1170	3570	4630	9590	14970
315	GEHA-Std	PPO-FEE	3880	2590	3340	4640	9200	15590
KM2	NALC Value Plan	PPO-FEE	2580	1550	3270	4660	9920	14950
112	Blue Cross Basic	PPO	4770	3180	3870	4770	8280	14180
322	NALC-Hi	PPO-FEE	4710	3180	4040	4780	7760	12180
382	Rural Carrier	PPO-FEE	4680	3120	4060	4950	8470	13120
415	MHBP Value Plan	PPO-FEE	3160	2150	4050	4980	9900	15350
225	Aetna HealthFund HDHP	HDHP	4890	1660	3710	5090	10440	17060
445	SAMBA-Std	PPO-FEE	4470	2980	4080	5120	9310	16980
422	Compass Rose	PPO-FEE	6650	4440	5270	5710	8080	11440
472	APWU-Hi	PPO-FEE	6510	4380	5670	6390	9720	17380
Z25	Aetna Advantage	PPO-FEE	3540	2360	4760	6430	13410	17360
312	GEHA-Hi	PPO-FEE	7720	5150	5800	6710	9970	15150
105	Blue Cross-Std	PPO-FEE	7260	4840	6170	6940	10450	14840
442	SAMBA-Hi	PPO-FEE	11560	7710	8730	9600	13170	19710

* These are the premiums after tax savings, offset by savings accounts for plans that offer them. If you have no or low health-care costs with these plans, it can result in actual saving to you, which we indicate with a negative number.

Persons Under 55: Postal Premiums (Category 1)

Family of Three

Plan code	Plan name	Plan type	Published premium	Estimated yearly out-of-pocket costs, including premium and typical hospital, medical, drug, and dental bills near: No costs*	Low use: $3,000 or less	Average cost	High use: $30,000 or more	Limit to you
D.C. Area Plans When You Use Preferred Providers								
E35	Kaiser-Std	HMO	3800	2540	2950	3890	6420	9540
T72	Kaiser Basic	HMO	2960	1970	2750	3920	7400	9970
B62	CareFirst HDHP	HDHP	3900	800	2590	3980	8210	9100
V42	United HDHP	HDHP	3220	650	2850	4300	8940	9600
E32	Kaiser-Hi	HMO	5540	3700	3980	4560	6140	8200
Y82	United Choice Primary	HMO	3450	2300	3190	4650	8790	17000
AS2	United Choice Plus Primary	PPO-FEE	3580	2390	3280	4740	8880	17090
L92	United Choice Plus Advanced	PPO-FEE	4210	2810	4320	5310	8810	8810
B65	CareFirst Blue Value Plus	HMO-POS	5720	3820	4350	5390	8260	13820
JN5	Aetna Open Access Basic	HMO	4740	3160	4040	5510	9600	15160
LR2	United Choice Open Access	HMO	5930	3950	4770	5850	9100	13950
QQ5	Aetna Saver	HMO	3920	2620	4780	6360	12130	15620
2G5	CareFirst-Std POS	HMO-POS	9700	6470	6580	7280	9000	11470
F52	Aetna HealthFund CDHP	CDHP	8280	3520	5550	7410	12400	16120
F55	Aetna Value Plan	PPO-FEE	8130	5420	6270	8000	12730	18020
JP2	MD-IPA	HMO	15090	10060	10750	11720	14580	20060
JN2	Aetna Open Access-Hi	HMO	16280	10860	11390	12160	14290	20860
National Plans When You Use Preferred Providers								
342	GEHA HDHP	HDHP	3740	700	2570	3620	6370	12500
482	MHBP HDHP	HDHP	3840	200	2600	4010	7620	14600
325	NALC CDHP	CDHP	3140	-270	1450	4010	10000	15330
255	GEHA Elevate	PPO-FEE	3310	2210	2920	4480	8690	16210
475	APWU CDHP	CDHP	4080	360	2710	4550	9070	15760
402	Foreign Service	PPO-FEE	4260	2840	3910	4580	6850	9840
252	GEHA Elevate Plus	PPO-FEE	4500	3000	3540	4670	7950	15000
455	MHBP-Std	PPO-FEE	3820	2590	3860	4740	7680	14590
132	FEP Blue Focus	PPO	3140	2090	3480	4780	9230	15090
315	GEHA-Std	PPO-FEE	3880	2590	3340	4960	9200	15590
322	NALC-Hi	PPO-FEE	4710	3180	4040	5000	7760	12180
112	Blue Cross Basic	PPO	4770	3180	3870	5020	8280	14180
N62	Aetna Direct CDHP	CDHP	4450	1170	3570	5050	9590	14970
KM2	NALC Value Plan	PPO-FEE	2580	1550	3270	5090	9920	14950
382	Rural Carrier	PPO-FEE	4680	3120	4060	5180	8470	13120
415	MHBP Value Plan	PPO-FEE	3160	2150	4050	5350	9900	15350
445	SAMBA-Std	PPO-FEE	4470	2980	4080	5420	9310	16980
225	Aetna HealthFund HDHP	HDHP	4890	1660	3710	5540	10440	17060
422	Compass Rose	PPO-FEE	6650	4440	5270	5880	8080	11440
472	APWU-Hi	PPO-FEE	6510	4380	5670	6630	9720	17380
312	GEHA-Hi	PPO-FEE	7720	5150	5800	6940	9970	15150
Z25	Aetna Advantage	PPO-FEE	3540	2360	4760	6960	13410	17360
105	Blue Cross-Std	PPO-FEE	7260	4840	6170	7210	10450	14840
442	SAMBA-Hi	PPO-FEE	11560	7710	8730	9870	13170	19710

* These are the premiums after tax savings, offset by savings accounts for plans that offer them. If you have no or low health-care costs with these plans, it can result in actual saving to you, which we indicate with a negative number.

Persons Under 55: Postal Premiums (Category 1)

				Family of Four				
				Estimated yearly out-of-pocket costs, including premium and typical hospital, medical, drug, and dental bills near:				
Plan code	Plan name	Plan type	Published premium	No costs*	Low use: $1,000 or less	Average cost	High use: $30,000 or more	Limit to you
D.C. Area Plans When You Use Preferred Providers								
E35	Kaiser-Std	HMO	3800	2540	2950	4080	6420	9540
T72	Kaiser Basic	HMO	2960	1970	2750	4160	7400	9970
B62	CareFirst HDHP	HDHP	3900	800	2590	4300	8210	9100
E32	Kaiser-Hi	HMO	5540	3700	3980	4680	6140	8200
V42	United HDHP	HDHP	3220	650	2850	4680	8940	9600
Y82	United Choice Primary	HMO	3450	2300	3190	4950	8790	17000
AS2	United Choice Plus Primary	PPO-FEE	3580	2390	3280	5040	8880	17090
L92	United Choice Plus Advanced	PPO-FEE	4210	2810	4320	5570	8810	8810
B65	CareFirst Blue Value Plus	HMO-POS	5720	3820	4350	5580	8260	13820
JN5	Aetna Open Access Basic	HMO	4740	3160	4040	5800	9600	15160
LR2	United Choice Open Access	HMO	5930	3950	4770	6090	9100	13950
QQ5	Aetna Saver	HMO	3920	2620	4780	6770	12130	15620
2G5	CareFirst-Std POS	HMO-POS	9700	6470	6580	7400	9000	11470
F52	Aetna HealthFund CDHP	CDHP	8280	3520	5550	7820	12400	16120
F55	Aetna Value Plan	PPO-FEE	8130	5420	6270	8340	12730	18020
JP2	MD-IPA	HMO	15090	10060	10750	11920	14580	20060
JN2	Aetna Open Access-Hi	HMO	16280	10860	11390	12330	14290	20860
National Plans When You Use Preferred Providers								
342	GEHA HDHP	HDHP	3740	700	2570	3890	6370	12500
482	MHBP HDHP	HDHP	3840	200	2600	4360	7620	14600
325	NALC CDHP	CDHP	3140	-270	1450	4550	10000	15330
402	Foreign Service	PPO-FEE	4260	2840	3910	4760	6850	9840
255	GEHA Elevate	PPO-FEE	3310	2210	2920	4780	8690	16210
252	GEHA Elevate Plus	PPO-FEE	4500	3000	3540	4890	7950	15000
475	APWU CDHP	CDHP	4080	360	2710	4970	9070	15760
455	MHBP-Std	PPO-FEE	3820	2590	3860	4980	7680	14590
132	FEP Blue Focus	PPO	3140	2090	3480	5080	9230	15090
322	NALC-Hi	PPO-FEE	4710	3180	4040	5210	7760	12180
112	Blue Cross Basic	PPO	4770	3180	3870	5260	8280	14180
315	GEHA-Std	PPO-FEE	3880	2590	3340	5260	9200	15590
382	Rural Carrier	PPO-FEE	4680	3120	4060	5400	8470	13120
N62	Aetna Direct CDHP	CDHP	4450	1170	3570	5440	9590	14970
KM2	NALC Value Plan	PPO-FEE	2580	1550	3270	5500	9920	14950
415	MHBP Value Plan	PPO-FEE	3160	2150	4050	5710	9900	15350
445	SAMBA-Std	PPO-FEE	4470	2980	4080	5710	9310	16980
225	Aetna HealthFund HDHP	HDHP	4890	1660	3710	5960	10440	17060
422	Compass Rose	PPO-FEE	6650	4440	5270	6040	8080	11440
472	APWU-Hi	PPO-FEE	6510	4380	5670	6860	9720	17380
312	GEHA-Hi	PPO-FEE	7720	5150	5800	7160	9970	15150
Z25	Aetna Advantage	PPO-FEE	3540	2360	4760	7450	13410	17360
105	Blue Cross-Std	PPO-FEE	7260	4840	6170	7470	10450	14840
442	SAMBA-Hi	PPO-FEE	11560	7710	8730	10120	13170	19710

* These are the premiums after tax savings, offset by savings accounts for plans that offer them. If you have no or low health-care costs with these plans, it can result in actual saving to you, which we indicate with a negative number.

Persons Under 55: Postal Premiums (Category 1)

Family of Five

Plan code	Plan name	Plan type	Published premium	Estimated yearly out-of-pocket costs, including premium and typical hospital, medical, drug, and dental bills near: No costs*	Low use: $3,000 or less	Average cost	High use: $30,000 or more	Limit to you
D.C. Area Plans When You Use Preferred Providers								
E35	Kaiser-Std	HMO	3800	2540	2950	4250	6420	9540
T72	Kaiser Basic	HMO	2960	1970	2750	4400	7400	9970
B62	CareFirst HDHP	HDHP	3900	800	2590	4610	8210	9100
E32	Kaiser-Hi	HMO	5540	3700	3980	4790	6140	8200
V42	United HDHP	HDHP	3220	650	2850	5020	8940	9600
Y82	United Choice Primary	HMO	3450	2300	3190	5250	8790	17000
AS2	United Choice Plus Primary	PPO-FEE	3580	2390	3280	5340	8880	17090
B65	CareFirst Blue Value Plus	HMO-POS	5720	3820	4350	5770	8260	13820
L92	United Choice Plus Advanced	PPO-FEE	4210	2810	4320	5800	8810	8810
JN5	Aetna Open Access Basic	HMO	4740	3160	4040	6080	9600	15160
LR2	United Choice Open Access	HMO	5930	3950	4770	6310	9100	13950
QQ5	Aetna Saver	HMO	3920	2620	4780	7150	12130	15620
2G5	CareFirst-Std POS	HMO-POS	9700	6470	6580	7520	9000	11470
F52	Aetna HealthFund CDHP	CDHP	8280	3520	5550	8210	12400	16120
F55	Aetna Value Plan	PPO-FEE	8130	5420	6270	8670	12730	18020
JP2	MD-IPA	HMO	15090	10060	10750	12120	14580	20060
JN2	Aetna Open Access-Hi	HMO	16280	10860	11390	12480	14290	20860
National Plans When You Use Preferred Providers								
342	GEHA HDHP	HDHP	3740	700	2570	4150	6370	12500
482	MHBP HDHP	HDHP	3840	200	2600	4680	7620	14600
402	Foreign Service	PPO-FEE	4260	2840	3910	4930	6850	9840
325	NALC CDHP	CDHP	3140	-270	1450	5050	10000	15330
255	GEHA Elevate	PPO-FEE	3310	2210	2920	5070	8690	16210
252	GEHA Elevate Plus	PPO-FEE	4500	3000	3540	5110	7950	15000
455	MHBP-Std	PPO-FEE	3820	2590	3860	5200	7680	14590
475	APWU CDHP	CDHP	4080	360	2710	5360	9070	15760
132	FEP Blue Focus	PPO	3140	2090	3480	5370	9230	15090
322	NALC-Hi	PPO-FEE	4710	3180	4040	5410	7760	12180
112	Blue Cross Basic	PPO	4770	3180	3870	5480	8280	14180
315	GEHA-Std	PPO-FEE	3880	2590	3340	5560	9200	15590
382	Rural Carrier	PPO-FEE	4680	3120	4060	5620	8470	13120
N62	Aetna Direct CDHP	CDHP	4450	1170	3570	5800	9590	14970
KM2	NALC Value Plan	PPO-FEE	2580	1550	3270	5890	9920	14950
445	SAMBA-Std	PPO-FEE	4470	2980	4080	5980	9310	16980
415	MHBP Value Plan	PPO-FEE	3160	2150	4050	6050	9900	15350
422	Compass Rose	PPO-FEE	6650	4440	5270	6200	8080	11440
225	Aetna HealthFund HDHP	HDHP	4890	1660	3710	6350	10440	17060
472	APWU-Hi	PPO-FEE	6510	4380	5670	7080	9720	17380
312	GEHA-Hi	PPO-FEE	7720	5150	5800	7380	9970	15150
105	Blue Cross-Std	PPO-FEE	7260	4840	6170	7710	10450	14840
Z25	Aetna Advantage	PPO-FEE	3540	2360	4760	7910	13410	17360
442	SAMBA-Hi	PPO-FEE	11560	7710	8730	10350	13170	19710

* These are the premiums after tax savings, offset by savings accounts for plans that offer them. If you have no or low health-care costs with these plans, it can result in actual saving to you, which we indicate with a negative number.

Persons Under 55: Postal Premiums (Category 2)		Self Only						
		Plan type	Published premium	Estimated yearly out-of-pocket costs, including premium and typical hospital, medical, drug, and dental bills near:				
Plan code	Plan name			No costs*	Low use: $1,000 or less	Average cost	High use: $30,000 or more	Limit to you
D.C. Area Plans When You Use Preferred Providers								
B61	CareFirst HDHP	HDHP	1420	50	590	1520	4950	4950
E34	Kaiser-Std	HMO	1420	950	1020	1580	4450	4450
T71	Kaiser Basic	HMO	1050	700	920	1600	4700	4700
V41	United HDHP	HDHP	1210	60	660	1620	5110	5110
E31	Kaiser-Hi	HMO	2200	1470	1490	1880	3720	3720
L91	United Choice Plus Advanced	PPO-FEE	1300	870	1400	1970	3870	3870
Y81	United Choice Primary	HMO	1260	840	1020	2010	8190	8190
AS1	United Choice Plus Primary	PPO-FEE	1310	870	1050	2040	8220	8220
B64	CareFirst Blue Value Plus	HMO-POS	2000	1330	1500	2200	6330	6330
LR1	United Choice Open Access	HMO	2110	1410	1600	2330	6410	6410
JN4	Aetna Open Access Basic	HMO	1890	1260	1460	2420	7260	7260
QQ4	Aetna Saver	HMO	1480	990	1690	2770	7490	7490
2G4	CareFirst-Std POS	HMO-POS	3680	2450	2450	2900	4950	4950
F51	Aetna HealthFund CDHP	CDHP	3480	1320	1870	3050	7620	7620
F54	Aetna Value Plan	PPO-FEE	3370	2250	2500	3460	8550	8550
JP1	MD-IPA	HMO	4050	2700	2840	3510	7300	7700
JN1	Aetna Open Access-Hi	HMO	7180	4790	4860	5420	8280	9790
National Plans When You Use Preferred Providers								
341	GEHA HDHP	HDHP	1280	-50	450	1280	4720	5850
324	NALC CDHP	CDHP	1180	-380	-10	1400	7420	7420
481	MHBP HDHP	HDHP	1430	-210	490	1550	5490	6990
474	APWU CDHP	CDHP	1490	-170	500	1790	7530	7530
254	GEHA Elevate	PPO-FEE	1020	680	910	1840	7680	7680
401	Foreign Service	PPO-FEE	1490	990	1270	1850	4860	5990
251	GEHA Elevate Plus	PPO-FEE	1570	1050	1170	1910	6370	7050
N61	Aetna Direct CDHP	CDHP	1530	120	820	1930	7020	7020
111	Blue Cross Basic	PPO	1640	1090	1220	2000	6320	6590
131	FEP Blue Focus	PPO	1150	760	1280	2020	7260	7260
314	GEHA-Std	PPO-FEE	1310	870	1100	2040	7370	7370
454	MHBP-Std	PPO-FEE	1420	990	1290	2110	6660	6990
KM1	NALC Value Plan	PPO-FEE	970	580	950	2170	7280	7280
421	Compass Rose	PPO-FEE	2300	1540	1750	2260	5180	6540
321	NALC-Hi	PPO-FEE	2020	1380	1660	2300	5740	7980
414	MHBP Value Plan	PPO-FEE	1130	790	1210	2320	7390	7390
444	SAMBA-Std	PPO-FEE	1700	1130	1470	2440	8130	8130
224	Aetna HealthFund HDHP	HDHP	2280	720	1240	2520	8420	8420
311	GEHA-Hi	PPO-FEE	2400	1600	1820	2520	6600	6600
471	APWU-Hi	PPO-FEE	2240	1530	2050	2750	7740	8030
Z24	Aetna Advantage	PPO-FEE	1150	770	1470	2840	8270	8270
381	Rural Carrier	PPO-FEE	2840	1890	2210	2900	6890	6890
104	Blue Cross-Std	PPO-FEE	2700	1800	2230	2960	6800	6800
441	SAMBA-Hi	PPO-FEE	4350	2900	3210	4060	8900	8900

* These are the premiums after tax savings, offset by savings accounts for plans that offer them. If you have no or low health-care costs with these plans, it can result in actual saving to you, which we indicate with a negative number.

Persons Under 55: Postal Premiums (Category 2)		Self Plus One							
		Plan type	Published premium	Estimated yearly out-of-pocket costs, including premium and typical hospital, medical, drug, and dental bills near:					
Plan code	Plan name			No costs*	Low use: $3,000 or less	Average cost	High use: $30,000 or more	Limit to you	
D.C. Area Plans When You Use Preferred Providers									
B63	CareFirst HDHP	HDHP	2840	90	1880	2920	7500	8390	
T73	Kaiser Basic	HMO	2330	1550	2330	3240	6980	9550	
E36	Kaiser-Std	HMO	3270	2180	2590	3340	6060	9180	
V43	United HDHP	HDHP	2600	240	2440	3490	8530	9190	
B66	CareFirst Blue Value Plus	HMO-POS	3520	2350	2880	3720	6790	12350	
Y83	United Choice Primary	HMO	2710	1810	2700	3840	8300	16510	
AS3	United Choice Plus Primary	PPO-FEE	2810	1880	2770	3910	8370	16580	
L93	United Choice Plus Advanced	PPO-FEE	2540	1690	3200	3920	7690	7690	
JN6	Aetna Open Access Basic	HMO	3740	2500	3380	4540	8940	14500	
LR3	United Choice Open Access	HMO	4610	3070	3890	4730	8220	13070	
E33	Kaiser-Hi	HMO	6120	4080	4360	4820	6520	8580	
2G6	CareFirst-Std POS	HMO-POS	6460	4310	4420	5000	6840	9310	
QQ6	Aetna Saver	HMO	3110	2080	4240	5400	11590	15080	
JP3	MD-IPA	HMO	6710	4470	5160	5910	8990	14470	
F53	Aetna HealthFund CDHP	CDHP	8630	3760	5790	7200	12640	16360	
F56	Aetna Value Plan	PPO-FEE	8250	5510	6360	7750	12820	18110	
JN3	Aetna Open Access-Hi	HMO	16550	11040	11570	12170	14470	21040	
National Plans When You Use Preferred Providers									
343	GEHA HDHP	HDHP	2750	30	1900	2640	5700	11830	
326	NALC CDHP	CDHP	2600	-630	1090	3090	9640	14970	
483	MHBP HDHP	HDHP	3160	-250	2150	3160	7170	14150	
476	APWU CDHP	CDHP	3230	-210	2140	3520	8500	15190	
256	GEHA Elevate	PPO-FEE	2350	1570	2280	3530	8050	15570	
N63	Aetna Direct CDHP	CDHP	3350	430	2830	3890	8850	14230	
253	GEHA Elevate Plus	PPO-FEE	3700	2470	3010	3910	7420	14470	
316	GEHA-Std	PPO-FEE	2810	1870	2620	3920	8480	14870	
133	FEP Blue Focus	PPO	2470	1640	3030	4020	8780	14640	
403	Foreign Service	PPO-FEE	3740	2490	3560	4030	6500	9490	
456	MHBP-Std	PPO-FEE	3270	2220	3490	4120	7310	14220	
113	Blue Cross Basic	PPO	3920	2610	3300	4200	7710	13610	
KM3	NALC Value Plan	PPO-FEE	2130	1260	2980	4370	9630	14660	
446	SAMBA-Std	PPO-FEE	3740	2500	3600	4640	8830	16500	
416	MHBP Value Plan	PPO-FEE	2670	1830	3730	4660	9580	15030	
383	Rural Carrier	PPO-FEE	4600	3070	4010	4900	8420	13070	
423	Compass Rose	PPO-FEE	5470	3650	4480	4920	7290	10650	
323	NALC-Hi	PPO-FEE	4950	3340	4200	4940	7920	12340	
473	APWU-Hi	PPO-FEE	4470	3010	4300	5020	8350	16010	
226	Aetna HealthFund HDHP	HDHP	5080	1790	3840	5220	10570	17190	
313	GEHA-Hi	PPO-FEE	5680	3790	4440	5350	8610	13790	
Z26	Aetna Advantage	PPO-FEE	2540	1690	4090	5760	12740	16690	
106	Blue Cross-Std	PPO-FEE	6220	4150	5480	6250	9760	14150	
443	SAMBA-Hi	PPO-FEE	9970	6650	7670	8540	12110	18650	

* These are the premiums after tax savings, offset by savings accounts for plans that offer them. If you have no or low health-care costs with these plans, it can result in actual saving to you, which we indicate with a negative number.

Persons Under 55: Postal Premiums (Category 2)				Family of Two					
				Estimated yearly out-of-pocket costs, including premium and typical hospital, medical, drug, and dental bills near:					
Plan code	Plan name	Plan type	Published premium	No costs*	Low use: $1,000 or less	Average cost	High use: $30,000 or more	Limit to you
D.C. Area Plans When You Use Preferred Providers								
B62	CareFirst HDHP	HDHP	3370	450	2240	3280	7860	8750
E35	Kaiser-Std	HMO	3290	2190	2600	3350	6070	9190
T72	Kaiser Basic	HMO	2560	1700	2480	3390	7130	9700
V42	United HDHP	HDHP	2790	360	2560	3610	8650	9310
Y82	United Choice Primary	HMO	2980	1990	2880	4020	8480	16690
E32	Kaiser-Hi	HMO	4950	3300	3580	4040	5740	7800
AS2	United Choice Plus Primary	PPO-FEE	3100	2070	2960	4100	8560	16770
L92	United Choice Plus Advanced	PPO-FEE	3640	2430	3940	4660	8430	8430
B65	CareFirst Blue Value Plus	HMO-POS	5130	3420	3950	4790	7860	13420
JN5	Aetna Open Access Basic	HMO	4150	2770	3650	4810	9210	14770
LR2	United Choice Open Access	HMO	5330	3560	4380	5220	8710	13560
QQ5	Aetna Saver	HMO	3390	2260	4420	5580	11770	15260
F52	Aetna HealthFund CDHP	CDHP	7690	3130	5160	6570	12010	15730
2G5	CareFirst-Std POS	HMO-POS	9110	6080	6190	6770	8610	11080
F55	Aetna Value Plan	PPO-FEE	7530	5030	5880	7270	12340	17630
JP2	MD-IPA	HMO	14500	9670	10360	11110	14190	19670
JN2	Aetna Open Access-Hi	HMO	15690	10470	11000	11600	13900	20470
National Plans When You Use Preferred Providers								
342	GEHA HDHP	HDHP	3240	360	2230	2970	6030	12160
325	NALC CDHP	CDHP	2710	-560	1160	3160	9710	15040
482	MHBP HDHP	HDHP	3320	-150	2250	3260	7270	14250
475	APWU CDHP	CDHP	3530	-10	2340	3720	8700	15390
255	GEHA Elevate	PPO-FEE	2860	1910	2620	3870	8390	15910
402	Foreign Service	PPO-FEE	3680	2460	3530	4000	6470	9460
252	GEHA Elevate Plus	PPO-FEE	3890	2590	3130	4030	7540	14590
455	MHBP-Std	PPO-FEE	3300	2250	3520	4150	7340	14250
132	FEP Blue Focus	PPO	2710	1810	3200	4190	8950	14810
N62	Aetna Direct CDHP	CDHP	3850	770	3170	4230	9190	14570
315	GEHA-Std	PPO-FEE	3360	2240	2990	4290	8850	15240
112	Blue Cross Basic	PPO	4180	2790	3480	4380	7890	13790
322	NALC-Hi	PPO-FEE	4120	2780	3640	4380	7360	11780
KM2	NALC Value Plan	PPO-FEE	2230	1320	3040	4430	9690	14720
382	Rural Carrier	PPO-FEE	4090	2730	3670	4560	8080	12730
225	Aetna HealthFund HDHP	HDHP	4290	1260	3310	4690	10040	16660
415	MHBP Value Plan	PPO-FEE	2730	1860	3760	4690	9610	15060
445	SAMBA-Std	PPO-FEE	3870	2580	3680	4720	8910	16580
422	Compass Rose	PPO-FEE	6060	4040	4870	5310	7680	11040
472	APWU-Hi	PPO-FEE	5920	3980	5270	5990	9320	16980
Z25	Aetna Advantage	PPO-FEE	3060	2040	4440	6110	13090	17040
312	GEHA-Hi	PPO-FEE	7120	4750	5400	6310	9570	14750
105	Blue Cross-Std	PPO-FEE	6670	4450	5780	6550	10060	14450
442	SAMBA-Hi	PPO-FEE	10970	7320	8340	9210	12780	19320

* These are the premiums after tax savings, offset by savings accounts for plans that offer them. If you have no or low health-care costs with these plans, it can result in actual saving to you, which we indicate with a negative number.

Persons Under 55: Postal Premiums (Category 2)		Family of Three							
				Estimated yearly out-of-pocket costs, including premium and typical hospital, medical, drug, and dental bills near:					
Plan code	Plan name	Plan type	Published premium	No costs*	Low use: $3,000 or less	Average cost	High use: $30,000 or more	Limit to you
D.C. Area Plans When You Use Preferred Providers								
E35	Kaiser-Std	HMO	3290	2190	2600	3540	6070	9190
B62	CareFirst HDHP	HDHP	3370	450	2240	3630	7860	8750
T72	Kaiser Basic	HMO	2560	1700	2480	3650	7130	9700
V42	United HDHP	HDHP	2790	360	2560	4010	8650	9310
E32	Kaiser-Hi	HMO	4950	3300	3580	4160	5740	7800
Y82	United Choice Primary	HMO	2980	1990	2880	4340	8480	16690
AS2	United Choice Plus Primary	PPO-FEE	3100	2070	2960	4420	8560	16770
L92	United Choice Plus Advanced	PPO-FEE	3640	2430	3940	4930	8430	8430
B65	CareFirst Blue Value Plus	HMO-POS	5130	3420	3950	4990	7860	13420
JN5	Aetna Open Access Basic	HMO	4150	2770	3650	5120	9210	14770
LR2	United Choice Open Access	HMO	5330	3560	4380	5460	8710	13560
QQ5	Aetna Saver	HMO	3390	2260	4420	6000	11770	15260
2G5	CareFirst-Std POS	HMO-POS	9110	6080	6190	6890	8610	11080
F52	Aetna HealthFund CDHP	CDHP	7690	3130	5160	7020	12010	15730
F55	Aetna Value Plan	PPO-FEE	7530	5030	5880	7610	12340	17630
JP2	MD-IPA	HMO	14500	9670	10360	11330	14190	19670
JN2	Aetna Open Access-Hi	HMO	15690	10470	11000	11770	13900	20470
National Plans When You Use Preferred Providers								
342	GEHA HDHP	HDHP	3240	360	2230	3280	6030	12160
482	MHBP HDHP	HDHP	3320	-150	2250	3660	7270	14250
325	NALC CDHP	CDHP	2710	-560	1160	3720	9710	15040
475	APWU CDHP	CDHP	3530	-10	2340	4180	8700	15390
255	GEHA Elevate	PPO-FEE	2860	1910	2620	4180	8390	15910
402	Foreign Service	PPO-FEE	3680	2460	3530	4200	6470	9460
252	GEHA Elevate Plus	PPO-FEE	3890	2590	3130	4260	7540	14590
455	MHBP-Std	PPO-FEE	3300	2250	3520	4400	7340	14250
132	FEP Blue Focus	PPO	2710	1810	3200	4500	8950	14810
322	NALC-Hi	PPO-FEE	4120	2780	3640	4600	7360	11780
315	GEHA-Std	PPO-FEE	3360	2240	2990	4610	8850	15240
112	Blue Cross Basic	PPO	4180	2790	3480	4630	7890	13790
N62	Aetna Direct CDHP	CDHP	3850	770	3170	4650	9190	14570
382	Rural Carrier	PPO-FEE	4090	2730	3670	4790	8080	12730
KM2	NALC Value Plan	PPO-FEE	2230	1320	3040	4860	9690	14720
445	SAMBA-Std	PPO-FEE	3870	2580	3680	5020	8910	16580
415	MHBP Value Plan	PPO-FEE	2730	1860	3760	5060	9610	15060
225	Aetna HealthFund HDHP	HDHP	4290	1260	3310	5140	10040	16660
422	Compass Rose	PPO-FEE	6060	4040	4870	5480	7680	11040
472	APWU-Hi	PPO-FEE	5920	3980	5270	6230	9320	16980
312	GEHA-Hi	PPO-FEE	7120	4750	5400	6540	9570	14750
Z25	Aetna Advantage	PPO-FEE	3060	2040	4440	6640	13090	17040
105	Blue Cross-Std	PPO-FEE	6670	4450	5780	6820	10060	14450
442	SAMBA-Hi	PPO-FEE	10970	7320	8340	9480	12780	19320

* These are the premiums after tax savings, offset by savings accounts for plans that offer them. If you have no or low health-care costs with these plans, it can result in actual saving to you, which we indicate with a negative number.

Persons Under 55: Postal Premiums (Category 2)

Plan code	Plan name	Family of Four: Plan type	Published premium	Estimated yearly out-of-pocket costs, including premium and typical hospital, medical, drug, and dental bills near: No costs*	Low use: $1,000 or less	Average cost	High use: $30,000 or more	Limit to you
D.C. Area Plans When You Use Preferred Providers								
E35	Kaiser-Std	HMO	3290	2190	2600	3730	6070	9190
T72	Kaiser Basic	HMO	2560	1700	2480	3890	7130	9700
B62	CareFirst HDHP	HDHP	3370	450	2240	3950	7860	8750
E32	Kaiser-Hi	HMO	4950	3300	3580	4280	5740	7800
V42	United HDHP	HDHP	2790	360	2560	4390	8650	9310
Y82	United Choice Primary	HMO	2980	1990	2880	4640	8480	16690
AS2	United Choice Plus Primary	PPO-FEE	3100	2070	2960	4720	8560	16770
B65	CareFirst Blue Value Plus	HMO-POS	5130	3420	3950	5180	7860	13420
L92	United Choice Plus Advanced	PPO-FEE	3640	2430	3940	5190	8430	8430
JN5	Aetna Open Access Basic	HMO	4150	2770	3650	5410	9210	14770
LR2	United Choice Open Access	HMO	5330	3560	4380	5700	8710	13560
QQ5	Aetna Saver	HMO	3390	2260	4420	6410	11770	15260
2G5	CareFirst-Std POS	HMO-POS	9110	6080	6190	7010	8610	11080
F52	Aetna HealthFund CDHP	CDHP	7690	3130	5160	7430	12010	15730
F55	Aetna Value Plan	PPO-FEE	7530	5030	5880	7950	12340	17630
JP2	MD-IPA	HMO	14500	9670	10360	11530	14190	19670
JN2	Aetna Open Access-Hi	HMO	15690	10470	11000	11940	13900	20470
National Plans When You Use Preferred Providers								
342	GEHA HDHP	HDHP	3240	360	2230	3550	6030	12160
482	MHBP HDHP	HDHP	3320	-150	2250	4010	7270	14250
325	NALC CDHP	CDHP	2710	-560	1160	4260	9710	15040
402	Foreign Service	PPO-FEE	3680	2460	3530	4380	6470	9460
255	GEHA Elevate	PPO-FEE	2860	1910	2620	4480	8390	15910
252	GEHA Elevate Plus	PPO-FEE	3890	2590	3130	4480	7540	14590
475	APWU CDHP	CDHP	3530	-10	2340	4600	8700	15390
455	MHBP-Std	PPO-FEE	3300	2250	3520	4640	7340	14250
132	FEP Blue Focus	PPO	2710	1810	3200	4800	8950	14810
322	NALC-Hi	PPO-FEE	4120	2780	3640	4810	7360	11780
112	Blue Cross Basic	PPO	4180	2790	3480	4870	7890	13790
315	GEHA-Std	PPO-FEE	3360	2240	2990	4910	8850	15240
382	Rural Carrier	PPO-FEE	4090	2730	3670	5010	8080	12730
N62	Aetna Direct CDHP	CDHP	3850	770	3170	5040	9190	14570
KM2	NALC Value Plan	PPO-FEE	2230	1320	3040	5270	9690	14720
445	SAMBA-Std	PPO-FEE	3870	2580	3680	5310	8910	16580
415	MHBP Value Plan	PPO-FEE	2730	1860	3760	5420	9610	15060
225	Aetna HealthFund HDHP	HDHP	4290	1260	3310	5560	10040	16660
422	Compass Rose	PPO-FEE	6060	4040	4870	5640	7680	11040
472	APWU-Hi	PPO-FEE	5920	3980	5270	6460	9320	16980
312	GEHA-Hi	PPO-FEE	7120	4750	5400	6760	9570	14750
105	Blue Cross-Std	PPO-FEE	6670	4450	5780	7080	10060	14450
Z25	Aetna Advantage	PPO-FEE	3060	2040	4440	7130	13090	17040
442	SAMBA-Hi	PPO-FEE	10970	7320	8340	9730	12780	19320

* These are the premiums after tax savings, offset by savings accounts for plans that offer them. If you have no or low health-care costs with these plans, it can result in actual saving to you, which we indicate with a negative number.

Persons Under 55: Postal Premiums (Category 2)		Family of Five							
		Plan type	Published premium	Estimated yearly out-of-pocket costs, including premium and typical hospital, medical, drug, and dental bills near:					
Plan code	Plan name			No costs*	Low use: $3,000 or less	Average cost	High use: $30,000 or more	Limit to you
D.C. Area Plans When You Use Preferred Providers								
E35	Kaiser-Std	HMO	3290	2190	2600	3900	6070	9190
T72	Kaiser Basic	HMO	2560	1700	2480	4130	7130	9700
B62	CareFirst HDHP	HDHP	3370	450	2240	4260	7860	8750
E32	Kaiser-Hi	HMO	4950	3300	3580	4390	5740	7800
V42	United HDHP	HDHP	2790	360	2560	4730	8650	9310
Y82	United Choice Primary	HMO	2980	1990	2880	4940	8480	16690
AS2	United Choice Plus Primary	PPO-FEE	3100	2070	2960	5020	8560	16770
B65	CareFirst Blue Value Plus	HMO-POS	5130	3420	3950	5370	7860	13420
L92	United Choice Plus Advanced	PPO-FEE	3640	2430	3940	5420	8430	8430
JN5	Aetna Open Access Basic	HMO	4150	2770	3650	5690	9210	14770
LR2	United Choice Open Access	HMO	5330	3560	4380	5920	8710	13560
QQ5	Aetna Saver	HMO	3390	2260	4420	6790	11770	15260
2G5	CareFirst-Std POS	HMO-POS	9110	6080	6190	7130	8610	11080
F52	Aetna HealthFund CDHP	CDHP	7690	3130	5160	7820	12010	15730
F55	Aetna Value Plan	PPO-FEE	7530	5030	5880	8280	12340	17630
JP2	MD-IPA	HMO	14500	9670	10360	11730	14190	19670
JN2	Aetna Open Access-Hi	HMO	15690	10470	11000	12090	13900	20470
National Plans When You Use Preferred Providers								
342	GEHA HDHP	HDHP	3240	360	2230	3810	6030	12160
482	MHBP HDHP	HDHP	3320	-150	2250	4330	7270	14250
402	Foreign Service	PPO-FEE	3680	2460	3530	4550	6470	9460
252	GEHA Elevate Plus	PPO-FEE	3890	2590	3130	4700	7540	14590
325	NALC CDHP	CDHP	2710	-560	1160	4760	9710	15040
255	GEHA Elevate	PPO-FEE	2860	1910	2620	4770	8390	15910
455	MHBP-Std	PPO-FEE	3300	2250	3520	4860	7340	14250
475	APWU CDHP	CDHP	3530	-10	2340	4990	8700	15390
322	NALC-Hi	PPO-FEE	4120	2780	3640	5010	7360	11780
112	Blue Cross Basic	PPO	4180	2790	3480	5090	7890	13790
132	FEP Blue Focus	PPO	2710	1810	3200	5090	8950	14810
315	GEHA-Std	PPO-FEE	3360	2240	2990	5210	8850	15240
382	Rural Carrier	PPO-FEE	4090	2730	3670	5230	8080	12730
N62	Aetna Direct CDHP	CDHP	3850	770	3170	5400	9190	14570
445	SAMBA-Std	PPO-FEE	3870	2580	3680	5580	8910	16580
KM2	NALC Value Plan	PPO-FEE	2230	1320	3040	5660	9690	14720
415	MHBP Value Plan	PPO-FEE	2730	1860	3760	5760	9610	15060
422	Compass Rose	PPO-FEE	6060	4040	4870	5800	7680	11040
225	Aetna HealthFund HDHP	HDHP	4290	1260	3310	5950	10040	16660
472	APWU-Hi	PPO-FEE	5920	3980	5270	6680	9320	16980
312	GEHA-Hi	PPO-FEE	7120	4750	5400	6980	9570	14750
105	Blue Cross-Std	PPO-FEE	6670	4450	5780	7320	10060	14450
Z25	Aetna Advantage	PPO-FEE	3060	2040	4440	7590	13090	17040
442	SAMBA-Hi	PPO-FEE	10970	7320	8340	9960	12780	19320

* These are the premiums after tax savings, offset by savings accounts for plans that offer them. If you have no or low health-care costs with these plans, it can result in actual saving to you, which we indicate with a negative number.

Persons 55 to 64: GS Premiums		Self Only						
		Plan type	Published premium	Estimated yearly out-of-pocket costs, including premium and typical hospital, medical, drug, and dental bills near:				
Plan code	Plan name			No costs*	Low use: $1,000 or less	Average cost	High use: $30,000 or more	Limit to you
D.C. Area Plans When You Use Preferred Providers								
E34	Kaiser-Std	HMO	1710	1140	1210	2160	4640	4640
T71	Kaiser Basic	HMO	1260	840	1060	2240	4840	4840
E31	Kaiser-Hi	HMO	2540	1700	1720	2370	3950	3950
B61	CareFirst HDHP	HDHP	1710	240	780	2390	5140	5140
V41	United HDHP	HDHP	1460	220	820	2480	5270	5270
L91	United Choice Plus Advanced	PPO-FEE	1560	1040	1570	2580	4040	4040
Y81	United Choice Primary	HMO	1520	1010	1190	2920	8360	8360
B64	CareFirst Blue Value Plus	HMO-POS	2340	1560	1730	2950	6560	6560
AS1	United Choice Plus Primary	PPO-FEE	1580	1050	1230	2960	8400	8400
LR1	United Choice Open Access	HMO	2450	1630	1820	3090	6630	6630
JN4	Aetna Open Access Basic	HMO	2240	1490	1690	3350	7490	7490
2G4	CareFirst-Std POS	HMO-POS	4020	2680	2680	3440	5180	5180
QQ4	Aetna Saver	HMO	1790	1190	1890	3800	7690	7690
F51	Aetna HealthFund CDHP	CDHP	3820	1550	2100	4140	7850	7850
JP1	MD-IPA	HMO	4390	2930	3070	4240	7530	7930
F54	Aetna Value Plan	PPO-FEE	3710	2470	2720	4390	8770	8770
JN1	Aetna Open Access-Hi	HMO	7520	5020	5090	6060	8510	10020
National Plans When You Use Preferred Providers								
341	GEHA HDHP	HDHP	1540	130	630	2090	4900	6030
401	Foreign Service	PPO-FEE	1790	1200	1480	2520	5070	6200
481	MHBP HDHP	HDHP	1720	-10	690	2550	5690	7190
324	NALC CDHP	CDHP	1420	-220	150	2560	7580	7580
251	GEHA Elevate Plus	PPO-FEE	1890	1260	1380	2670	6580	7260
254	GEHA Elevate	PPO-FEE	1230	820	1050	2690	7820	7820
131	FEP Blue Focus	PPO	1380	920	1440	2790	7420	7420
111	Blue Cross Basic	PPO	1970	1320	1450	2800	6550	6820
421	Compass Rose	PPO-FEE	2640	1760	1970	2870	5400	6760
314	GEHA-Std	PPO-FEE	1570	1050	1280	2920	7550	7550
454	MHBP-Std	PPO-FEE	1710	1180	1480	2920	6850	7180
474	APWU CDHP	CDHP	1790	30	700	2940	7730	7730
N61	Aetna Direct CDHP	CDHP	1840	330	1030	2980	7230	7230
321	NALC-Hi	PPO-FEE	2360	1610	1890	3040	5970	8210
KM1	NALC Value Plan	PPO-FEE	1170	710	1080	3160	7410	7410
311	GEHA-Hi	PPO-FEE	2740	1830	2050	3280	6830	6830
414	MHBP Value Plan	PPO-FEE	1360	950	1370	3290	7550	7550
444	SAMBA-Std	PPO-FEE	2040	1360	1700	3390	8360	8360
471	APWU-Hi	PPO-FEE	2580	1760	2280	3570	7970	8260
381	Rural Carrier	PPO-FEE	3180	2120	2440	3660	7120	7120
224	Aetna HealthFund HDHP	HDHP	2620	940	1460	3670	8640	8640
104	Blue Cross-Std	PPO-FEE	3040	2030	2460	3750	7030	7030
Z24	Aetna Advantage	PPO-FEE	1390	930	1630	4010	8430	8430
441	SAMBA-Hi	PPO-FEE	4690	3130	3440	4930	9130	9130

* These are the premiums after tax savings, offset by savings accounts for plans that offer them. If you have no or low health-care costs with these plans, it can result in actual saving to you, which we indicate with a negative number.

Persons 55 to 64: GS Premiums		Self Plus One						
		Plan type	Published premium	Estimated yearly out-of-pocket costs, including premium and typical hospital, medical, drug, and dental bills near:				
Plan code	Plan name			No costs*	Low use: $3,000 or less	Average cost	High use: $30,000 or more	Limit to you
D.C. Area Plans When You Use Preferred Providers								
E36	Kaiser-Std	HMO	3940	2630	3040	4600	6510	9630
T73	Kaiser Basic	HMO	2800	1870	2650	4620	7300	9870
B63	CareFirst HDHP	HDHP	3420	480	2270	4660	7890	8780
B66	CareFirst Blue Value Plus	HMO-POS	4240	2830	3360	5110	7270	12830
L93	United Choice Plus Advanced	PPO-FEE	3060	2040	3550	5310	8040	8040
V43	United HDHP	HDHP	3140	590	2790	5380	8880	9540
Y83	United Choice Primary	HMO	3270	2180	3070	5600	8670	16880
AS3	United Choice Plus Primary	PPO-FEE	3390	2260	3150	5680	8750	16960
E33	Kaiser-Hi	HMO	6840	4560	4840	5820	7000	9060
2G6	CareFirst-Std POS	HMO-POS	7190	4790	4900	6030	7320	9790
LR3	United Choice Open Access	HMO	5340	3560	4380	6250	8710	13560
JN6	Aetna Open Access Basic	HMO	4470	2980	3860	6330	9420	14980
JP3	MD-IPA	HMO	7440	4960	5650	7320	9480	14960
QQ6	Aetna Saver	HMO	3750	2500	4660	7560	12010	15500
F53	Aetna HealthFund CDHP	CDHP	9360	4240	6270	9460	13120	16840
F56	Aetna Value Plan	PPO-FEE	8980	5990	6840	9710	13300	18590
JN3	Aetna Open Access-Hi	HMO	17280	11520	12050	13380	14950	21520
National Plans When You Use Preferred Providers								
343	GEHA HDHP	HDHP	3310	410	2280	4200	6080	12210
483	MHBP HDHP	HDHP	3810	180	2580	5080	7600	14580
256	GEHA Elevate	PPO-FEE	2830	1890	2600	5220	8370	15890
403	Foreign Service	PPO-FEE	4470	2980	4050	5320	6990	9980
253	GEHA Elevate Plus	PPO-FEE	4430	2950	3490	5390	7900	14950
456	MHBP-Std	PPO-FEE	3940	2670	3940	5610	7760	14670
326	NALC CDHP	CDHP	3130	-270	1450	5670	10000	15330
316	GEHA-Std	PPO-FEE	3380	2260	3010	5680	8870	15260
133	FEP Blue Focus	PPO	2970	1980	3370	5720	9120	14980
113	Blue Cross Basic	PPO	4640	3100	3790	5740	8200	14100
476	APWU CDHP	CDHP	3900	230	2580	5790	8940	15630
N63	Aetna Direct CDHP	CDHP	4030	890	3290	6040	9310	14690
423	Compass Rose	PPO-FEE	6190	4130	4960	6130	7770	11130
323	NALC-Hi	PPO-FEE	5680	3820	4680	6350	8400	12820
383	Rural Carrier	PPO-FEE	5330	3550	4490	6370	8900	13550
446	SAMBA-Std	PPO-FEE	4470	2980	4080	6390	9310	16980
KM3	NALC Value Plan	PPO-FEE	2570	1550	3270	6410	9920	14950
473	APWU-Hi	PPO-FEE	5190	3500	4790	6580	8840	16500
416	MHBP Value Plan	PPO-FEE	3220	2190	4090	6580	9940	15390
313	GEHA-Hi	PPO-FEE	6410	4270	4920	6820	9090	14270
226	Aetna HealthFund HDHP	HDHP	5810	2270	4320	7530	11050	17670
106	Blue Cross-Std	PPO-FEE	6950	4630	5960	7860	10240	14630
Z26	Aetna Advantage	PPO-FEE	3060	2040	4440	8230	13090	17040
443	SAMBA-Hi	PPO-FEE	10700	7140	8160	10130	12600	19140

* These are the premiums after tax savings, offset by savings accounts for plans that offer them. If you have no or low health-care costs with these plans, it can result in actual saving to you, which we indicate with a negative number.

Persons 55 to 64: GS Premiums		Family of Two						
				Estimated yearly out-of-pocket costs, including premium and typical hospital, medical, drug, and dental bills near:				
Plan code	Plan name	Plan type	Published premium	No costs*	Low use: $1,000 or less	Average cost	High use: $30,000 or more	Limit to you
D.C. Area Plans When You Use Preferred Providers								
E35	Kaiser-Std	HMO	3960	2640	3050	4610	6520	9640
T72	Kaiser Basic	HMO	3080	2050	2830	4800	7480	10050
B62	CareFirst HDHP	HDHP	4060	910	2700	5090	8320	9210
E32	Kaiser-Hi	HMO	5740	3830	4110	5090	6270	8330
V42	United HDHP	HDHP	3360	740	2940	5530	9030	9690
Y82	United Choice Primary	HMO	3590	2400	3290	5820	8890	17100
AS2	United Choice Plus Primary	PPO-FEE	3730	2490	3380	5910	8980	17190
L92	United Choice Plus Advanced	PPO-FEE	4390	2930	4440	6200	8930	8930
B65	CareFirst Blue Value Plus	HMO-POS	5920	3950	4480	6230	8390	13950
JN5	Aetna Open Access Basic	HMO	4940	3290	4170	6640	9730	15290
LR2	United Choice Open Access	HMO	6120	4080	4900	6770	9230	14080
QQ5	Aetna Saver	HMO	4090	2730	4890	7790	12240	15730
2G5	CareFirst-Std POS	HMO-POS	9900	6600	6710	7840	9130	11600
F52	Aetna HealthFund CDHP	CDHP	8480	3660	5690	8880	12540	16260
F55	Aetna Value Plan	PPO-FEE	8320	5550	6400	9270	12860	18150
JP2	MD-IPA	HMO	15290	10200	10890	12560	14720	20200
JN2	Aetna Open Access-Hi	HMO	16480	10990	11520	12850	14420	20990
National Plans When You Use Preferred Providers								
342	GEHA HDHP	HDHP	3900	800	2670	4590	6470	12600
482	MHBP HDHP	HDHP	4000	310	2710	5210	7730	14710
402	Foreign Service	PPO-FEE	4440	2960	4030	5300	6970	9960
252	GEHA Elevate Plus	PPO-FEE	4690	3130	3670	5570	8080	15130
255	GEHA Elevate	PPO-FEE	3450	2300	3010	5630	8780	16300
455	MHBP-Std	PPO-FEE	3980	2700	3970	5640	7790	14700
325	NALC CDHP	CDHP	3270	-180	1540	5760	10090	15420
322	NALC-Hi	PPO-FEE	4910	3310	4170	5840	7890	12310
132	FEP Blue Focus	PPO	3270	2180	3570	5920	9320	15180
112	Blue Cross Basic	PPO	4970	3320	4010	5960	8420	14320
475	APWU CDHP	CDHP	4250	470	2820	6030	9180	15870
382	Rural Carrier	PPO-FEE	4880	3250	4190	6070	8600	13250
315	GEHA-Std	PPO-FEE	4040	2700	3450	6120	9310	15700
N62	Aetna Direct CDHP	CDHP	4640	1290	3690	6440	9710	15090
KM2	NALC Value Plan	PPO-FEE	2680	1630	3350	6490	10000	15030
445	SAMBA-Std	PPO-FEE	4660	3110	4210	6520	9440	17110
422	Compass Rose	PPO-FEE	6850	4570	5400	6570	8210	11570
415	MHBP Value Plan	PPO-FEE	3290	2230	4130	6620	9980	15430
225	Aetna HealthFund HDHP	HDHP	5080	1790	3840	7050	10570	17190
472	APWU-Hi	PPO-FEE	6710	4510	5800	7590	9850	17510
312	GEHA-Hi	PPO-FEE	7910	5280	5930	7830	10100	15280
105	Blue Cross-Std	PPO-FEE	7460	4970	6300	8200	10580	14970
Z25	Aetna Advantage	PPO-FEE	3690	2460	4860	8650	13510	17460
442	SAMBA-Hi	PPO-FEE	11760	7850	8870	10840	13310	19850

* These are the premiums after tax savings, offset by savings accounts for plans that offer them. If you have no or low health-care costs with these plans, it can result in actual saving to you, which we indicate with a negative number.

Persons 55 to 64: GS Premiums		Family of Three							
		Plan type	Published premium	Estimated yearly out-of-pocket costs, including premium and typical hospital, medical, drug, and dental bills near:					
Plan code	Plan name			No costs*	Low use: $3,000 or less	Average cost	High use: $30,000 or more	Limit to you
D.C. Area Plans When You Use Preferred Providers									
E35	Kaiser-Std	HMO	3960	2640	3050	4770	6520	9640
T72	Kaiser Basic	HMO	3080	2050	2830	5020	7480	10050
E32	Kaiser-Hi	HMO	5740	3830	4110	5190	6270	8330
B62	CareFirst HDHP	HDHP	4060	910	2700	5360	8320	9210
V42	United HDHP	HDHP	3360	740	2940	5820	9030	9690
Y82	United Choice Primary	HMO	3590	2400	3290	6090	8890	17100
AS2	United Choice Plus Primary	PPO-FEE	3730	2490	3380	6180	8980	17190
B65	CareFirst Blue Value Plus	HMO-POS	5920	3950	4480	6410	8390	13950
L92	United Choice Plus Advanced	PPO-FEE	4390	2930	4440	6410	8930	8930
JN5	Aetna Open Access Basic	HMO	4940	3290	4170	6890	9730	15290
LR2	United Choice Open Access	HMO	6120	4080	4900	6970	9230	14080
2G5	CareFirst-Std POS	HMO-POS	9900	6600	6710	7950	9130	11600
QQ5	Aetna Saver	HMO	4090	2730	4890	8140	12240	15730
F52	Aetna HealthFund CDHP	CDHP	8480	3660	5690	9210	12540	16260
F55	Aetna Value Plan	PPO-FEE	8320	5550	6400	9570	12860	18150
JP2	MD-IPA	HMO	15290	10200	10890	12740	14720	20200
JN2	Aetna Open Access-Hi	HMO	16480	10990	11520	12990	14420	20990
National Plans When You Use Preferred Providers									
342	GEHA HDHP	HDHP	3900	800	2670	4800	6470	12600
402	Foreign Service	PPO-FEE	4440	2960	4030	5450	6970	9960
482	MHBP HDHP	HDHP	4000	310	2710	5480	7730	14710
252	GEHA Elevate Plus	PPO-FEE	4690	3130	3670	5770	8080	15130
455	MHBP-Std	PPO-FEE	3980	2700	3970	5830	7790	14700
255	GEHA Elevate	PPO-FEE	3450	2300	3010	5900	8780	16300
322	NALC-Hi	PPO-FEE	4910	3310	4170	6020	7890	12310
112	Blue Cross Basic	PPO	4970	3320	4010	6170	8420	14320
132	FEP Blue Focus	PPO	3270	2180	3570	6190	9320	15180
325	NALC CDHP	CDHP	3270	-180	1540	6210	10090	15420
382	Rural Carrier	PPO-FEE	4880	3250	4190	6270	8600	13250
475	APWU CDHP	CDHP	4250	470	2820	6360	9180	15870
315	GEHA-Std	PPO-FEE	4040	2700	3450	6400	9310	15700
422	Compass Rose	PPO-FEE	6850	4570	5400	6710	8210	11570
N62	Aetna Direct CDHP	CDHP	4640	1290	3690	6750	9710	15090
445	SAMBA-Std	PPO-FEE	4660	3110	4210	6770	9440	17110
KM2	NALC Value Plan	PPO-FEE	2680	1630	3350	6830	10000	15030
415	MHBP Value Plan	PPO-FEE	3290	2230	4130	6920	9980	15430
225	Aetna HealthFund HDHP	HDHP	5080	1790	3840	7380	10570	17190
472	APWU-Hi	PPO-FEE	6710	4510	5800	7790	9850	17510
312	GEHA-Hi	PPO-FEE	7910	5280	5930	8030	10100	15280
105	Blue Cross-Std	PPO-FEE	7460	4970	6300	8410	10580	14970
Z25	Aetna Advantage	PPO-FEE	3690	2460	4860	9050	13510	17460
442	SAMBA-Hi	PPO-FEE	11760	7850	8870	11060	13310	19850

* These are the premiums after tax savings, offset by savings accounts for plans that offer them. If you have no or low health-care costs with these plans, it can result in actual saving to you, which we indicate with a negative number.

Persons 55 to 64: Postal Premiums (Category 1)		Self Only						
				Estimated yearly out-of-pocket costs, including premium and typical hospital, medical, drug, and dental bills near:				
Plan code	Plan name	Plan type	Published premium	No costs*	Low use: $1,000 or less	Average cost	High use: $30,000 or more	Limit to you
D.C. Area Plans When You Use Preferred Providers								
E34	Kaiser-Std	HMO	1650	1100	1170	2120	4600	4600
T71	Kaiser Basic	HMO	1210	810	1030	2210	4810	4810
E31	Kaiser-Hi	HMO	2460	1640	1660	2310	3890	3890
B61	CareFirst HDHP	HDHP	1640	200	740	2350	5100	5100
V41	United HDHP	HDHP	1400	180	780	2440	5230	5230
L91	United Choice Plus Advanced	PPO-FEE	1500	1000	1530	2540	4000	4000
Y81	United Choice Primary	HMO	1460	970	1150	2880	8320	8320
B64	CareFirst Blue Value Plus	HMO-POS	2260	1510	1680	2900	6510	6510
AS1	United Choice Plus Primary	PPO-FEE	1510	1010	1190	2920	8360	8360
LR1	United Choice Open Access	HMO	2360	1580	1770	3040	6580	6580
JN4	Aetna Open Access Basic	HMO	2150	1430	1630	3290	7430	7430
2G4	CareFirst-Std POS	HMO-POS	3930	2620	2620	3380	5120	5120
QQ4	Aetna Saver	HMO	1710	1140	1840	3750	7640	7640
F51	Aetna HealthFund CDHP	CDHP	3740	1490	2040	4080	7790	7790
JP1	MD-IPA	HMO	4300	2870	3010	4180	7470	7870
F54	Aetna Value Plan	PPO-FEE	3620	2420	2670	4340	8720	8720
JN1	Aetna Open Access-Hi	HMO	7440	4960	5030	6000	8450	9960
National Plans When You Use Preferred Providers								
341	GEHA HDHP	HDHP	1480	90	590	2050	4860	5990
401	Foreign Service	PPO-FEE	1720	1150	1430	2470	5020	6150
481	MHBP HDHP	HDHP	1650	-60	640	2500	5640	7140
324	NALC CDHP	CDHP	1360	-250	120	2530	7550	7550
251	GEHA Elevate Plus	PPO-FEE	1810	1210	1330	2620	6530	7210
254	GEHA Elevate	PPO-FEE	1180	790	1020	2660	7790	7790
111	Blue Cross Basic	PPO	1900	1260	1390	2740	6490	6760
381	Rural Carrier	PPO-FEE	1800	1200	1520	2740	6200	6200
131	FEP Blue Focus	PPO	1330	880	1400	2750	7380	7380
421	Compass Rose	PPO-FEE	2560	1710	1920	2820	5350	6710
314	GEHA-Std	PPO-FEE	1510	1010	1240	2880	7510	7510
454	MHBP-Std	PPO-FEE	1640	1140	1440	2880	6810	7140
474	APWU CDHP	CDHP	1720	-20	650	2890	7680	7680
N61	Aetna Direct CDHP	CDHP	1760	280	980	2930	7180	7180
321	NALC-Hi	PPO-FEE	2280	1550	1830	2980	5910	8150
KM1	NALC Value Plan	PPO-FEE	1120	680	1050	3130	7380	7380
311	GEHA-Hi	PPO-FEE	2660	1770	1990	3220	6770	6770
414	MHBP Value Plan	PPO-FEE	1310	910	1330	3250	7510	7510
444	SAMBA-Std	PPO-FEE	1960	1310	1650	3340	8310	8310
471	APWU-Hi	PPO-FEE	2500	1700	2220	3510	7910	8200
224	Aetna HealthFund HDHP	HDHP	2530	890	1410	3620	8590	8590
104	Blue Cross-Std	PPO-FEE	2950	1970	2400	3690	6970	6970
Z24	Aetna Advantage	PPO-FEE	1340	890	1590	3970	8390	8390
441	SAMBA-Hi	PPO-FEE	4610	3070	3380	4870	9070	9070

* These are the premiums after tax savings, offset by savings accounts for plans that offer them. If you have no or low health-care costs with these plans, it can result in actual saving to you, which we indicate with a negative number.

Persons 55 to 64: Postal Premiums (Category 1)

Plan code	Plan name	Plan type	Published premium	Self Plus One: Estimated yearly out-of-pocket costs, including premium and typical hospital, medical, drug, and dental bills near: No costs*	Low use: $3,000 or less	Average cost	High use: $30,000 or more	Limit to you
D.C. Area Plans When You Use Preferred Providers								
E36	Kaiser-Std	HMO	3790	2530	2940	4500	6410	9530
T73	Kaiser Basic	HMO	2690	1800	2580	4550	7230	9800
B63	CareFirst HDHP	HDHP	3280	390	2180	4570	7800	8690
B66	CareFirst Blue Value Plus	HMO-POS	4070	2710	3240	4990	7150	12710
L93	United Choice Plus Advanced	PPO-FEE	2930	1960	3470	5230	7960	7960
V43	United HDHP	HDHP	3010	510	2710	5300	8800	9460
Y83	United Choice Primary	HMO	3140	2090	2980	5510	8580	16790
AS3	United Choice Plus Primary	PPO-FEE	3260	2170	3060	5590	8660	16870
E33	Kaiser-Hi	HMO	6660	4440	4720	5700	6880	8940
2G6	CareFirst-Std POS	HMO-POS	7000	4670	4780	5910	7200	9670
LR3	United Choice Open Access	HMO	5150	3440	4260	6130	8590	13440
JN6	Aetna Open Access Basic	HMO	4290	2860	3740	6210	9300	14860
JP3	MD-IPA	HMO	7260	4840	5530	7200	9360	14840
QQ6	Aetna Saver	HMO	3600	2400	4560	7460	11910	15400
F53	Aetna HealthFund CDHP	CDHP	9170	4120	6150	9340	13000	16720
F56	Aetna Value Plan	PPO-FEE	8800	5870	6720	9590	13180	18470
JN3	Aetna Open Access-Hi	HMO	17100	11400	11930	13260	14830	21400
National Plans When You Use Preferred Providers								
343	GEHA HDHP	HDHP	3180	320	2190	4110	5990	12120
483	MHBP HDHP	HDHP	3650	80	2480	4980	7500	14480
256	GEHA Elevate	PPO-FEE	2720	1810	2520	5140	8290	15810
403	Foreign Service	PPO-FEE	4280	2860	3930	5200	6870	9860
253	GEHA Elevate Plus	PPO-FEE	4240	2830	3370	5270	7780	14830
456	MHBP-Std	PPO-FEE	3780	2570	3840	5510	7660	14570
326	NALC CDHP	CDHP	3010	-360	1360	5580	9910	15240
316	GEHA-Std	PPO-FEE	3250	2170	2920	5590	8780	15170
113	Blue Cross Basic	PPO	4460	2980	3670	5620	8080	13980
133	FEP Blue Focus	PPO	2850	1900	3290	5640	9040	14900
476	APWU CDHP	CDHP	3740	130	2480	5690	8840	15530
N63	Aetna Direct CDHP	CDHP	3870	780	3180	5930	9200	14580
423	Compass Rose	PPO-FEE	6010	4010	4840	6010	7650	11010
323	NALC-Hi	PPO-FEE	5490	3700	4560	6230	8280	12700
383	Rural Carrier	PPO-FEE	5140	3430	4370	6250	8780	13430
446	SAMBA-Std	PPO-FEE	4290	2860	3960	6270	9190	16860
KM3	NALC Value Plan	PPO-FEE	2470	1480	3200	6340	9850	14880
473	APWU-Hi	PPO-FEE	5010	3380	4670	6460	8720	16380
416	MHBP Value Plan	PPO-FEE	3090	2110	4010	6500	9860	15310
313	GEHA-Hi	PPO-FEE	6230	4150	4800	6700	8970	14150
226	Aetna HealthFund HDHP	HDHP	5620	2150	4200	7410	10930	17550
106	Blue Cross-Std	PPO-FEE	6760	4510	5840	7740	10120	14510
Z26	Aetna Advantage	PPO-FEE	2940	1960	4360	8150	13010	16960
443	SAMBA-Hi	PPO-FEE	10520	7010	8030	10000	12470	19010

* These are the premiums after tax savings, offset by savings accounts for plans that offer them. If you have no or low health-care costs with these plans, it can result in actual saving to you, which we indicate with a negative number.

Persons 55 to 64: Postal Premiums (Category 1)		Family of Two						
		Plan type	Published premium	Estimated yearly out-of-pocket costs, including premium and typical hospital, medical, drug, and dental bills near:				
Plan code	Plan name			No costs*	Low use: $1,000 or less	Average cost	High use: $30,000 or more	Limit to you
D.C. Area Plans When You Use Preferred Providers								
E35	Kaiser-Std	HMO	3800	2540	2950	4510	6420	9540
T72	Kaiser Basic	HMO	2960	1970	2750	4720	7400	9970
E32	Kaiser-Hi	HMO	5540	3700	3980	4960	6140	8200
B62	CareFirst HDHP	HDHP	3900	800	2590	4980	8210	9100
V42	United HDHP	HDHP	3220	650	2850	5440	8940	9600
Y82	United Choice Primary	HMO	3450	2300	3190	5720	8790	17000
AS2	United Choice Plus Primary	PPO-FEE	3580	2390	3280	5810	8880	17090
L92	United Choice Plus Advanced	PPO-FEE	4210	2810	4320	6080	8810	8810
B65	CareFirst Blue Value Plus	HMO-POS	5720	3820	4350	6100	8260	13820
JN5	Aetna Open Access Basic	HMO	4740	3160	4040	6510	9600	15160
LR2	United Choice Open Access	HMO	5930	3950	4770	6640	9100	13950
QQ5	Aetna Saver	HMO	3920	2620	4780	7680	12130	15620
2G5	CareFirst-Std POS	HMO-POS	9700	6470	6580	7710	9000	11470
F52	Aetna HealthFund CDHP	CDHP	8280	3520	5550	8740	12400	16120
F55	Aetna Value Plan	PPO-FEE	8130	5420	6270	9140	12730	18020
JP2	MD-IPA	HMO	15090	10060	10750	12420	14580	20060
JN2	Aetna Open Access-Hi	HMO	16280	10860	11390	12720	14290	20860
National Plans When You Use Preferred Providers								
342	GEHA HDHP	HDHP	3740	700	2570	4490	6370	12500
482	MHBP HDHP	HDHP	3840	200	2600	5100	7620	14600
402	Foreign Service	PPO-FEE	4260	2840	3910	5180	6850	9840
252	GEHA Elevate Plus	PPO-FEE	4500	3000	3540	5440	7950	15000
455	MHBP-Std	PPO-FEE	3820	2590	3860	5530	7680	14590
255	GEHA Elevate	PPO-FEE	3310	2210	2920	5540	8690	16210
325	NALC CDHP	CDHP	3140	-270	1450	5670	10000	15330
322	NALC-Hi	PPO-FEE	4710	3180	4040	5710	7760	12180
112	Blue Cross Basic	PPO	4770	3180	3870	5820	8280	14180
132	FEP Blue Focus	PPO	3140	2090	3480	5830	9230	15090
475	APWU CDHP	CDHP	4080	360	2710	5920	9070	15760
382	Rural Carrier	PPO-FEE	4680	3120	4060	5940	8470	13120
315	GEHA-Std	PPO-FEE	3880	2590	3340	6010	9200	15590
N62	Aetna Direct CDHP	CDHP	4450	1170	3570	6320	9590	14970
445	SAMBA-Std	PPO-FEE	4470	2980	4080	6390	9310	16980
KM2	NALC Value Plan	PPO-FEE	2580	1550	3270	6410	9920	14950
422	Compass Rose	PPO-FEE	6650	4440	5270	6440	8080	11440
415	MHBP Value Plan	PPO-FEE	3160	2150	4050	6540	9900	15350
225	Aetna HealthFund HDHP	HDHP	4890	1660	3710	6920	10440	17060
472	APWU-Hi	PPO-FEE	6510	4380	5670	7460	9720	17380
312	GEHA-Hi	PPO-FEE	7720	5150	5800	7700	9970	15150
105	Blue Cross-Std	PPO-FEE	7260	4840	6170	8070	10450	14840
Z25	Aetna Advantage	PPO-FEE	3540	2360	4760	8550	13410	17360
442	SAMBA-Hi	PPO-FEE	11560	7710	8730	10700	13170	19710

* These are the premiums after tax savings, offset by savings accounts for plans that offer them. If you have no or low health-care costs with these plans, it can result in actual saving to you, which we indicate with a negative number.

Persons 55 to 64: Postal Premiums (Category 1)

Family of Three

Plan code	Plan name	Plan type	Published premium	Estimated yearly out-of-pocket costs, including premium and typical hospital, medical, drug, and dental bills near: No costs*	Low use: $3,000 or less	Average cost	High use: $30,000 or more	Limit to you
D.C. Area Plans When You Use Preferred Providers								
E35	Kaiser-Std	HMO	3800	2540	2950	4670	6420	9540
T72	Kaiser Basic	HMO	2960	1970	2750	4940	7400	9970
E32	Kaiser-Hi	HMO	5540	3700	3980	5060	6140	8200
B62	CareFirst HDHP	HDHP	3900	800	2590	5250	8210	9100
V42	United HDHP	HDHP	3220	650	2850	5730	8940	9600
Y82	United Choice Primary	HMO	3450	2300	3190	5990	8790	17000
AS2	United Choice Plus Primary	PPO-FEE	3580	2390	3280	6080	8880	17090
B65	CareFirst Blue Value Plus	HMO-POS	5720	3820	4350	6280	8260	13820
L92	United Choice Plus Advanced	PPO-FEE	4210	2810	4320	6290	8810	8810
JN5	Aetna Open Access Basic	HMO	4740	3160	4040	6760	9600	15160
LR2	United Choice Open Access	HMO	5930	3950	4770	6840	9100	13950
2G5	CareFirst-Std POS	HMO-POS	9700	6470	6580	7820	9000	11470
QQ5	Aetna Saver	HMO	3920	2620	4780	8030	12130	15620
F52	Aetna HealthFund CDHP	CDHP	8280	3520	5550	9070	12400	16120
F55	Aetna Value Plan	PPO-FEE	8130	5420	6270	9440	12730	18020
JP2	MD-IPA	HMO	15090	10060	10750	12600	14580	20060
JN2	Aetna Open Access-Hi	HMO	16280	10860	11390	12860	14290	20860
National Plans When You Use Preferred Providers								
342	GEHA HDHP	HDHP	3740	700	2570	4700	6370	12500
402	Foreign Service	PPO-FEE	4260	2840	3910	5330	6850	9840
482	MHBP HDHP	HDHP	3840	200	2600	5370	7620	14600
252	GEHA Elevate Plus	PPO-FEE	4500	3000	3540	5640	7950	15000
455	MHBP-Std	PPO-FEE	3820	2590	3860	5720	7680	14590
255	GEHA Elevate	PPO-FEE	3310	2210	2920	5810	8690	16210
322	NALC-Hi	PPO-FEE	4710	3180	4040	5890	7760	12180
112	Blue Cross Basic	PPO	4770	3180	3870	6030	8280	14180
132	FEP Blue Focus	PPO	3140	2090	3480	6100	9230	15090
325	NALC CDHP	CDHP	3140	-270	1450	6120	10000	15330
382	Rural Carrier	PPO-FEE	4680	3120	4060	6140	8470	13120
475	APWU CDHP	CDHP	4080	360	2710	6250	9070	15760
315	GEHA-Std	PPO-FEE	3880	2590	3340	6290	9200	15590
422	Compass Rose	PPO-FEE	6650	4440	5270	6580	8080	11440
N62	Aetna Direct CDHP	CDHP	4450	1170	3570	6630	9590	14970
445	SAMBA-Std	PPO-FEE	4470	2980	4080	6640	9310	16980
KM2	NALC Value Plan	PPO-FEE	2580	1550	3270	6750	9920	14950
415	MHBP Value Plan	PPO-FEE	3160	2150	4050	6840	9900	15350
225	Aetna HealthFund HDHP	HDHP	4890	1660	3710	7250	10440	17060
472	APWU-Hi	PPO-FEE	6510	4380	5670	7660	9720	17380
312	GEHA-Hi	PPO-FEE	7720	5150	5800	7900	9970	15150
105	Blue Cross-Std	PPO-FEE	7260	4840	6170	8280	10450	14840
Z25	Aetna Advantage	PPO-FEE	3540	2360	4760	8950	13410	17360
442	SAMBA-Hi	PPO-FEE	11560	7710	8730	10920	13170	19710

* These are the premiums after tax savings, offset by savings accounts for plans that offer them. If you have no or low health-care costs with these plans, it can result in actual saving to you, which we indicate with a negative number.

Persons 55 to 64: Postal Premiums (Category 2)		Self Only						
		Plan type	Published premium	Estimated yearly out-of-pocket costs, including premium and typical hospital, medical, drug, and dental bills near:				
Plan code	Plan name			No costs*	Low use: $1,000 or less	Average cost	High use: $30,000 or more	Limit to you
D.C. Area Plans When You Use Preferred Providers								
E34	Kaiser-Std	HMO	1420	950	1020	1970	4450	4450
T71	Kaiser Basic	HMO	1050	700	920	2100	4700	4700
E31	Kaiser-Hi	HMO	2200	1470	1490	2140	3720	3720
B61	CareFirst HDHP	HDHP	1420	50	590	2200	4950	4950
V41	United HDHP	HDHP	1210	60	660	2320	5110	5110
L91	United Choice Plus Advanced	PPO-FEE	1300	870	1400	2410	3870	3870
B64	CareFirst Blue Value Plus	HMO-POS	2000	1330	1500	2720	6330	6330
Y81	United Choice Primary	HMO	1260	840	1020	2750	8190	8190
AS1	United Choice Plus Primary	PPO-FEE	1310	870	1050	2780	8220	8220
LR1	United Choice Open Access	HMO	2110	1410	1600	2870	6410	6410
JN4	Aetna Open Access Basic	HMO	1890	1260	1460	3120	7260	7260
2G4	CareFirst-Std POS	HMO-POS	3680	2450	2450	3210	4950	4950
QQ4	Aetna Saver	HMO	1480	990	1690	3600	7490	7490
F51	Aetna HealthFund CDHP	CDHP	3480	1320	1870	3910	7620	7620
JP1	MD-IPA	HMO	4050	2700	2840	4010	7300	7700
F54	Aetna Value Plan	PPO-FEE	3370	2250	2500	4170	8550	8550
JN1	Aetna Open Access-Hi	HMO	7180	4790	4860	5830	8280	9790
National Plans When You Use Preferred Providers								
341	GEHA HDHP	HDHP	1280	-50	450	1910	4720	5850
401	Foreign Service	PPO-FEE	1490	990	1270	2310	4860	5990
481	MHBP HDHP	HDHP	1430	-210	490	2350	5490	6990
324	NALC CDHP	CDHP	1180	-380	-10	2400	7420	7420
251	GEHA Elevate Plus	PPO-FEE	1570	1050	1170	2460	6370	7050
254	GEHA Elevate	PPO-FEE	1020	680	910	2550	7680	7680
111	Blue Cross Basic	PPO	1640	1090	1220	2570	6320	6590
131	FEP Blue Focus	PPO	1150	760	1280	2630	7260	7260
421	Compass Rose	PPO-FEE	2300	1540	1750	2650	5180	6540
454	MHBP-Std	PPO-FEE	1420	990	1290	2730	6660	6990
474	APWU CDHP	CDHP	1490	-170	500	2740	7530	7530
314	GEHA-Std	PPO-FEE	1310	870	1100	2740	7370	7370
N61	Aetna Direct CDHP	CDHP	1530	120	820	2770	7020	7020
321	NALC-Hi	PPO-FEE	2020	1380	1660	2810	5740	7980
KM1	NALC Value Plan	PPO-FEE	970	580	950	3030	7280	7280
311	GEHA-Hi	PPO-FEE	2400	1600	1820	3050	6600	6600
414	MHBP Value Plan	PPO-FEE	1130	790	1210	3130	7390	7390
444	SAMBA-Std	PPO-FEE	1700	1130	1470	3160	8130	8130
471	APWU-Hi	PPO-FEE	2240	1530	2050	3340	7740	8030
381	Rural Carrier	PPO-FEE	2840	1890	2210	3430	6890	6890
224	Aetna HealthFund HDHP	HDHP	2280	720	1240	3450	8420	8420
104	Blue Cross-Std	PPO-FEE	2700	1800	2230	3520	6800	6800
Z24	Aetna Advantage	PPO-FEE	1150	770	1470	3850	8270	8270
441	SAMBA-Hi	PPO-FEE	4350	2900	3210	4700	8900	8900

* These are the premiums after tax savings, offset by savings accounts for plans that offer them. If you have no or low health-care costs with these plans, it can result in actual saving to you, which we indicate with a negative number.

Persons 55 to 64: Postal Premiums (Category 2)		Self Plus One						
		Plan type	Published premium	Estimated yearly out-of-pocket costs, including premium and typical hospital, medical, drug, and dental bills near:				
Plan code	Plan name			No costs*	Low use: $3,000 or less	Average cost	High use: $30,000 or more	Limit to you
D.C. Area Plans When You Use Preferred Providers								
E36	Kaiser-Std	HMO	3270	2180	2590	4150	6060	9180
B63	CareFirst HDHP	HDHP	2840	90	1880	4270	7500	8390
T73	Kaiser Basic	HMO	2330	1550	2330	4300	6980	9550
B66	CareFirst Blue Value Plus	HMO-POS	3520	2350	2880	4630	6790	12350
L93	United Choice Plus Advanced	PPO-FEE	2540	1690	3200	4960	7690	7690
V43	United HDHP	HDHP	2600	240	2440	5030	8530	9190
Y83	United Choice Primary	HMO	2710	1810	2700	5230	8300	16510
AS3	United Choice Plus Primary	PPO-FEE	2810	1880	2770	5300	8370	16580
E33	Kaiser-Hi	HMO	6120	4080	4360	5340	6520	8580
2G6	CareFirst-Std POS	HMO-POS	6460	4310	4420	5550	6840	9310
LR3	United Choice Open Access	HMO	4610	3070	3890	5760	8220	13070
JN6	Aetna Open Access Basic	HMO	3740	2500	3380	5850	8940	14500
JP3	MD-IPA	HMO	6710	4470	5160	6830	8990	14470
QQ6	Aetna Saver	HMO	3110	2080	4240	7140	11590	15080
F53	Aetna HealthFund CDHP	CDHP	8630	3760	5790	8980	12640	16360
F56	Aetna Value Plan	PPO-FEE	8250	5510	6360	9230	12820	18110
JN3	Aetna Open Access-Hi	HMO	16550	11040	11570	12900	14470	21040
National Plans When You Use Preferred Providers								
343	GEHA HDHP	HDHP	2750	30	1900	3820	5700	11830
483	MHBP HDHP	HDHP	3160	-250	2150	4650	7170	14150
403	Foreign Service	PPO-FEE	3740	2490	3560	4830	6500	9490
256	GEHA Elevate	PPO-FEE	2350	1570	2280	4900	8050	15570
253	GEHA Elevate Plus	PPO-FEE	3700	2470	3010	4910	7420	14470
456	MHBP-Std	PPO-FEE	3270	2220	3490	5160	7310	14220
113	Blue Cross Basic	PPO	3920	2610	3300	5250	7710	13610
316	GEHA-Std	PPO-FEE	2810	1870	2620	5290	8480	14870
326	NALC CDHP	CDHP	2600	-630	1090	5310	9640	14970
476	APWU CDHP	CDHP	3230	-210	2140	5350	8500	15190
133	FEP Blue Focus	PPO	2470	1640	3030	5380	8780	14640
N63	Aetna Direct CDHP	CDHP	3350	430	2830	5580	8850	14230
423	Compass Rose	PPO-FEE	5470	3650	4480	5650	7290	10650
323	NALC-Hi	PPO-FEE	4950	3340	4200	5870	7920	12340
383	Rural Carrier	PPO-FEE	4600	3070	4010	5890	8420	13070
446	SAMBA-Std	PPO-FEE	3740	2500	3600	5910	8830	16500
473	APWU-Hi	PPO-FEE	4470	3010	4300	6090	8350	16010
KM3	NALC Value Plan	PPO-FEE	2130	1260	2980	6120	9630	14660
416	MHBP Value Plan	PPO-FEE	2670	1830	3730	6220	9580	15030
313	GEHA-Hi	PPO-FEE	5680	3790	4440	6340	8610	13790
226	Aetna HealthFund HDHP	HDHP	5080	1790	3840	7050	10570	17190
106	Blue Cross-Std	PPO-FEE	6220	4150	5480	7380	9760	14150
Z26	Aetna Advantage	PPO-FEE	2540	1690	4090	7880	12740	16690
443	SAMBA-Hi	PPO-FEE	9970	6650	7670	9640	12110	18650

* These are the premiums after tax savings, offset by savings accounts for plans that offer them. If you have no or low health-care costs with these plans, it can result in actual saving to you, which we indicate with a negative number.

Persons 55 to 64: Postal Premiums (Category 2)		Plan type	Published premium	Family of Two: Estimated yearly out-of-pocket costs, including premium and typical hospital, medical, drug, and dental bills near:				
Plan code	Plan name			No costs*	Low use: $1,000 or less	Average cost	High use: $30,000 or more	Limit to you
D.C. Area Plans When You Use Preferred Providers								
E35	Kaiser-Std	HMO	3290	2190	2600	4160	6070	9190
T72	Kaiser Basic	HMO	2560	1700	2480	4450	7130	9700
E32	Kaiser-Hi	HMO	4950	3300	3580	4560	5740	7800
B62	CareFirst HDHP	HDHP	3370	450	2240	4630	7860	8750
V42	United HDHP	HDHP	2790	360	2560	5150	8650	9310
Y82	United Choice Primary	HMO	2980	1990	2880	5410	8480	16690
AS2	United Choice Plus Primary	PPO-FEE	3100	2070	2960	5490	8560	16770
B65	CareFirst Blue Value Plus	HMO-POS	5130	3420	3950	5700	7860	13420
L92	United Choice Plus Advanced	PPO-FEE	3640	2430	3940	5700	8430	8430
JN5	Aetna Open Access Basic	HMO	4150	2770	3650	6120	9210	14770
LR2	United Choice Open Access	HMO	5330	3560	4380	6250	8710	13560
QQ5	Aetna Saver	HMO	3390	2260	4420	7320	11770	15260
2G5	CareFirst-Std POS	HMO-POS	9110	6080	6190	7320	8610	11080
F52	Aetna HealthFund CDHP	CDHP	7690	3130	5160	8350	12010	15730
F55	Aetna Value Plan	PPO-FEE	7530	5030	5880	8750	12340	17630
JP2	MD-IPA	HMO	14500	9670	10360	12030	14190	19670
JN2	Aetna Open Access-Hi	HMO	15690	10470	11000	12330	13900	20470
National Plans When You Use Preferred Providers								
342	GEHA HDHP	HDHP	3240	360	2230	4150	6030	12160
482	MHBP HDHP	HDHP	3320	-150	2250	4750	7270	14250
402	Foreign Service	PPO-FEE	3680	2460	3530	4800	6470	9460
252	GEHA Elevate Plus	PPO-FEE	3890	2590	3130	5030	7540	14590
455	MHBP-Std	PPO-FEE	3300	2250	3520	5190	7340	14250
255	GEHA Elevate	PPO-FEE	2860	1910	2620	5240	8390	15910
322	NALC-Hi	PPO-FEE	4120	2780	3640	5310	7360	11780
325	NALC CDHP	CDHP	2710	-560	1160	5380	9710	15040
112	Blue Cross Basic	PPO	4180	2790	3480	5430	7890	13790
475	APWU CDHP	CDHP	3530	-10	2340	5550	8700	15390
132	FEP Blue Focus	PPO	2710	1810	3200	5550	8950	14810
382	Rural Carrier	PPO-FEE	4090	2730	3670	5550	8080	12730
315	GEHA-Std	PPO-FEE	3360	2240	2990	5660	8850	15240
N62	Aetna Direct CDHP	CDHP	3850	770	3170	5920	9190	14570
445	SAMBA-Std	PPO-FEE	3870	2580	3680	5990	8910	16580
422	Compass Rose	PPO-FEE	6060	4040	4870	6040	7680	11040
KM2	NALC Value Plan	PPO-FEE	2230	1320	3040	6180	9690	14720
415	MHBP Value Plan	PPO-FEE	2730	1860	3760	6250	9610	15060
225	Aetna HealthFund HDHP	HDHP	4290	1260	3310	6520	10040	16660
472	APWU-Hi	PPO-FEE	5920	3980	5270	7060	9320	16980
312	GEHA-Hi	PPO-FEE	7120	4750	5400	7300	9570	14750
105	Blue Cross-Std	PPO-FEE	6670	4450	5780	7680	10060	14450
Z25	Aetna Advantage	PPO-FEE	3060	2040	4440	8230	13090	17040
442	SAMBA-Hi	PPO-FEE	10970	7320	8340	10310	12780	19320

* These are the premiums after tax savings, offset by savings accounts for plans that offer them. If you have no or low health-care costs with these plans, it can result in actual saving to you, which we indicate with a negative number.

Persons 55 to 64: Postal Premiums (Category 2)		Family of Three						
				Estimated yearly out-of-pocket costs, including premium and typical hospital, medical, drug, and dental bills near:				
Plan code	Plan name	Plan type	Published premium	No costs*	Low use: $3,000 or less	Average cost	High use: $30,000 or more	Limit to you
D.C. Area Plans When You Use Preferred Providers								
E35	Kaiser-Std	HMO	3290	2190	2600	4320	6070	9190
E32	Kaiser-Hi	HMO	4950	3300	3580	4660	5740	7800
T72	Kaiser Basic	HMO	2560	1700	2480	4670	7130	9700
B62	CareFirst HDHP	HDHP	3370	450	2240	4900	7860	8750
V42	United HDHP	HDHP	2790	360	2560	5440	8650	9310
Y82	United Choice Primary	HMO	2980	1990	2880	5680	8480	16690
AS2	United Choice Plus Primary	PPO-FEE	3100	2070	2960	5760	8560	16770
B65	CareFirst Blue Value Plus	HMO-POS	5130	3420	3950	5880	7860	13420
L92	United Choice Plus Advanced	PPO-FEE	3640	2430	3940	5910	8430	8430
JN5	Aetna Open Access Basic	HMO	4150	2770	3650	6370	9210	14770
LR2	United Choice Open Access	HMO	5330	3560	4380	6450	8710	13560
2G5	CareFirst-Std POS	HMO-POS	9110	6080	6190	7430	8610	11080
QQ5	Aetna Saver	HMO	3390	2260	4420	7670	11770	15260
F52	Aetna HealthFund CDHP	CDHP	7690	3130	5160	8680	12010	15730
F55	Aetna Value Plan	PPO-FEE	7530	5030	5880	9050	12340	17630
JP2	MD-IPA	HMO	14500	9670	10360	12210	14190	19670
JN2	Aetna Open Access-Hi	HMO	15690	10470	11000	12470	13900	20470
National Plans When You Use Preferred Providers								
342	GEHA HDHP	HDHP	3240	360	2230	4360	6030	12160
402	Foreign Service	PPO-FEE	3680	2460	3530	4950	6470	9460
482	MHBP HDHP	HDHP	3320	-150	2250	5020	7270	14250
252	GEHA Elevate Plus	PPO-FEE	3890	2590	3130	5230	7540	14590
455	MHBP-Std	PPO-FEE	3300	2250	3520	5380	7340	14250
322	NALC-Hi	PPO-FEE	4120	2780	3640	5490	7360	11780
255	GEHA Elevate	PPO-FEE	2860	1910	2620	5510	8390	15910
112	Blue Cross Basic	PPO	4180	2790	3480	5640	7890	13790
382	Rural Carrier	PPO-FEE	4090	2730	3670	5750	8080	12730
132	FEP Blue Focus	PPO	2710	1810	3200	5820	8950	14810
325	NALC CDHP	CDHP	2710	-560	1160	5830	9710	15040
475	APWU CDHP	CDHP	3530	-10	2340	5880	8700	15390
315	GEHA-Std	PPO-FEE	3360	2240	2990	5940	8850	15240
422	Compass Rose	PPO-FEE	6060	4040	4870	6180	7680	11040
N62	Aetna Direct CDHP	CDHP	3850	770	3170	6230	9190	14570
445	SAMBA-Std	PPO-FEE	3870	2580	3680	6240	8910	16580
KM2	NALC Value Plan	PPO-FEE	2230	1320	3040	6520	9690	14720
415	MHBP Value Plan	PPO-FEE	2730	1860	3760	6550	9610	15060
225	Aetna HealthFund HDHP	HDHP	4290	1260	3310	6850	10040	16660
472	APWU-Hi	PPO-FEE	5920	3980	5270	7260	9320	16980
312	GEHA-Hi	PPO-FEE	7120	4750	5400	7500	9570	14750
105	Blue Cross-Std	PPO-FEE	6670	4450	5780	7890	10060	14450
Z25	Aetna Advantage	PPO-FEE	3060	2040	4440	8630	13090	17040
442	SAMBA-Hi	PPO-FEE	10970	7320	8340	10530	12780	19320

* These are the premiums after tax savings, offset by savings accounts for plans that offer them. If you have no or low health-care costs with these plans, it can result in actual saving to you, which we indicate with a negative number.

Half-Time Employees Under 55: GS Premiums

Plan code	Plan name	Plan type	Published premium	Self Only: Estimated yearly out-of-pocket costs, including premium and typical hospital, medical, drug, and dental bills near: No costs*	Low use: $1,000 or less	Average cost	High use: $30,000 or more	Limit to you
D.C. Area Plans When You Use Preferred Providers								
T71	Kaiser Basic	HMO	3150	2100	2320	3000	6100	6100
V41	United HDHP	HDHP	3650	1680	2280	3240	6730	6730
B61	CareFirst HDHP	HDHP	4280	1950	2490	3420	6850	6850
E34	Kaiser-Std	HMO	4290	2860	2930	3490	6360	6360
Y81	United Choice Primary	HMO	3800	2530	2710	3700	9880	9880
L91	United Choice Plus Advanced	PPO-FEE	3910	2610	3140	3710	5610	5610
AS1	United Choice Plus Primary	PPO-FEE	3940	2630	2810	3800	9980	9980
E31	Kaiser-Hi	HMO	5610	3740	3760	4150	5990	5990
B64	CareFirst Blue Value Plus	HMO-POS	5410	3610	3780	4480	8610	8610
LR1	United Choice Open Access	HMO	5510	3680	3870	4600	8680	8680
JN4	Aetna Open Access Basic	HMO	5300	3540	3740	4700	9540	9540
QQ4	Aetna Saver	HMO	4460	2980	3680	4760	9480	9480
2G4	CareFirst-Std POS	HMO-POS	7080	4720	4720	5170	7220	7220
F51	Aetna HealthFund CDHP	CDHP	6890	3590	4140	5320	9890	9890
F54	Aetna Value Plan	PPO-FEE	6770	4520	4770	5730	10820	10820
JP1	MD-IPA	HMO	7450	4970	5110	5780	9570	9970
JN1	Aetna Open Access-Hi	HMO	10590	7060	7130	7690	10550	12060
National Plans When You Use Preferred Providers								
324	NALC CDHP	CDHP	3550	1200	1570	2980	9000	9000
341	GEHA HDHP	HDHP	3850	1670	2170	3000	6440	7570
254	GEHA Elevate	PPO-FEE	3080	2050	2280	3210	9050	9050
481	MHBP HDHP	HDHP	4300	1710	2410	3470	7410	8910
KM1	NALC Value Plan	PPO-FEE	2910	1880	2250	3470	8580	8580
131	FEP Blue Focus	PPO	3450	2300	2820	3560	8800	8800
474	APWU CDHP	CDHP	4480	1820	2490	3780	9520	9520
314	GEHA-Std	PPO-FEE	3940	2620	2850	3790	9120	9120
414	MHBP Value Plan	PPO-FEE	3400	2310	2730	3840	8910	8910
401	Foreign Service	PPO-FEE	4480	2990	3270	3850	6860	7990
N61	Aetna Direct CDHP	CDHP	4590	2160	2860	3970	9060	9060
251	GEHA Elevate Plus	PPO-FEE	4720	3150	3270	4010	8470	9150
454	MHBP-Std	PPO-FEE	4280	2900	3200	4020	8570	8900
111	Blue Cross Basic	PPO	4940	3290	3420	4200	8520	8790
Z24	Aetna Advantage	PPO-FEE	3480	2320	3020	4390	9820	9820
421	Compass Rose	PPO-FEE	5710	3810	4020	4530	7450	8810
321	NALC-Hi	PPO-FEE	5430	3660	3940	4580	8020	10260
444	SAMBA-Std	PPO-FEE	5100	3400	3740	4710	10400	10400
224	Aetna HealthFund HDHP	HDHP	5680	2990	3510	4790	10690	10690
311	GEHA-Hi	PPO-FEE	5810	3870	4090	4790	8870	8870
471	APWU-Hi	PPO-FEE	5650	3800	4320	5020	10010	10300
381	Rural Carrier	PPO-FEE	6240	4160	4480	5170	9160	9160
104	Blue Cross-Std	PPO-FEE	6100	4070	4500	5230	9070	9070
441	SAMBA-Hi	PPO-FEE	7760	5170	5480	6330	11170	11170

* These are the premiums after tax savings, offset by savings accounts for plans that offer them. If you have no or low health-care costs with these plans, it can result in actual saving to you, which we indicate with a negative number.

Half-Time Employees Under 55: GS Premiums		Self Plus One							
		Plan type	Published premium	Estimated yearly out-of-pocket costs, including premium and typical hospital, medical, drug, and dental bills near:					
Plan code	Plan name			No costs*	Low use: $3,000 or less	Average cost	High use: $30,000 or more	Limit to you
D.C. Area Plans When You Use Preferred Providers									
T73	Kaiser Basic	HMO	7010	4680	5460	6370	10110	12680
B63	CareFirst HDHP	HDHP	8550	3900	5690	6730	11310	12200
V43	United HDHP	HDHP	7850	3730	5930	6980	12020	12680
L93	United Choice Plus Advanced	PPO-FEE	7640	5090	6600	7320	11090	11090
Y83	United Choice Primary	HMO	8170	5450	6340	7480	11940	20150
AS3	United Choice Plus Primary	PPO-FEE	8480	5650	6540	7680	12140	20350
E36	Kaiser-Std	HMO	9860	6580	6990	7740	10460	13580
B66	CareFirst Blue Value Plus	HMO-POS	10590	7060	7590	8430	11500	17060
JN6	Aetna Open Access Basic	HMO	11030	7350	8230	9390	13790	19350
QQ6	Aetna Saver	HMO	9380	6260	8420	9580	15770	19260
LR3	United Choice Open Access	HMO	11890	7930	8750	9590	13080	17930
E33	Kaiser-Hi	HMO	13400	8940	9220	9680	11380	13440
2G6	CareFirst-Std POS	HMO-POS	13740	9160	9270	9850	11690	14160
JP3	MD-IPA	HMO	13990	9330	10020	10770	13850	19330
F53	Aetna HealthFund CDHP	CDHP	15910	8610	10640	12050	17490	21210
F56	Aetna Value Plan	PPO-FEE	15540	10360	11210	12600	17670	22960
JN3	Aetna Open Access-Hi	HMO	23830	15900	16430	17030	19330	25900
National Plans When You Use Preferred Providers									
343	GEHA HDHP	HDHP	8290	3730	5600	6340	9400	15530
326	NALC CDHP	CDHP	7840	2860	4580	6580	13130	18460
256	GEHA Elevate	PPO-FEE	7070	4720	5430	6680	11200	18720
KM3	NALC Value Plan	PPO-FEE	6430	4120	5840	7230	12490	17520
133	FEP Blue Focus	PPO	7430	4950	6340	7330	12090	17950
483	MHBP HDHP	HDHP	9510	3990	6390	7400	11410	18390
316	GEHA-Std	PPO-FEE	8460	5640	6390	7690	12250	18640
476	APWU CDHP	CDHP	9740	4130	6480	7860	12840	19530
416	MHBP Value Plan	PPO-FEE	8060	5420	7320	8250	13170	18620
N63	Aetna Direct CDHP	CDHP	10080	4920	7320	8380	13340	18720
456	MHBP-Std	PPO-FEE	9860	6620	7890	8520	11710	18620
253	GEHA Elevate Plus	PPO-FEE	10980	7320	7860	8760	12270	19320
403	Foreign Service	PPO-FEE	11020	7350	8420	8890	11360	14350
113	Blue Cross Basic	PPO	11200	7470	8160	9060	12570	18470
Z26	Aetna Advantage	PPO-FEE	7650	5100	7500	9170	16150	20100
446	SAMBA-Std	PPO-FEE	11020	7350	8450	9490	13680	21350
383	Rural Carrier	PPO-FEE	11880	7920	8860	9750	13270	17920
423	Compass Rose	PPO-FEE	12750	8500	9330	9770	12140	15500
323	NALC-Hi	PPO-FEE	12230	8190	9050	9790	12770	17190
473	APWU-Hi	PPO-FEE	11750	7870	9160	9880	13210	20870
226	Aetna HealthFund HDHP	HDHP	12360	6640	8690	10070	15420	22040
313	GEHA-Hi	PPO-FEE	12960	8650	9300	10210	13470	18650
106	Blue Cross-Std	PPO-FEE	13500	9000	10330	11100	14610	19000
443	SAMBA-Hi	PPO-FEE	17250	11510	12530	13400	16970	23510

* These are the premiums after tax savings, offset by savings accounts for plans that offer them. If you have no or low health-care costs with these plans, it can result in actual saving to you, which we indicate with a negative number.

Half-Time Employees Under 55: GS Premiums		Family of Three						
		Plan type	Published premium	Estimated yearly out-of-pocket costs, including premium and typical hospital, medical, drug, and dental bills near:				
Plan code	Plan name			No costs*	Low use: $1,000 or less	Average cost	High use: $30,000 or more	Limit to you
D.C. Area Plans When You Use Preferred Providers								
T72	Kaiser Basic	HMO	7700	5130	5910	7080	10560	13130
V42	United HDHP	HDHP	8390	4100	6300	7750	12390	13050
E35	Kaiser-Std	HMO	9910	6610	7020	7960	10490	13610
B62	CareFirst HDHP	HDHP	10160	4980	6770	8160	12390	13280
Y82	United Choice Primary	HMO	8990	5990	6880	8340	12480	20690
AS2	United Choice Plus Primary	PPO-FEE	9330	6220	7110	8570	12710	20920
E32	Kaiser-Hi	HMO	12850	8570	8850	9430	11010	13070
L92	United Choice Plus Advanced	PPO-FEE	10970	7310	8820	9810	13310	13310
B65	CareFirst Blue Value Plus	HMO-POS	13030	8690	9220	10260	13130	18690
JN5	Aetna Open Access Basic	HMO	12040	8030	8910	10380	14470	20030
QQ5	Aetna Saver	HMO	10220	6810	8970	10550	16320	19810
LR2	United Choice Open Access	HMO	13230	8820	9640	10720	13970	18820
2G5	CareFirst-Std POS	HMO-POS	17000	11340	11450	12150	13870	16340
F52	Aetna HealthFund CDHP	CDHP	15580	8390	10420	12280	17270	20990
F55	Aetna Value Plan	PPO-FEE	15430	10290	11140	12870	17600	22890
JP2	MD-IPA	HMO	22390	14930	15620	16590	19450	24930
JN2	Aetna Open Access-Hi	HMO	23580	15730	16260	17030	19160	25730
National Plans When You Use Preferred Providers								
325	NALC CDHP	CDHP	8170	3080	4800	7360	13350	18680
342	GEHA HDHP	HDHP	9750	4700	6570	7620	10370	16500
KM2	NALC Value Plan	PPO-FEE	6710	4310	6030	7850	12680	17710
255	GEHA Elevate	PPO-FEE	8610	5740	6450	8010	12220	19740
482	MHBP HDHP	HDHP	9990	4310	6710	8120	11730	18710
132	FEP Blue Focus	PPO	8170	5450	6840	8140	12590	18450
415	MHBP Value Plan	PPO-FEE	8220	5520	7420	8720	13270	18720
455	MHBP-Std	PPO-FEE	9950	6680	7950	8830	11770	18680
475	APWU CDHP	CDHP	10630	4720	7070	8910	13430	20120
315	GEHA-Std	PPO-FEE	10110	6740	7490	9110	13350	19740
402	Foreign Service	PPO-FEE	11090	7400	8470	9140	11410	14400
252	GEHA Elevate Plus	PPO-FEE	11710	7810	8350	9480	12760	19810
N62	Aetna Direct CDHP	CDHP	11590	5930	8330	9810	14350	19730
322	NALC-Hi	PPO-FEE	12010	8050	8910	9870	12630	17050
112	Blue Cross Basic	PPO	12080	8050	8740	9890	13150	19050
382	Rural Carrier	PPO-FEE	11980	7990	8930	10050	13340	17990
445	SAMBA-Std	PPO-FEE	11640	7770	8870	10210	14100	21770
225	Aetna HealthFund HDHP	HDHP	12190	6530	8580	10410	15310	21930
Z25	Aetna Advantage	PPO-FEE	9220	6150	8550	10750	17200	21150
422	Compass Rose	PPO-FEE	13950	9310	10140	10750	12950	16310
472	APWU-Hi	PPO-FEE	13810	9250	10540	11500	14590	22250
312	GEHA-Hi	PPO-FEE	15020	10020	10670	11810	14840	20020
105	Blue Cross-Std	PPO-FEE	14560	9710	11040	12080	15320	19710
442	SAMBA-Hi	PPO-FEE	18870	12580	13600	14740	18040	24580

* These are the premiums after tax savings, offset by savings accounts for plans that offer them. If you have no or low health-care costs with these plans, it can result in actual saving to you, which we indicate with a negative number.

Four-Fifths-Time Employees Under 55: GS Premiums				Self Only				
				Estimated yearly out-of-pocket costs, including premium and typical hospital, medical, drug, and dental bills near:				
Plan code	Plan name	Plan type	Published premium	No costs*	Low use: $1,000 or less	Average cost	High use: $30,000 or more	Limit to you
D.C. Area Plans When You Use Preferred Providers								
T71	Kaiser Basic	HMO	2020	1350	2240	2920	6020	6020
E34	Kaiser-Std	HMO	2740	1830	2810	3370	6240	6240
Y81	United Choice Primary	HMO	2430	1620	2610	3600	9780	9780
L91	United Choice Plus Advanced	PPO-FEE	2500	1670	3030	3600	5500	5500
AS1	United Choice Plus Primary	PPO-FEE	2520	1680	2700	3690	9870	9870
V41	United HDHP	HDHP	2340	810	2940	3900	7390	7390
E31	Kaiser-Hi	HMO	3770	2510	3790	4180	6020	6020
B61	CareFirst HDHP	HDHP	2740	930	3280	4210	7640	7640
B64	CareFirst Blue Value Plus	HMO-POS	3570	2380	3740	4440	8570	8570
LR1	United Choice Open Access	HMO	3670	2450	3860	4590	8670	8670
JN4	Aetna Open Access Basic	HMO	3460	2310	3660	4620	9460	9460
QQ4	Aetna Saver	HMO	2860	1910	3560	4640	9360	9360
2G4	CareFirst-Std POS	HMO-POS	5240	3500	5240	5690	7740	7740
F54	Aetna Value Plan	PPO-FEE	4940	3290	5190	6150	11240	11240
JP1	MD-IPA	HMO	5620	3750	5760	6430	10220	10620
F51	Aetna HealthFund CDHP	CDHP	5050	2370	5600	6780	11350	11350
JN1	Aetna Open Access-Hi	HMO	8750	5830	8820	9380	12240	13750
National Plans When You Use Preferred Providers								
254	GEHA Elevate	PPO-FEE	1970	1310	2200	3130	8970	8970
KM1	NALC Value Plan	PPO-FEE	1870	1180	2240	3460	8570	8570
131	FEP Blue Focus	PPO	2210	1470	2730	3470	8710	8710
314	GEHA-Std	PPO-FEE	2520	1680	2750	3690	9020	9020
414	MHBP Value Plan	PPO-FEE	2180	1490	2600	3710	8780	8780
401	Foreign Service	PPO-FEE	2870	1910	3150	3730	6740	7870
341	GEHA HDHP	HDHP	2470	750	2970	3800	7240	8370
454	MHBP-Std	PPO-FEE	2740	1870	3040	3860	8410	8740
251	GEHA Elevate Plus	PPO-FEE	3020	2020	3140	3880	8340	9020
324	NALC CDHP	CDHP	2270	350	2640	4050	10070	10070
111	Blue Cross Basic	PPO	3160	2110	3290	4070	8390	8660
Z24	Aetna Advantage	PPO-FEE	2230	1490	2930	4300	9730	9730
481	MHBP HDHP	HDHP	2750	680	3450	4510	8450	9950
321	NALC-Hi	PPO-FEE	3590	2430	3870	4510	7950	10190
444	SAMBA-Std	PPO-FEE	3270	2180	3610	4580	10270	10270
421	Compass Rose	PPO-FEE	3870	2580	4080	4590	7510	8870
N61	Aetna Direct CDHP	CDHP	2940	1060	3640	4750	9840	9840
474	APWU CDHP	CDHP	2870	750	3540	4830	10570	10570
311	GEHA-Hi	PPO-FEE	3970	2650	4190	4890	8970	8970
471	APWU-Hi	PPO-FEE	3810	2580	4330	5030	10020	10310
381	Rural Carrier	PPO-FEE	4400	2940	4720	5410	9400	9400
104	Blue Cross-Std	PPO-FEE	4270	2850	4700	5430	9270	9270
224	Aetna HealthFund HDHP	HDHP	3840	1760	4360	5640	11540	11540
441	SAMBA-Hi	PPO-FEE	5920	3950	6230	7080	11920	11920

* These are the premiums after tax savings, offset by savings accounts for plans that offer them. If you have no or low health-care costs with these plans, it can result in actual saving to you, which we indicate with a negative number.

Four-Fifths-Time Employees Under 55: GS Premiums		Self Plus One						
		Plan type	Published premium	Estimated yearly out-of-pocket costs, including premium and typical hospital, medical, drug, and dental bills near:				
Plan code	Plan name			No costs*	Low use: $3,000 or less	Average cost	High use: $30,000 or more	Limit to you
D.C. Area Plans When You Use Preferred Providers								
B63	CareFirst HDHP	HDHP	5470	1850	3640	4680	9260	10150
T73	Kaiser Basic	HMO	4490	2990	3770	4680	8420	10990
V43	United HDHP	HDHP	5020	1850	4050	5100	10140	10800
E36	Kaiser-Std	HMO	6310	4210	4620	5370	8090	11210
L93	United Choice Plus Advanced	PPO-FEE	4890	3260	4770	5490	9260	9260
Y83	United Choice Primary	HMO	5230	3490	4380	5520	9980	18190
AS3	United Choice Plus Primary	PPO-FEE	5430	3620	4510	5650	10110	18320
B66	CareFirst Blue Value Plus	HMO-POS	6780	4520	5050	5890	8960	14520
JN6	Aetna Open Access Basic	HMO	7090	4730	5610	6770	11170	16730
LR3	United Choice Open Access	HMO	7960	5310	6130	6970	10460	15310
E33	Kaiser-Hi	HMO	9460	6310	6590	7050	8750	10810
2G6	CareFirst-Std POS	HMO-POS	9810	6540	6650	7230	9070	11540
QQ6	Aetna Saver	HMO	6000	4000	6160	7320	13510	17000
JP3	MD-IPA	HMO	10060	6710	7400	8150	11230	16710
F53	Aetna HealthFund CDHP	CDHP	11980	5990	8020	9430	14870	18590
F56	Aetna Value Plan	PPO-FEE	11600	7740	8590	9980	15050	20340
JN3	Aetna Open Access-Hi	HMO	19900	13270	13800	14400	16700	23270
National Plans When You Use Preferred Providers								
343	GEHA HDHP	HDHP	5300	1740	3610	4350	7410	13540
326	NALC CDHP	CDHP	5010	980	2700	4700	11250	16580
256	GEHA Elevate	PPO-FEE	4530	3020	3730	4980	9500	17020
483	MHBP HDHP	HDHP	6090	1700	4100	5110	9120	16100
476	APWU CDHP	CDHP	6240	1790	4140	5520	10500	17190
133	FEP Blue Focus	PPO	4750	3170	4560	5550	10310	16170
316	GEHA-Std	PPO-FEE	5420	3610	4360	5660	10220	16610
KM3	NALC Value Plan	PPO-FEE	4120	2580	4300	5690	10950	15980
N63	Aetna Direct CDHP	CDHP	6450	2500	4900	5960	10920	16300
253	GEHA Elevate Plus	PPO-FEE	7050	4700	5240	6140	9650	16700
456	MHBP-Std	PPO-FEE	6310	4250	5520	6150	9340	16250
403	Foreign Service	PPO-FEE	7090	4730	5800	6270	8740	11730
416	MHBP Value Plan	PPO-FEE	5160	3480	5380	6310	11230	16680
113	Blue Cross Basic	PPO	7270	4850	5540	6440	9950	15850
446	SAMBA-Std	PPO-FEE	7090	4730	5830	6870	11060	18730
383	Rural Carrier	PPO-FEE	7950	5300	6240	7130	10650	15300
423	Compass Rose	PPO-FEE	8820	5880	6710	7150	9520	12880
323	NALC-Hi	PPO-FEE	8300	5570	6430	7170	10150	14570
473	APWU-Hi	PPO-FEE	7810	5250	6540	7260	10590	18250
Z26	Aetna Advantage	PPO-FEE	4900	3270	5670	7340	14320	18270
226	Aetna HealthFund HDHP	HDHP	8430	4020	6070	7450	12800	19420
313	GEHA-Hi	PPO-FEE	9030	6020	6670	7580	10840	16020
106	Blue Cross-Std	PPO-FEE	9570	6380	7710	8480	11990	16380
443	SAMBA-Hi	PPO-FEE	13320	8880	9900	10770	14340	20880

* These are the premiums after tax savings, offset by savings accounts for plans that offer them. If you have no or low health-care costs with these plans, it can result in actual saving to you, which we indicate with a negative number.

Four-Fifths-Time Employees Under 55: GS Premiums		Family of Three							
		Plan type	Published premium	Estimated yearly out-of-pocket costs, including premium and typical hospital, medical, drug, and dental bills near:					
Plan code	Plan name			No costs*	Low use: $3,000 or less	Average cost	High use: $30,000 or more	Limit to you
D.C. Area Plans When You Use Preferred Providers								
T72	Kaiser Basic	HMO	4930	3290	4070	5240	8720	11290
E35	Kaiser-Std	HMO	6340	4230	4640	5580	8110	11230
B62	CareFirst HDHP	HDHP	6500	2540	4330	5720	9950	10840
V42	United HDHP	HDHP	5370	2080	4280	5730	10370	11030
Y82	United Choice Primary	HMO	5750	3840	4730	6190	10330	18540
AS2	United Choice Plus Primary	PPO-FEE	5970	3980	4870	6330	10470	18680
E32	Kaiser-Hi	HMO	8580	5730	6010	6590	8170	10230
L92	United Choice Plus Advanced	PPO-FEE	7020	4680	6190	7180	10680	10680
B65	CareFirst Blue Value Plus	HMO-POS	8760	5840	6370	7410	10280	15840
JN5	Aetna Open Access Basic	HMO	7780	5190	6070	7540	11630	17190
LR2	United Choice Open Access	HMO	8960	5980	6800	7880	11130	15980
QQ5	Aetna Saver	HMO	6540	4360	6520	8100	13870	17360
2G5	CareFirst-Std POS	HMO-POS	12740	8500	8610	9310	11030	13500
F52	Aetna HealthFund CDHP	CDHP	11320	5550	7580	9440	14430	18150
F55	Aetna Value Plan	PPO-FEE	11160	7450	8300	10030	14760	20050
JP2	MD-IPA	HMO	18130	12090	12780	13750	16610	22090
JN2	Aetna Open Access-Hi	HMO	19320	12890	13420	14190	16320	22890
National Plans When You Use Preferred Providers								
342	GEHA HDHP	HDHP	6240	2360	4230	5280	8030	14160
325	NALC CDHP	CDHP	5230	1120	2840	5400	11390	16720
482	MHBP HDHP	HDHP	6390	1910	4310	5720	9330	16310
255	GEHA Elevate	PPO-FEE	5510	3680	4390	5950	10160	17680
132	FEP Blue Focus	PPO	5230	3490	4880	6180	10630	16490
KM2	NALC Value Plan	PPO-FEE	4290	2700	4420	6240	11070	16100
475	APWU CDHP	CDHP	6800	2170	4520	6360	10880	17570
455	MHBP-Std	PPO-FEE	6370	4290	5560	6440	9380	16290
402	Foreign Service	PPO-FEE	7100	4740	5810	6480	8750	11740
252	GEHA Elevate Plus	PPO-FEE	7500	5000	5540	6670	9950	17000
315	GEHA-Std	PPO-FEE	6470	4320	5070	6690	10930	17320
415	MHBP Value Plan	PPO-FEE	5260	3550	5450	6750	11300	16750
322	NALC-Hi	PPO-FEE	7750	5200	6060	7020	9780	14200
N62	Aetna Direct CDHP	CDHP	7420	3150	5550	7030	11570	16950
112	Blue Cross Basic	PPO	7810	5210	5900	7050	10310	16210
382	Rural Carrier	PPO-FEE	7720	5150	6090	7210	10500	15150
445	SAMBA-Std	PPO-FEE	7450	4970	6070	7410	11300	18970
225	Aetna HealthFund HDHP	HDHP	7920	3690	5740	7570	12470	19090
422	Compass Rose	PPO-FEE	9690	6460	7290	7900	10100	13460
Z25	Aetna Advantage	PPO-FEE	5900	3940	6340	8540	14990	18940
472	APWU-Hi	PPO-FEE	9550	6400	7690	8650	11740	19400
312	GEHA-Hi	PPO-FEE	10760	7170	7820	8960	11990	17170
105	Blue Cross-Std	PPO-FEE	10300	6870	8200	9240	12480	16870
442	SAMBA-Hi	PPO-FEE	14600	9740	10760	11900	15200	21740

* These are the premiums after tax savings, offset by savings accounts for plans that offer them. If you have no or low health-care costs with these plans, it can result in actual saving to you, which we indicate with a negative number.

Persons Under 55 Who Pay Full Premiums

Plan code	Plan name	Plan type	Published premium	Self Only — Estimated yearly out-of-pocket costs, including premium and typical hospital, medical, drug, and dental bills near: No costs*	Low use: $3,000 or less	Average cost	High use: $30,000 or more	Limit to you
D.C. Area Plans When You Use Preferred Providers								
T71	Kaiser Basic	HMO	5040	5040	5260	5940	9040	9040
V41	United HDHP	HDHP	5840	5090	5690	6650	10140	10140
Y81	United Choice Primary	HMO	6080	6080	6260	7250	13430	13430
L91	United Choice Plus Advanced	PPO-FEE	6260	6260	6790	7360	9260	9260
B61	CareFirst HDHP	HDHP	6840	5940	6480	7410	10840	10840
AS1	United Choice Plus Primary	PPO-FEE	6310	6310	6490	7480	13660	13660
E34	Kaiser-Std	HMO	6860	6860	6930	7490	10360	10360
QQ4	Aetna Saver	HMO	7140	7140	7840	8920	13640	13640
E31	Kaiser-Hi	HMO	8670	8670	8690	9080	10920	10920
B64	CareFirst Blue Value Plus	HMO-POS	8470	8470	8640	9340	13470	13470
LR1	United Choice Open Access	HMO	8580	8580	8770	9500	13580	13580
JN4	Aetna Open Access Basic	HMO	8370	8370	8570	9530	14370	14370
2G4	CareFirst-Std POS	HMO-POS	10150	10150	10150	10600	12650	12650
F51	Aetna HealthFund CDHP	CDHP	9950	8950	9500	10680	15250	15250
F54	Aetna Value Plan	PPO-FEE	9840	9840	10090	11050	16140	16140
JP1	MD-IPA	HMO	10520	10520	10660	11330	15120	15520
JN1	Aetna Open Access-Hi	HMO	13650	13650	13720	14280	17140	18650
National Plans When You Use Preferred Providers								
254	GEHA Elevate	PPO-FEE	4920	4920	5150	6080	11920	11920
KM1	NALC Value Plan	PPO-FEE	4660	4560	4930	6150	11260	11260
324	NALC CDHP	CDHP	5680	4480	4850	6260	12280	12280
341	GEHA HDHP	HDHP	6170	5270	5770	6600	10040	11170
131	FEP Blue Focus	PPO	5530	5530	6050	6790	12030	12030
414	MHBP Value Plan	PPO-FEE	5440	5440	5860	6970	12040	12040
481	MHBP HDHP	HDHP	6880	5680	6380	7440	11380	12880
314	GEHA-Std	PPO-FEE	6300	6300	6530	7470	12800	12800
Z24	Aetna Advantage	PPO-FEE	5570	5570	6270	7640	13070	13070
474	APWU CDHP	CDHP	7170	5970	6640	7930	13670	13670
454	MHBP-Std	PPO-FEE	6850	6850	7150	7970	12520	12850
401	Foreign Service	PPO-FEE	7170	7170	7450	8030	11040	12170
N61	Aetna Direct CDHP	CDHP	7350	6450	7150	8260	13350	13350
251	GEHA Elevate Plus	PPO-FEE	7560	7560	7680	8420	12880	13560
111	Blue Cross Basic	PPO	7900	7900	8030	8810	13130	13400
321	NALC-Hi	PPO-FEE	8490	8490	8770	9410	12850	15090
444	SAMBA-Std	PPO-FEE	8170	8170	8510	9480	15170	15170
421	Compass Rose	PPO-FEE	8770	8770	8980	9490	12410	13770
224	Aetna HealthFund HDHP	HDHP	8750	7950	8470	9750	15650	15650
311	GEHA-Hi	PPO-FEE	8870	8870	9090	9790	13870	13870
471	APWU-Hi	PPO-FEE	8710	8710	9230	9930	14920	15210
381	Rural Carrier	PPO-FEE	9310	9310	9630	10320	14310	14310
104	Blue Cross-Std	PPO-FEE	9170	9170	9600	10330	14170	14170
441	SAMBA-Hi	PPO-FEE	10820	10820	11130	11980	16820	16820

* These are the premiums after tax savings, offset by savings accounts for plans that offer them. If you have no or low health-care costs with these plans, it can result in actual saving to you, which we indicate with a negative number.

Persons Under 55 Who Pay Full Premiums		Self Plus One						
		Plan type	Published premium	Estimated yearly out-of-pocket costs, including premium and typical hospital, medical, drug, and dental bills near:				
Plan code	Plan name			No costs*	Low use: $3,000 or less	Average cost	High use: $30,000 or more	Limit to you
D.C. Area Plans When You Use Preferred Providers								
T73	Kaiser Basic	HMO	11220	11220	12000	12910	16650	19220
L93	United Choice Plus Advanced	PPO-FEE	12220	12220	13730	14450	18220	18220
B63	CareFirst HDHP	HDHP	13680	11880	13670	14710	19290	20180
V43	United HDHP	HDHP	13430	11930	14130	15180	20220	20880
Y83	United Choice Primary	HMO	14380	14380	15270	16410	20870	29080
E36	Kaiser-Std	HMO	15770	15770	16180	16930	19650	22770
AS3	United Choice Plus Primary	PPO-FEE	14920	14920	15810	16950	21410	29620
B66	CareFirst Blue Value Plus	HMO-POS	16940	16940	17470	18310	21380	26940
QQ6	Aetna Saver	HMO	15010	15010	17170	18330	24520	28010
JN6	Aetna Open Access Basic	HMO	17580	17580	18460	19620	24020	29580
E33	Kaiser-Hi	HMO	19950	19950	20230	20690	22390	24450
2G6	CareFirst-Std POS	HMO-POS	20290	20290	20400	20980	22820	25290
JP3	MD-IPA	HMO	20540	20540	21230	21980	25060	30540
LR3	United Choice Open Access	HMO	20330	20330	21150	21990	25480	30330
F53	Aetna HealthFund CDHP	CDHP	22460	20460	22490	23900	29340	33060
F56	Aetna Value Plan	PPO-FEE	22090	22090	22940	24330	29400	34690
JN3	Aetna Open Access-Hi	HMO	30390	30390	30920	31520	33820	40390
National Plans When You Use Preferred Providers								
KM3	NALC Value Plan	PPO-FEE	10290	10090	11810	13200	18460	23490
256	GEHA Elevate	PPO-FEE	11320	11320	12030	13280	17800	25320
326	NALC CDHP	CDHP	12540	10140	11860	13860	20410	25740
343	GEHA HDHP	HDHP	13260	11460	13330	14070	17130	23260
133	FEP Blue Focus	PPO	11880	11880	13270	14260	19020	24880
316	GEHA-Std	PPO-FEE	13540	13540	14290	15590	20150	26540
416	MHBP Value Plan	PPO-FEE	12890	12890	14790	15720	20640	26090
483	MHBP HDHP	HDHP	15220	12820	15220	16230	20240	27220
Z26	Aetna Advantage	PPO-FEE	12250	12250	14650	16320	23300	27250
476	APWU CDHP	CDHP	15590	13190	15540	16920	21900	28590
456	MHBP-Std	PPO-FEE	15770	15770	17040	17670	20860	27770
N63	Aetna Direct CDHP	CDHP	16120	14320	16720	17780	22740	28120
253	GEHA Elevate Plus	PPO-FEE	17530	17530	18070	18970	22480	29530
403	Foreign Service	PPO-FEE	17570	17570	18640	19110	21580	24570
113	Blue Cross Basic	PPO	17750	17750	18440	19340	22850	28750
446	SAMBA-Std	PPO-FEE	17580	17580	18680	19720	23910	31580
383	Rural Carrier	PPO-FEE	18430	18430	19370	20260	23780	28430
473	APWU-Hi	PPO-FEE	18300	18300	19590	20310	23640	31300
323	NALC-Hi	PPO-FEE	18780	18780	19640	20380	23360	27780
423	Compass Rose	PPO-FEE	19300	19300	20130	20570	22940	26300
226	Aetna HealthFund HDHP	HDHP	18910	17310	19360	20740	26090	32710
313	GEHA-Hi	PPO-FEE	19520	19520	20170	21080	24340	29520
106	Blue Cross-Std	PPO-FEE	20050	20050	21380	22150	25660	30050
443	SAMBA-Hi	PPO-FEE	23810	23810	24830	25700	29270	35810

* These are the premiums after tax savings, offset by savings accounts for plans that offer them. If you have no or low health-care costs with these plans, it can result in actual saving to you, which we indicate with a negative number.

Persons Under 55 Who Pay Full Premiums

Family of Three

Plan code	Plan name	Plan type	Published premium	Estimated yearly out-of-pocket costs, including premium and typical hospital, medical, drug, and dental bills near: No costs*	Low use: $1,000 or less	Average cost	High use: $30,000 or more	Limit to you
D.C. Area Plans When You Use Preferred Providers								
T72	Kaiser Basic	HMO	12310	12310	13090	14260	17740	20310
V42	United HDHP	HDHP	13430	11930	14130	15580	20220	20880
Y82	United Choice Primary	HMO	14380	14380	15270	16730	20870	29080
E35	Kaiser-Std	HMO	15850	15850	16260	17200	19730	22850
AS2	United Choice Plus Primary	PPO-FEE	14920	14920	15810	17270	21410	29620
B62	CareFirst HDHP	HDHP	16250	14450	16240	17630	21860	22750
L92	United Choice Plus Advanced	PPO-FEE	17550	17550	19060	20050	23550	23550
QQ5	Aetna Saver	HMO	16350	16350	18510	20090	25860	29350
E32	Kaiser-Hi	HMO	19950	19950	20230	20810	22390	24450
JN5	Aetna Open Access Basic	HMO	19140	19140	20020	21490	25580	31140
B65	CareFirst Blue Value Plus	HMO-POS	20130	20130	20660	21700	24570	30130
LR2	United Choice Open Access	HMO	20330	20330	21150	22230	25480	30330
F52	Aetna HealthFund CDHP	CDHP	22690	20690	22720	24580	29570	33290
2G5	CareFirst-Std POS	HMO-POS	24110	24110	24220	24920	26640	29110
F55	Aetna Value Plan	PPO-FEE	22530	22530	23380	25110	29840	35130
JP2	MD-IPA	HMO	29490	29490	30180	31150	34010	39490
JN2	Aetna Open Access-Hi	HMO	30690	30690	31220	31990	34120	40690
National Plans When You Use Preferred Providers								
KM2	NALC Value Plan	PPO-FEE	10730	10530	12250	14070	18900	23930
325	NALC CDHP	CDHP	13070	10670	12390	14950	20940	26270
132	FEP Blue Focus	PPO	13070	13070	14460	15760	20210	26070
255	GEHA Elevate	PPO-FEE	13780	13780	14490	16050	20260	27780
415	MHBP Value Plan	PPO-FEE	13150	13150	15050	16350	20900	26350
342	GEHA HDHP	HDHP	15600	13800	15670	16720	19470	25600
482	MHBP HDHP	HDHP	15980	13580	15980	17390	21000	27980
455	MHBP-Std	PPO-FEE	15920	15920	17190	18070	21010	27920
315	GEHA-Std	PPO-FEE	16170	16170	16920	18540	22780	29170
475	APWU CDHP	CDHP	17010	14610	16960	18800	23320	30010
Z25	Aetna Advantage	PPO-FEE	14750	14750	17150	19350	25800	29750
402	Foreign Service	PPO-FEE	17750	17750	18820	19490	21760	24750
252	GEHA Elevate Plus	PPO-FEE	18740	18740	19280	20410	23690	30740
N62	Aetna Direct CDHP	CDHP	18540	16740	19140	20620	25160	30540
322	NALC-Hi	PPO-FEE	19120	19120	19980	20940	23700	28120
112	Blue Cross Basic	PPO	19180	19180	19870	21020	24280	30180
445	SAMBA-Std	PPO-FEE	18630	18630	19730	21070	24960	32630
382	Rural Carrier	PPO-FEE	19080	19080	20020	21140	24430	29080
225	Aetna HealthFund HDHP	HDHP	19290	17690	19740	21570	26470	33090
422	Compass Rose	PPO-FEE	21060	21060	21890	22500	24700	28060
472	APWU-Hi	PPO-FEE	20910	20910	22200	23160	26250	33910
312	GEHA-Hi	PPO-FEE	22120	22120	22770	23910	26940	32120
105	Blue Cross-Std	PPO-FEE	21660	21660	22990	24030	27270	31660
442	SAMBA-Hi	PPO-FEE	25970	25970	26990	28130	31430	37970

* These are the premiums after tax savings, offset by savings accounts for plans that offer them. If you have no or low health-care costs with these plans, it can result in actual saving to you, which we indicate with a negative number.

Chapter 4

Cost Comparisons and Advice for Annuitants

As explained in Chapter 2 "Comparing Plan Costs," we rate and compare health plans based on their likely cost to you, taking into account your pay system, employment or retirement status, family size, age, health status, location, and other factors. A key element of our ratings are estimates of likely out-of-pocket costs under each plan, based on actuarial estimates of the size and likelihood of low, average, and high spending for families of different sizes and ages. Our ratings also reflect varying premium levels and tax situations faced by different eligibility groups. For example, unlike employees annuitants do not obtain "Premium Conversion" tax advantages.

Online *Guide* users see a summary cost comparison table for their group, and then have the option to look at tables providing more detailed cost comparisons. Readers of the printed *Guide* see both summary and detailed cost information for their comparison group for all national plans and local plans available in the DC area.

All of these comparisons take into account not only premiums and potential health care costs, but also plan features such as Health Savings Accounts, personal accounts, and Wellness benefits that involve cash rewards. We also include dental benefits and premiums, both for dental benefits built into some health plans and for the costs and benefits of standalone dental plans. For annuitants, our estimates and comparisons also take into account both Medicare benefits and Medicare premiums, depending on choices about Medicare enrollment. In summary, we provide a comprehensive set of financial comparisons that allow users to make "apple to apple" comparisons of costs for both premiums and likely health care expenses under each plan and across all plans for which they are eligible.

Very importantly, our comparisons take into account that a few plans provide both a Medicare "wraparound" and a fund that will pay part of the Medicare Part B premium. The three national plans that provide a complete wraparound for hospital and doctor costs and also fund Part B costs are Aetna Direct (funding up to $900 towards the Part B premium), Blue Cross Basic option ($800), and GEHA High option ($600). Most of the west coast Kaiser plans, and most of the UnitedHealthcare plans including several in the Washington area, offer even larger subsidies if you have Medicare Parts A and B and are willing to join their Medicare Advantage plans. The amounts these plans pay is almost as high as the 2020 Part B premium.

All of our calculations should be considered approximations that will be broadly accurate in the great majority of situations but that cannot provide precise predictions that cover every possible situation. What our calculations also do, therefore, is take into account the risks of ruinously high health care costs from an unexpected illness or accident, and compare the maximum out-of-pocket and premium costs under each plan.

Using the Cost Comparison Tables for Annuitants

We provide rating comparisons for self-only, self plus one, and families of two for annuitants in the print Guide, and additionally for families of sizes three through five online. Comparisons include:

- **Annuitants without Medicare.**
- **Annuitants with Medicare Parts A and B who pay regular premium rates.** These tables include not only the FEHB premium, but also the Part B Medicare premium.
- **Annuitants with Medicare Parts A and B who pay higher "income-tested" rates** (online only).
- **Annuitants who have only Part A of Medicare**, the hospital benefit. You can compare these with the preceding ratings to see how much you gain, or in most cases lose, by paying the Part B premium.

There are many comparisons, but **only one cost comparison table applies to your current situation.** Of course, your situation may change if your family changes or if you change your Medicare decisions—and you can compare tables to see those differences. For example, if you are trying to decide whether to enroll in Medicare Part B or not, you can compare plans with or without this option—but be careful to read our advice on this decision, since there are important advantages to Part B enrollment that for most annuitants outweigh its premium costs.

By looking at the different columns in a table, you can find how you will come out under each plan if your expenses range from none to the maximum you could pay in a year. Very importantly for those with Medicare Part B, the "Published premium" column, as well as following columns, includes both FEHB and Part B premiums. These columns also credit you with the savings you gain from a Health Savings Account (HSA) or personal health care account or Health Reimbursement Arrangement (HRA) in plans that give you these benefits (annuitants get the HSA amount as an HRA contribution, as explained in our chapter on "Plan Types and Flexibility"). Personal care accounts and HRAs are the equivalent of a reduction in premium. If you don't spend that account at the end of the year you will have a bank balance in that amount that carries over to the next year. Therefore, the "No costs" column includes your yearly premium adjusted, as pertinent, for the Medicare Part B Premium, HRA account, and any membership dues. These will be your only out-of-pocket costs if you have no medical bills. We rank the plans in order of average cost to emphasize the importance of each plan's treatment of "average" expenses for a family of a particular size and type.

> ***You Can Keep Flexibility Only at a Price***
>
> Good arguments for paying the Medicare Part B premium are to preserve your choices over time, as both FEHB and Medicare evolve, to get you low costs for providers who are not in your plan network, and to reduce cost-sharing. However, to use this choice choose a plan designed to keep these costs low.

You begin by making profile choices to find the table that relates to families of your age, premium category, and size. Unless you know something to the contrary, you should expect average expenses in the coming year. The plans that are likely to cost families the least have the lowest dollar figures in this column. But do not choose the highest-ranked plan until you consider whether there is some reason the average column does not apply to you or your family.

In your cost table you will notice that differences among closely ranked plans are often very small. Differences of $100 or less are not important. A different mix of bills from those we use to compare plans could overcome these. Differences of several hundred dollars or more, however, reflect significant variations in how expensively the plans handle most cases.

Notice that most of the higher-ranked plans will save you money in every situation—whether your expenses are high or low—compared to the plans ranked lower in each group on your comparison. You can also see that many HMOs and CDHP and HDHP plans will save you hundreds of dollars compared to most national PPO plans, but that many will not.

Preferred Providers and Annuitants Over Age 65

We rate plan costs based on the assumption that you will always or almost always want to use preferred providers, also known as "staying in the network". However, network problems largely disappear if you have Medicare Parts A and B, since most of the national plans waive doctor and hospital cost-sharing whether you obtain care in or out of the network. Even in HMOs that don't waive these costs, you can use Medicare to go out of network and pay only the 20% coinsurance under Medicare. Therefore, **for retirees who participate in Medicare Parts A and B preferred provider restrictions largely disappear when enrolled in almost all plans.** You can go to any hospital and almost any doctor without losing coverage. Moreover, persons over age 65 are by law guaranteed a Medicare rate and can use all doctors who have not opted out of Medicare without fearing very high charges, even while enrolled in plans that offer no reduced cost sharing for those with Part B of Medicare.

You should be aware, however, that there are many complexities. For example, some doctors do not accept new Medicare patients, even if the patients are in a plan whose network includes these doctors. Some doctors accept no insurance of any kind. And still others will accept new Medicare patients but do not "take assignment" and have their patients pay in full and submit Medicare claims. In such cases a 15% higher Medicare rate called the "limiting charge" may apply. The great majority of doctors do not present such problems, so your best option will often be to avoid those who do.

Savings for Couples Using Self Only Enrollments

For a husband and wife who are **both** Federal annuitants and who have no dependent children, it is possible to save on premium costs by enrolling separately as self only rather than together as self plus one. The premiums for two self only enrollments are usually less than the self plus one premium. This option can be particularly valuable in cases where each spouse prefers a different plan, perhaps because no one plan covers both family physicians in its network.

Be cautious, however, because each person will have to meet a separate catastrophic limit rather than the single limit that applies to self plus one. Most plans do not increase your risk because they include individual limits of about half the amount of the overall self plus one or family limit. Moreover, while you are still technically subject to meeting two catastrophic limits if you both enroll self-only, the fee structure of most HMOs makes it almost impossible to reach those limits. Finally, if two Federal annuitants both have Medicare Parts A and B your risk exposure is low in all plans, and very low in plans that offer a Part B wrap-around. For these reasons, you are almost always safe with two self only enrollments. But do check the plan brochure's catastrophic limits carefully before making this decision.

> ***Huge Annuitant Cost Saving***
>
> Annuitants with Medicare Parts A and B can suspend their FEHBP enrollment, join a Medicare Advantage plan, and pay only the Medicare premium. They can reenroll in an FEHBP plan in the future without penalty, and in the meantime enjoy good catastrophic protection, have low copays, and save thousands in premium costs.

However, couples in which one is a federal annuitant and the other still federally employed should almost never use two self only enrollments. It is always less expensive for the employed spouse to enroll in a self plus one or family option, and get about a one-third savings from Premium Conversion.

Savings for Couples or Single Parents with One Child Under Self Plus One Enrollment

Married couples with no children to cover, and single parents with one child to cover, can enroll as self plus one rather than as a family and, depending on the plan chosen, usually save two or three hundred dollars a year in premium costs, and often more. Since the benefits of the plan are identical (or in a few cases even better) in the self plus one plan, this is a clear saving. You should use our comparison table for self plus one with adults of your age to make your initial plan comparison.

In addition to the regular Open Season, where you can switch plans or enrollment category or both, OPM allows annuitants to switch "down" to from family to self plus one at any time during the year. This can only be used for the plan you are already enrolled in, not to switch plans, unless there is a "qualifying life event" such as death of family member or divorce.

Annuitants Without Medicare Part B

Older persons, on average, incur much higher expenses than do younger persons. Children's expenses average about $2,000 a year, and those of an adult below 55 years of age about $6,000 per year. Expenses for people age 65 and older average over $12,000 per year. Of course, most enrollees have much lower bills. The average cost is pulled up by a small fraction that has much higher bills, a fraction that rises sharply with age. To reflect these large differences, our cost tables for annuitants compare plans on the basis of expenses faced by older persons. We provide separate results for annuitants age 55 to 64, and over age 65, as their expense profiles are quite different. In either age group, the plans with better coverage tend to rank higher despite bigger premiums. In using our print comparisons a safe approach for couples in which only one member has Medicare coverage is to use the cost comparisons for retirees without Medicare (in the online Guide we provide specific estimates for these situations).

Once you reach age 65, a special rule applies whether or not you enroll in Medicare Part B. **It is illegal for doctors who have not opted out entirely from Medicare to charge patients covered by Medicare more than a "limiting charge." This restriction applies to all FEHB annuitants over age 65, whether or not they have Medicare.** Under this provision, you will not be exposed to high charges that neither Medicare nor your FEHB plan recognizes as reasonable. You do **not** have to sign up for Medicare Part B to get this guarantee. Therefore, unlike employees, if you are over 65 you can use non-preferred providers without fear of being charged substantially more than the plan will recognize as reasonable. You do, of course, have to pay higher deductibles and coinsurance if the provider is not in your plan's network.

Annuitants with Medicare Part A or Parts A and B

Obviously, if Medicare covers you, the rankings in our regular cost comparisons do not apply, since Medicare is "primary" for retirees and will pay most expenses. Therefore, we present tables for single persons and couples with either both Parts A and B of Medicare, or Part A only. Since couples can choose either self plus one or family enrollments, we provide comparisons for both. Although these tables are presented in terms of preferred providers, it is important to understand that the main advantage of preferred providers, guaranteed low rates, is available once you reach age 65 from almost any doctor you might use, whether or not you have Medicare Part B. The online *Guide* also presents a comparison for couples in which one spouse does not have Medicare and the other has both Parts A and B. Each comparison takes into account:

- Premium costs for the FEHB plan and, in the "both Part A and B" tables, for Medicare Part B (Part A has no premium for Federal annuitants who retired after 1983);
- Each plan's coverage for services, such as prescription drugs and dental care, that are not covered by Medicare Parts A and B; and
- Elimination of all or most hospital and medical cost-sharing offered by many plans for Medicare Part A and B enrollees.

Should You Stay Enrolled in the FEHB Program After Age 65?

You could drop the FEHB program once you enroll in Parts A and B. But this would be a bad decision. Medicare Part B requires you to pay 20 percent of the cost of doctors' fees, and deductibles, with no upper limit. The Medicare Part A hospital deductible is about $1,400 and the Part B medical deductible is almost $200. To obtain Medicare coverage roughly comparable to FEHB plans you would have to pay a Part B premium of almost $145 a month, or about $1,700 for the year (many pay more, as discussed below), and a Part D premium for drug coverage of about $40 a month and $480 for the year (there is a wide range of prescription drug premiums, some lower and some higher). The total premium cost for all three parts of Medicare is over $2,000 a person—higher than in many FEHB plans and with cost-sharing worse than most and no protection against catastrophically high expenses. You could improve your protection by enrolling in what are called "Medigap" plans, but only at the cost of paying another $2,000 a year in premium, the exact amount depending on the Medigap plan chosen. Therefore, if paying both FEHB and Medicare premiums presses you financially, and you are not sure which program to retain, **the FEHB program alone is a better bargain than Medicare alone, unless you are willing to enroll in a Medicare Advantage plan** (discussed below). And even then, you should never drop the FEHB program completely, but "suspend" enrollment with the option of rejoining in the next Open Season. Moreover, almost all Federal annuitants over age 65 have premium-free Medicare Part A, and in combination with almost all FEHB plans will never have to pay more than a few hundred dollars for hospital costs. Finally, FEHB plans, unlike Medicare (except in parts of Canada and Mexico), cover you if you travel or live abroad.

Should You Enroll in Part B After Age 65?

There are advantages to enrolling in Part B as a complement to an FEHB plan (technically, Medicare is "primary" and pays first). Almost all of the national plans waive their hospital and medical deductibles, copays, and coinsurance for members enrolled in both Medicare Part A (hospital) and Part B (medical). In effect, they "wrap around" Medicare. HMOs generally have only nominal deductibles or copayments and most of them do not provide such waivers. However, an increasing number do. For example, in the Washington, DC area CareFirst and M.D. IPA provide wraparound benefits to retirees with both parts of Medicare. In other parts of the nation, the Humana plans offer similar savings. With Medicare Parts A and B and most national Federal plans, you will have close to 100 percent coverage of almost all medical expenses (a few services are not covered by either program and would not get this coverage). Coverage for dental and prescription drug expenses will still differ depending on which plan you choose.

However, Medicare Part B will rarely save you nearly as much money as you spend on the Part B premium. This is because the cost sharing for physician visits and tests in almost all FEHB plans is already so low. And as we discuss below, for those who pay more for Part B than the normal premium, it is almost always a bad buy in purely financial terms.

By comparing tables for those with Part A only, versus those with Parts A and B, you will see that in most plans you are likely to spend several hundred dollars a year more for this combination than by retaining the FEHB plan alone. Simply put, Medicare Part B is of limited dollar value to someone already covered by a good health plan. **If you join an HMO, the Medicare premium gains you very little in dollar benefits. If you are willing to use preferred providers in national plans, or to join an HMO and use its network, you can usually save several hundred dollars per year or more—often a thousand dollars a year or more—by not joining, or dropping, Medicare Part B**. Even if you do not use preferred providers, you will do almost as well without Medicare Part B, because of the special rate ceiling that limits what Medicare-participating doctors can charge to Medicare allowed charges.

Part B does have some important advantages. Perhaps most importantly, in almost all the plans that wrap around Part B, **enrollment in Part B gives you the freedom to go outside the plan's network at no cost**.

Even if you enroll in one of the plans that don't wrap around, you can use your Part B benefit to **go outside the plan's doctor network and pay only 20% of the Medicare allowed charge**. For example, for using a specialist at the Mayo Clinic, you could simply charge the visit to Part B without your HMO or PPO plan's permission,

Part B provides more generous benefits than most FEHB plans in a few categories, such as physical therapy and home health care, and it covers more of the costs of some injected specialty drugs, prostheses and durable medical equipment than many. Still, Medicare Part B rarely reduces overall costs enough to pay for the extra premium. For those plans that provide a wraparound, in almost all situations Part B will likely save you several hundred dollars a year and often as much as half the Part B premium—but rarely as much as the "for sure" premium expense.

Also importantly, Part B gives you the option of joining a Medicare Advantage plan—either PPO or HMO—through Medicare and suspending your FEHB enrollment and premium payment. It also gives you the option under some plans of enrolling in both FEHB and MA plans simultaneously and getting a large premium reimbursement.

Continues on page 79

Annuitants 55 to 64 Without Medicare				Self Only				
				Estimated yearly out-of-pocket costs, including premium and typical hospital, medical, drug, and dental bills near:				
Plan code	Plan name	Plan type	Published premium	No costs*	Low use: $3,000 or less	Average cost	High use: $30,000 or more	Limit to you
D.C. Area Plans When You Use Preferred Providers								
T71	Kaiser Basic	HMO	1260	1260	1480	2660	5260	5260
E34	Kaiser-Std	HMO	1710	1710	1780	2730	5210	5210
B61	CareFirst HDHP	HDHP	1710	810	1350	2960	5710	5710
V41	United HDHP	HDHP	1460	710	1310	2970	5760	5760
L91	United Choice Plus Advanced	PPO-FEE	1560	1560	2090	3100	4560	4560
E31	Kaiser-Hi	HMO	2540	2540	2560	3210	4790	4790
Y81	United Choice Primary	HMO	1520	1520	1700	3430	8870	8870
AS1	United Choice Plus Primary	PPO-FEE	1580	1580	1760	3490	8930	8930
B64	CareFirst Blue Value Plus	HMO-POS	2340	2340	2510	3730	7340	7340
LR1	United Choice Open Access	HMO	2450	2450	2640	3910	7450	7450
JN4	Aetna Open Access Basic	HMO	2240	2240	2440	4100	8240	8240
QQ4	Aetna Saver	HMO	1790	1790	2490	4400	8290	8290
2G4	CareFirst-Std POS	HMO-POS	4020	4020	4020	4780	6520	6520
F51	Aetna HealthFund CDHP	CDHP	3820	2820	3370	5410	9120	9120
F54	Aetna Value Plan	PPO-FEE	3710	3710	3960	5630	10010	10010
JP1	MD-IPA	HMO	4390	4390	4530	5700	8990	9390
JN1	Aetna Open Access-Hi	HMO	7520	7520	7590	8560	11010	12520
National Plans When You Use Preferred Providers								
341	GEHA HDHP	HDHP	1540	640	1140	2600	5410	6540
324	NALC CDHP	CDHP	1420	220	590	3000	8020	8020
481	MHBP HDHP	HDHP	1720	520	1220	3080	6220	7720
254	GEHA Elevate	PPO-FEE	1230	1230	1460	3100	8230	8230
401	Foreign Service	PPO-FEE	1790	1790	2070	3110	5660	6790
131	FEP Blue Focus	PPO	1380	1380	1900	3250	7880	7880
251	GEHA Elevate Plus	PPO-FEE	1890	1890	2010	3300	7210	7890
314	GEHA-Std	PPO-FEE	1570	1570	1800	3440	8070	8070
111	Blue Cross Basic	PPO	1970	1970	2100	3450	7200	7470
454	MHBP-Std	PPO-FEE	1710	1710	2010	3450	7380	7710
474	APWU CDHP	CDHP	1790	590	1260	3500	8290	8290
KM1	NALC Value Plan	PPO-FEE	1170	1070	1440	3520	7770	7770
N61	Aetna Direct CDHP	CDHP	1840	940	1640	3590	7840	7840
414	MHBP Value Plan	PPO-FEE	1360	1360	1780	3700	7960	7960
421	Compass Rose	PPO-FEE	2640	2640	2850	3750	6280	7640
321	NALC-Hi	PPO-FEE	2360	2360	2640	3790	6720	8960
444	SAMBA-Std	PPO-FEE	2040	2040	2380	4070	9040	9040
311	GEHA-Hi	PPO-FEE	2740	2740	2960	4190	7740	7740
471	APWU-Hi	PPO-FEE	2580	2580	3100	4390	8790	9080
Z24	Aetna Advantage	PPO-FEE	1390	1390	2090	4470	8890	8890
224	Aetna HealthFund HDHP	HDHP	2620	1820	2340	4550	9520	9520
381	Rural Carrier	PPO-FEE	3180	3180	3500	4720	8180	8180
104	Blue Cross-Std	PPO-FEE	3040	3040	3470	4760	8040	8040
441	SAMBA-Hi	PPO-FEE	4690	4690	5000	6490	10690	10690

* These are the premiums after tax savings, offset by savings accounts for plans that offer them. If you have no or low health-care costs with these plans, it can result in actual saving to you, which we indicate with a negative number.

Annuitants 55 to 64 Without Medicare		Self Plus One						
		Plan type	Published premium	Estimated yearly out-of-pocket costs, including premium and typical hospital, medical, drug, and dental bills near:				
Plan code	Plan name			No costs*	Low use: $3,000 or less	Average cost	High use: $30,000 or more	Limit to you
D.C. Area Plans When You Use Preferred Providers								
T73	Kaiser Basic	HMO	2800	2800	3580	5550	8230	10800
B63	CareFirst HDHP	HDHP	3420	1620	3410	5800	9030	9920
E36	Kaiser-Std	HMO	3940	3940	4350	5910	7820	10940
L93	United Choice Plus Advanced	PPO-FEE	3060	3060	4570	6330	9060	9060
V43	United HDHP	HDHP	3140	1640	3840	6430	9930	10590
B66	CareFirst Blue Value Plus	HMO-POS	4240	4240	4770	6520	8680	14240
Y83	United Choice Primary	HMO	3270	3270	4160	6690	9760	17970
AS3	United Choice Plus Primary	PPO-FEE	3390	3390	4280	6810	9880	18090
JN6	Aetna Open Access Basic	HMO	4470	4470	5350	7820	10910	16470
LR3	United Choice Open Access	HMO	5340	5340	6160	8030	10490	15340
E33	Kaiser-Hi	HMO	6840	6840	7120	8100	9280	11340
2G6	CareFirst-Std POS	HMO-POS	7190	7190	7300	8430	9720	12190
QQ6	Aetna Saver	HMO	3750	3750	5910	8810	13260	16750
JP3	MD-IPA	HMO	7440	7440	8130	9800	11960	17440
F53	Aetna HealthFund CDHP	CDHP	9360	7360	9390	12580	16240	19960
F56	Aetna Value Plan	PPO-FEE	8980	8980	9830	12700	16290	21580
JN3	Aetna Open Access-Hi	HMO	17280	17280	17810	19140	20710	27280
National Plans When You Use Preferred Providers								
343	GEHA HDHP	HDHP	3310	1510	3380	5300	7180	13310
256	GEHA Elevate	PPO-FEE	2830	2830	3540	6160	9310	16830
483	MHBP HDHP	HDHP	3810	1410	3810	6310	8830	15810
326	NALC CDHP	CDHP	3130	730	2450	6670	11000	16330
133	FEP Blue Focus	PPO	2970	2970	4360	6710	10110	15970
316	GEHA-Std	PPO-FEE	3380	3380	4130	6800	9990	16380
403	Foreign Service	PPO-FEE	4470	4470	5540	6810	8480	11470
253	GEHA Elevate Plus	PPO-FEE	4430	4430	4970	6870	9380	16430
456	MHBP-Std	PPO-FEE	3940	3940	5210	6880	9030	15940
476	APWU CDHP	CDHP	3900	1500	3850	7060	10210	16900
KM3	NALC Value Plan	PPO-FEE	2570	2370	4090	7230	10740	15770
113	Blue Cross Basic	PPO	4640	4640	5330	7280	9740	15640
N63	Aetna Direct CDHP	CDHP	4030	2230	4630	7380	10650	16030
416	MHBP Value Plan	PPO-FEE	3220	3220	5120	7610	10970	16420
446	SAMBA-Std	PPO-FEE	4470	4470	5570	7880	10800	18470
383	Rural Carrier	PPO-FEE	5330	5330	6270	8150	10680	15330
423	Compass Rose	PPO-FEE	6190	6190	7020	8190	9830	13190
323	NALC-Hi	PPO-FEE	5680	5680	6540	8210	10260	14680
473	APWU-Hi	PPO-FEE	5190	5190	6480	8270	10530	18190
313	GEHA-Hi	PPO-FEE	6410	6410	7060	8960	11230	16410
Z26	Aetna Advantage	PPO-FEE	3060	3060	5460	9250	14110	18060
226	Aetna HealthFund HDHP	HDHP	5810	4210	6260	9470	12990	19610
106	Blue Cross-Std	PPO-FEE	6950	6950	8280	10180	12560	16950
443	SAMBA-Hi	PPO-FEE	10700	10700	11720	13690	16160	22700

* These are the premiums after tax savings, offset by savings accounts for plans that offer them. If you have no or low health-care costs with these plans, it can result in actual saving to you, which we indicate with a negative number.

Annuitants 55 to 64 Without Medicare		Family of Two		Estimated yearly out-of-pocket costs, including premium and typical hospital, medical, drug, and dental bills near:				
Plan code	Plan name	Plan type	Published premium	No costs*	Low use: $3,000 or less	Average cost	High use: $30,000 or more	Limit to you
D.C. Area Plans When You Use Preferred Providers								
T72	Kaiser Basic	HMO	3080	3080	3860	5830	8510	11080
E35	Kaiser-Std	HMO	3960	3960	4370	5930	7840	10960
B62	CareFirst HDHP	HDHP	4060	2260	4050	6440	9670	10560
V42	United HDHP	HDHP	3360	1860	4060	6650	10150	10810
E32	Kaiser-Hi	HMO	5740	5740	6020	7000	8180	10240
Y82	United Choice Primary	HMO	3590	3590	4480	7010	10080	18290
AS2	United Choice Plus Primary	PPO-FEE	3730	3730	4620	7150	10220	18430
L92	United Choice Plus Advanced	PPO-FEE	4390	4390	5900	7660	10390	10390
B65	CareFirst Blue Value Plus	HMO-POS	5920	5920	6450	8200	10360	15920
JN5	Aetna Open Access Basic	HMO	4940	4940	5820	8290	11380	16940
LR2	United Choice Open Access	HMO	6120	6120	6940	8810	11270	16120
QQ5	Aetna Saver	HMO	4090	4090	6250	9150	13600	17090
2G5	CareFirst-Std POS	HMO-POS	9900	9900	10010	11140	12430	14900
F52	Aetna HealthFund CDHP	CDHP	8480	6480	8510	11700	15360	19080
F55	Aetna Value Plan	PPO-FEE	8320	8320	9170	12040	15630	20920
JP2	MD-IPA	HMO	15290	15290	15980	17650	19810	25290
JN2	Aetna Open Access-Hi	HMO	16480	16480	17010	18340	19910	26480
National Plans When You Use Preferred Providers								
342	GEHA HDHP	HDHP	3900	2100	3970	5890	7770	13900
482	MHBP HDHP	HDHP	4000	1600	4000	6500	9020	16000
402	Foreign Service	PPO-FEE	4440	4440	5510	6780	8450	11440
255	GEHA Elevate	PPO-FEE	3450	3450	4160	6780	9930	17450
325	NALC CDHP	CDHP	3270	870	2590	6810	11140	16470
455	MHBP-Std	PPO-FEE	3980	3980	5250	6920	9070	15980
132	FEP Blue Focus	PPO	3270	3270	4660	7010	10410	16270
252	GEHA Elevate Plus	PPO-FEE	4690	4690	5230	7130	9640	16690
KM2	NALC Value Plan	PPO-FEE	2680	2480	4200	7340	10850	15880
475	APWU CDHP	CDHP	4250	1850	4200	7410	10560	17250
322	NALC-Hi	PPO-FEE	4910	4910	5770	7440	9490	13910
315	GEHA-Std	PPO-FEE	4040	4040	4790	7460	10650	17040
112	Blue Cross Basic	PPO	4970	4970	5660	7610	10070	15970
415	MHBP Value Plan	PPO-FEE	3290	3290	5190	7680	11040	16490
382	Rural Carrier	PPO-FEE	4880	4880	5820	7700	10230	14880
N62	Aetna Direct CDHP	CDHP	4640	2840	5240	7990	11260	16640
445	SAMBA-Std	PPO-FEE	4660	4660	5760	8070	10990	18660
225	Aetna HealthFund HDHP	HDHP	5080	3480	5530	8740	12260	18880
422	Compass Rose	PPO-FEE	6850	6850	7680	8850	10490	13850
472	APWU-Hi	PPO-FEE	6710	6710	8000	9790	12050	19710
Z25	Aetna Advantage	PPO-FEE	3690	3690	6090	9880	14740	18690
312	GEHA-Hi	PPO-FEE	7910	7910	8560	10460	12730	17910
105	Blue Cross-Std	PPO-FEE	7460	7460	8790	10690	13070	17460
442	SAMBA-Hi	PPO-FEE	11760	11760	12780	14750	17220	23760

* These are the premiums after tax savings, offset by savings accounts for plans that offer them. If you have no or low health-care costs with these plans, it can result in actual saving to you, which we indicate with a negative number.

Annuitants 65 and Older with Medicare Parts A & B				Self Only				
				Estimated yearly out-of-pocket costs, including premium and typical hospital, medical, drug, and dental bills near:				
Plan code	Plan name	Plan type	Published premium	No costs*	Low use: $3,000 or less	Average cost	High use: $30,000 or more	Limit to you
D.C. Area Plans When You Use Preferred Providers								
B61	CareFirst HDHP	HDHP	3340	2440	2810	3710	5710	7340
E34	Kaiser-Std	HMO	3340	3340	3390	4290	5960	6840
T71	Kaiser Basic	HMO	2890	2890	3100	4430	6890	6890
B64	CareFirst Blue Value Plus	HMO-POS	3970	3970	4100	4690	5680	8970
E31	Kaiser-Hi	HMO	4170	4170	4170	4710	5540	6420
L91	United Choice Plus Advanced	PPO-FEE	3190	3190	3720	4960	6190	6190
V41	United HDHP	HDHP	3090	2340	2940	4970	7390	7390
Y81	United Choice Primary	HMO	3150	3150	3330	5230	8880	10500
AS1	United Choice Plus Primary	PPO-FEE	3200	3200	3380	5280	8930	10550
LR1	United Choice Open Access	HMO	4070	4070	4210	5780	8690	9070
2G4	CareFirst-Std POS	HMO-POS	5640	5640	5640	6030	6630	8140
JN4	Aetna Open Access Basic	HMO	3860	3860	4060	6050	9860	9860
QQ4	Aetna Saver	HMO	3410	3410	4110	6280	9910	9910
JP1	MD-IPA	HMO	6020	6020	6110	6850	7920	11020
F51	Aetna HealthFund CDHP	CDHP	5450	4450	5000	7440	10750	10750
F54	Aetna Value Plan	PPO-FEE	5340	5340	5590	7610	11640	11640
JN1	Aetna Open Access-Hi	HMO	9150	9150	9220	10460	12640	14150
National Plans When You Use Preferred Providers								
481	MHBP HDHP	HDHP	3350	2150	2360	3380	4770	9350
111	Blue Cross Basic	PPO	3600	2800	2870	3740	5000	8300
131	FEP Blue Focus	PPO	3010	3010	3130	3760	5070	9510
N61	Aetna Direct CDHP	CDHP	3460	2560	2750	3820	5260	9460
Z24	Aetna Advantage	PPO-FEE	3020	3020	3200	4220	5580	9370
401	Foreign Service	PPO-FEE	3420	3420	3500	4410	5650	8420
454	MHBP-Std	PPO-FEE	3340	3340	3440	4410	5690	9340
341	GEHA HDHP	HDHP	3170	2270	2770	4480	6500	8170
314	GEHA-Std	PPO-FEE	3200	3200	3320	4580	6530	9700
251	GEHA Elevate Plus	PPO-FEE	3520	3520	3620	4590	6090	9520
311	GEHA-Hi	PPO-FEE	4370	3770	3850	4600	5680	8770
421	Compass Rose	PPO-FEE	4270	4270	4270	4670	5250	9270
321	NALC-Hi	PPO-FEE	3990	3990	4120	4830	5730	10590
254	GEHA Elevate	PPO-FEE	2860	2860	3090	4900	8620	9860
444	SAMBA-Std	PPO-FEE	3670	3670	3850	4950	6470	10670
324	NALC CDHP	CDHP	3050	1850	2220	4990	8670	9650
471	APWU-Hi	PPO-FEE	4210	4210	4360	5160	6390	10710
KM1	NALC Value Plan	PPO-FEE	2790	2690	3060	5410	8620	9390
474	APWU CDHP	CDHP	3420	2220	2890	5440	8770	9920
414	MHBP Value Plan	PPO-FEE	2990	2990	3410	5710	9590	9590
104	Blue Cross-Std	PPO-FEE	4670	4670	4780	5750	7040	9670
381	Rural Carrier	PPO-FEE	4800	4800	5100	6030	7480	9800
224	Aetna HealthFund HDHP	HDHP	4240	3440	3960	6520	10270	11140
441	SAMBA-Hi	PPO-FEE	6320	6320	6480	7500	8850	12320

* These are the premiums after tax savings, offset by savings accounts for plans that offer them. If you have no or low health-care costs with these plans, it can result in actual saving to you, which we indicate with a negative number.

Annuitants 65 and Older with Medicare Parts A & B		Self Plus One							
		Plan type	Published premium	Estimated yearly out-of-pocket costs, including premium and typical hospital, medical, drug, and dental bills near:					
Plan code	Plan name			No costs*	Low use: $3,000 or less	Average cost	High use: $30,000 or more	Limit to you	
D.C. Area Plans When You Use Preferred Providers									
B63	CareFirst HDHP	HDHP	6670	4870	5410	6750	7890	13170	
B66	CareFirst Blue Value Plus	HMO-POS	7490	7490	7720	8570	9070	17490	
T73	Kaiser Basic	HMO	6060	6060	6770	8730	10180	14060	
E36	Kaiser-Std	HMO	7200	7200	7480	8820	9720	14200	
L93	United Choice Plus Advanced	PPO-FEE	6310	6310	7780	10110	12310	12310	
V43	United HDHP	HDHP	6390	4890	7090	10350	12580	13840	
Y83	United Choice Primary	HMO	6520	6520	7410	10430	12530	21220	
AS3	United Choice Plus Primary	PPO-FEE	6640	6640	7530	10550	12650	21340	
2G6	CareFirst-Std POS	HMO-POS	10440	10440	10440	10960	11230	15440	
E33	Kaiser-Hi	HMO	10100	10100	10230	10990	11420	14600	
JN6	Aetna Open Access Basic	HMO	7720	7720	8600	11570	13680	19720	
LR3	United Choice Open Access	HMO	8590	8590	9310	11570	13140	18590	
JP3	MD-IPA	HMO	10690	10690	11070	12050	12590	20690	
QQ6	Aetna Saver	HMO	7000	7000	9160	12610	15430	20000	
F53	Aetna HealthFund CDHP	CDHP	12610	10610	12640	16610	19130	23210	
F56	Aetna Value Plan	PPO-FEE	12230	12230	13080	16630	19060	24830	
JN3	Aetna Open Access-Hi	HMO	20530	20530	21060	22780	23960	30530	
National Plans When You Use Preferred Providers									
483	MHBP HDHP	HDHP	7060	4660	5350	6590	7280	19060	
N63	Aetna Direct CDHP	CDHP	7280	5480	6140	7470	8180	19280	
133	FEP Blue Focus	PPO	6220	6220	6610	7690	8280	19220	
113	Blue Cross Basic	PPO	7900	6300	6670	7810	8450	17300	
Z26	Aetna Advantage	PPO-FEE	6310	6310	6960	8200	8870	19010	
316	GEHA-Std	PPO-FEE	6640	6640	7010	8830	9820	19640	
456	MHBP-Std	PPO-FEE	7190	7190	7680	8840	9460	19190	
343	GEHA HDHP	HDHP	6570	4770	6640	9020	10260	16570	
253	GEHA Elevate Plus	PPO-FEE	7680	7680	8000	9230	9950	19680	
403	Foreign Service	PPO-FEE	7720	7720	8130	9240	9850	14720	
313	GEHA-Hi	PPO-FEE	9660	8460	8710	9680	10220	18460	
446	SAMBA-Std	PPO-FEE	7720	7720	8360	9740	10500	21720	
256	GEHA Elevate	PPO-FEE	6080	6080	6790	9770	11960	20080	
423	Compass Rose	PPO-FEE	9450	9450	9460	9960	10180	16450	
473	APWU-Hi	PPO-FEE	8450	8450	8900	10000	10630	21450	
323	NALC-Hi	PPO-FEE	8930	8930	9380	10280	10670	17930	
383	Rural Carrier	PPO-FEE	8580	8580	9300	10640	11570	18580	
326	NALC CDHP	CDHP	6390	3990	5710	10800	13540	19590	
476	APWU CDHP	CDHP	7150	4750	7100	10950	13100	20150	
KM3	NALC Value Plan	PPO-FEE	5820	5620	7340	11090	13270	19020	
416	MHBP Value Plan	PPO-FEE	6470	6470	8370	11470	13740	19670	
106	Blue Cross-Std	PPO-FEE	10200	10200	10710	11890	12520	20200	
226	Aetna HealthFund HDHP	HDHP	9060	7460	9510	13370	15700	22860	
443	SAMBA-Hi	PPO-FEE	13950	13950	14550	15790	16450	25950	

* These are the premiums after tax savings, offset by savings accounts for plans that offer them. If you have no or low health-care costs with these plans, it can result in actual saving to you, which we indicate with a negative number.

Annuitants 65 and Older with Medicare Parts A & B		Family of Two							
		Plan type	Published premium	Estimated yearly out-of-pocket costs, including premium and typical hospital, medical, drug, and dental bills near:					
Plan code	Plan name			No costs*	Low use: $3,000 or less	Average cost	High use: $30,000 or more	Limit to you	
D.C. Area Plans When You Use Preferred Providers									
B62	CareFirst HDHP	HDHP	7320	5520	6060	7400	8540	13820	
E35	Kaiser-Std	HMO	7210	7210	7490	8830	9730	14210	
T72	Kaiser Basic	HMO	6330	6330	7040	9000	10450	14330	
E32	Kaiser-Hi	HMO	8990	8990	9120	9880	10310	13490	
B65	CareFirst Blue Value Plus	HMO-POS	9170	9170	9400	10250	10750	19170	
V42	United HDHP	HDHP	6610	5110	7310	10570	12800	14060	
Y82	United Choice Primary	HMO	6850	6850	7740	10760	12860	21550	
AS2	United Choice Plus Primary	PPO-FEE	6980	6980	7870	10890	12990	21680	
L92	United Choice Plus Advanced	PPO-FEE	7640	7640	9110	11440	13640	13640	
JN5	Aetna Open Access Basic	HMO	8190	8190	9070	12040	14150	20190	
LR2	United Choice Open Access	HMO	9380	9380	10100	12360	13930	19380	
QQ5	Aetna Saver	HMO	7340	7340	9500	12950	15770	20340	
2G5	CareFirst-Std POS	HMO-POS	13150	13150	13150	13670	13940	18150	
F52	Aetna HealthFund CDHP	CDHP	11730	9730	11760	15730	18250	22330	
F55	Aetna Value Plan	PPO-FEE	11580	11580	12430	15980	18410	24180	
JP2	MD-IPA	HMO	18540	18540	18920	19900	20440	28540	
JN2	Aetna Open Access-Hi	HMO	19730	19730	20260	21980	23160	29730	
National Plans When You Use Preferred Providers									
482	MHBP HDHP	HDHP	7250	4850	5540	6780	7470	19250	
132	FEP Blue Focus	PPO	6520	6520	6910	7990	8580	19520	
N62	Aetna Direct CDHP	CDHP	7890	6090	6750	8080	8790	19890	
112	Blue Cross Basic	PPO	8220	6620	6990	8130	8770	17620	
Z25	Aetna Advantage	PPO-FEE	6940	6940	7590	8830	9500	19640	
455	MHBP-Std	PPO-FEE	7230	7230	7720	8880	9500	19230	
402	Foreign Service	PPO-FEE	7690	7690	8100	9210	9820	14690	
252	GEHA Elevate Plus	PPO-FEE	7940	7940	8260	9490	10210	19940	
315	GEHA-Std	PPO-FEE	7300	7300	7670	9490	10480	20300	
322	NALC-Hi	PPO-FEE	8160	8160	8610	9510	9900	17160	
342	GEHA HDHP	HDHP	7150	5350	7220	9600	10840	17150	
445	SAMBA-Std	PPO-FEE	7910	7910	8550	9930	10690	21910	
382	Rural Carrier	PPO-FEE	8130	8130	8850	10190	11120	18130	
255	GEHA Elevate	PPO-FEE	6700	6700	7410	10390	12580	20700	
422	Compass Rose	PPO-FEE	10100	10100	10110	10610	10830	17100	
325	NALC CDHP	CDHP	6520	4120	5840	10930	13670	19720	
312	GEHA-Hi	PPO-FEE	11170	9970	10220	11190	11730	19970	
KM2	NALC Value Plan	PPO-FEE	5930	5730	7450	11200	13380	19130	
475	APWU CDHP	CDHP	7500	5100	7450	11300	13450	20500	
472	APWU-Hi	PPO-FEE	9960	9960	10410	11510	12140	22960	
415	MHBP Value Plan	PPO-FEE	6540	6540	8440	11540	13810	19740	
105	Blue Cross-Std	PPO-FEE	10710	10710	11220	12400	13030	20710	
225	Aetna HealthFund HDHP	HDHP	8340	6740	8790	12650	14980	22140	
442	SAMBA-Hi	PPO-FEE	15010	15010	15610	16850	17510	27010	

* These are the premiums after tax savings, offset by savings accounts for plans that offer them. If you have no or low health-care costs with these plans, it can result in actual saving to you, which we indicate with a negative number.

Annuitants 65 and Older with Medicare Part A Only		Self Only						
				Estimated yearly out-of-pocket costs, including premium and typical hospital, medical, drug, and dental bills near:				
Plan code	Plan name	Plan type	Published premium	No costs*	Low use: $3,000 or less	Average cost	High use: $30,000 or more	Limit to you
D.C. Area Plans When You Use Preferred Providers								
T71	Kaiser Basic	HMO	1260	1260	1480	2990	5260	5260
E34	Kaiser-Std	HMO	1710	1710	1780	3010	5210	5210
B61	CareFirst HDHP	HDHP	1710	810	1350	3260	5710	5710
L91	United Choice Plus Advanced	PPO-FEE	1560	1560	2090	3360	4560	4560
V41	United HDHP	HDHP	1460	710	1310	3380	5760	5760
E31	Kaiser-Hi	HMO	2540	2540	2560	3390	4790	4790
Y81	United Choice Primary	HMO	1520	1520	1700	3600	7250	8870
AS1	United Choice Plus Primary	PPO-FEE	1580	1580	1760	3660	7310	8930
B64	CareFirst Blue Value Plus	HMO-POS	2340	2340	2510	3790	6410	7340
LR1	United Choice Open Access	HMO	2450	2450	2640	4280	7450	7450
JN4	Aetna Open Access Basic	HMO	2240	2240	2440	4430	8240	8240
QQ4	Aetna Saver	HMO	1790	1790	2490	4690	8290	8290
2G4	CareFirst-Std POS	HMO-POS	4020	4020	4020	4830	6350	6520
F51	Aetna HealthFund CDHP	CDHP	3820	2820	3370	5810	9120	9120
F54	Aetna Value Plan	PPO-FEE	3710	3710	3960	5980	10010	10010
JP1	MD-IPA	HMO	4390	4390	4530	6040	8990	9390
JN1	Aetna Open Access-Hi	HMO	7520	7520	7590	8840	11010	12520
National Plans When You Use Preferred Providers								
341	GEHA HDHP	HDHP	1540	640	1140	2860	4930	6540
254	GEHA Elevate	PPO-FEE	1230	1230	1460	3270	6990	8230
324	NALC CDHP	CDHP	1420	220	590	3390	7280	8020
401	Foreign Service	PPO-FEE	1790	1790	2070	3400	5660	6790
131	FEP Blue Focus	PPO	1380	1380	1900	3430	7540	7880
481	MHBP HDHP	HDHP	1720	520	1220	3520	6220	7720
251	GEHA Elevate Plus	PPO-FEE	1890	1890	2010	3610	6810	7890
454	MHBP-Std	PPO-FEE	1710	1710	2010	3710	6660	7710
111	Blue Cross Basic	PPO	1970	1970	2100	3770	6850	7470
314	GEHA-Std	PPO-FEE	1570	1570	1800	3790	7780	8070
474	APWU CDHP	CDHP	1790	590	1260	3810	7140	8290
KM1	NALC Value Plan	PPO-FEE	1170	1070	1440	3840	7240	7770
N61	Aetna Direct CDHP	CDHP	1840	940	1640	3940	7660	7840
421	Compass Rose	PPO-FEE	2640	2640	2850	3960	6080	7640
414	MHBP Value Plan	PPO-FEE	1360	1360	1780	4080	7960	7960
321	NALC-Hi	PPO-FEE	2360	2360	2640	4120	6720	8960
444	SAMBA-Std	PPO-FEE	2040	2040	2380	4320	7970	9040
311	GEHA-Hi	PPO-FEE	2740	2740	2960	4410	7210	7740
471	APWU-Hi	PPO-FEE	2580	2580	3100	4510	7350	9080
224	Aetna HealthFund HDHP	HDHP	2620	1820	2340	4930	8830	9520
381	Rural Carrier	PPO-FEE	3180	3180	3500	5070	8180	8180
Z24	Aetna Advantage	PPO-FEE	1390	1390	2090	5080	8890	8890
104	Blue Cross-Std	PPO-FEE	3040	3040	3470	5080	8040	8040
441	SAMBA-Hi	PPO-FEE	4690	4690	5000	6710	9770	10690

* These are the premiums after tax savings, offset by savings accounts for plans that offer them. If you have no or low health-care costs with these plans, it can result in actual saving to you, which we indicate with a negative number.

Annuitants 65 and Older with Medicare Part A Only

Plan code	Plan name	Plan type	Published premium	Self Plus One — Estimated yearly out-of-pocket costs, including premium and typical hospital, medical, drug, and dental bills near: No costs*	Low use: $3,000 or less	Average cost	High use: $30,000 or more	Limit to you
D.C. Area Plans When You Use Preferred Providers								
T73	Kaiser Basic	HMO	2800	2800	3580	6230	8230	10800
B63	CareFirst HDHP	HDHP	3420	1620	3410	6370	8550	9920
E36	Kaiser-Std	HMO	3940	3940	4350	6400	7820	10940
B66	CareFirst Blue Value Plus	HMO-POS	4240	4240	4770	6720	8080	14240
L93	United Choice Plus Advanced	PPO-FEE	3060	3060	4570	6880	9060	9060
Y83	United Choice Primary	HMO	3270	3270	4160	7170	9280	17970
AS3	United Choice Plus Primary	PPO-FEE	3390	3390	4280	7290	9400	18090
V43	United HDHP	HDHP	3140	1640	3840	7290	9930	10590
JN6	Aetna Open Access Basic	HMO	4470	4470	5350	8310	10430	16470
E33	Kaiser-Hi	HMO	6840	6840	7120	8400	9280	11340
2G6	CareFirst-Std POS	HMO-POS	7190	7190	7300	8500	9240	12190
LR3	United Choice Open Access	HMO	5340	5340	6160	8640	10490	15340
QQ6	Aetna Saver	HMO	3750	3750	5910	9530	12540	16750
JP3	MD-IPA	HMO	7440	7440	8130	10340	11960	17440
F53	Aetna HealthFund CDHP	CDHP	9360	7360	9390	13350	15880	19960
F56	Aetna Value Plan	PPO-FEE	8980	8980	9830	13400	15810	21580
JN3	Aetna Open Access-Hi	HMO	17280	17280	17810	19550	20710	27280
National Plans When You Use Preferred Providers								
343	GEHA HDHP	HDHP	3310	1510	3380	5780	7060	13310
256	GEHA Elevate	PPO-FEE	2830	2830	3540	6670	8710	16830
483	MHBP HDHP	HDHP	3810	1410	3810	7050	8830	15810
133	FEP Blue Focus	PPO	2970	2970	4360	7140	9390	15970
253	GEHA Elevate Plus	PPO-FEE	4430	4430	4970	7250	8980	16430
403	Foreign Service	PPO-FEE	4470	4470	5540	7260	8480	11470
456	MHBP-Std	PPO-FEE	3940	3940	5210	7450	9030	15940
316	GEHA-Std	PPO-FEE	3380	3380	4130	7480	9680	16380
326	NALC CDHP	CDHP	3130	730	2450	7650	10520	16330
476	APWU CDHP	CDHP	3900	1500	3850	7690	9850	16900
113	Blue Cross Basic	PPO	4640	4640	5330	7690	9390	15640
KM3	NALC Value Plan	PPO-FEE	2570	2370	4090	7950	10260	15770
N63	Aetna Direct CDHP	CDHP	4030	2230	4630	8000	10170	16030
416	MHBP Value Plan	PPO-FEE	3220	3220	5120	8230	10490	16420
423	Compass Rose	PPO-FEE	6190	6190	7020	8470	9630	13190
446	SAMBA-Std	PPO-FEE	4470	4470	5570	8530	10600	18470
473	APWU-Hi	PPO-FEE	5190	5190	6480	8580	10170	18190
323	NALC-Hi	PPO-FEE	5680	5680	6540	8750	10260	14680
383	Rural Carrier	PPO-FEE	5330	5330	6270	8750	10680	15330
313	GEHA-Hi	PPO-FEE	6410	6410	7060	9380	11000	16410
226	Aetna HealthFund HDHP	HDHP	5810	4210	6260	10180	12630	19610
106	Blue Cross-Std	PPO-FEE	6950	6950	8280	10590	12210	16950
Z26	Aetna Advantage	PPO-FEE	3060	3060	5460	10990	14810	18060
443	SAMBA-Hi	PPO-FEE	10700	10700	11720	14230	15960	22700

* These are the premiums after tax savings, offset by savings accounts for plans that offer them. If you have no or low health-care costs with these plans, it can result in actual saving to you, which we indicate with a negative number.

Annuitants 65 and Older with Medicare Part A Only		Family of Two						
		Plan type	Published premium	Estimated yearly out-of-pocket costs, including premium and typical hospital, medical, drug, and dental bills near:				
Plan code	Plan name			No costs*	Low use: $3,000 or less	Average cost	High use: $30,000 or more	Limit to you
D.C. Area Plans When You Use Preferred Providers								
E35	Kaiser-Std	HMO	3960	3960	4370	6420	7840	10960
T72	Kaiser Basic	HMO	3080	3080	3860	6510	8510	11080
B62	CareFirst HDHP	HDHP	4060	2260	4050	7010	9190	10560
E32	Kaiser-Hi	HMO	5740	5740	6020	7300	8180	10240
Y82	United Choice Primary	HMO	3590	3590	4480	7490	9600	18290
V42	United HDHP	HDHP	3360	1860	4060	7510	10150	10810
AS2	United Choice Plus Primary	PPO-FEE	3730	3730	4620	7630	9740	18430
L92	United Choice Plus Advanced	PPO-FEE	4390	4390	5900	8210	10390	10390
B65	CareFirst Blue Value Plus	HMO-POS	5920	5920	6450	8400	9760	15920
JN5	Aetna Open Access Basic	HMO	4940	4940	5820	8780	10900	16940
LR2	United Choice Open Access	HMO	6120	6120	6940	9420	11270	16120
QQ5	Aetna Saver	HMO	4090	4090	6250	9870	12880	17090
2G5	CareFirst-Std POS	HMO-POS	9900	9900	10010	11210	11950	14900
F52	Aetna HealthFund CDHP	CDHP	8480	6480	8510	12470	15000	19080
F55	Aetna Value Plan	PPO-FEE	8320	8320	9170	12740	15150	20920
JP2	MD-IPA	HMO	15290	15290	15980	18190	19810	25290
JN2	Aetna Open Access-Hi	HMO	16480	16480	17010	18750	19910	26480
National Plans When You Use Preferred Providers								
342	GEHA HDHP	HDHP	3900	2100	3970	6370	7650	13900
402	Foreign Service	PPO-FEE	4440	4440	5510	7230	8450	11440
482	MHBP HDHP	HDHP	4000	1600	4000	7240	9020	16000
255	GEHA Elevate	PPO-FEE	3450	3450	4160	7290	9330	17450
132	FEP Blue Focus	PPO	3270	3270	4660	7440	9690	16270
455	MHBP-Std	PPO-FEE	3980	3980	5250	7490	9070	15980
252	GEHA Elevate Plus	PPO-FEE	4690	4690	5230	7510	9240	16690
325	NALC CDHP	CDHP	3270	870	2590	7790	10660	16470
322	NALC-Hi	PPO-FEE	4910	4910	5770	7980	9490	13910
112	Blue Cross Basic	PPO	4970	4970	5660	8020	9720	15970
475	APWU CDHP	CDHP	4250	1850	4200	8040	10200	17250
KM2	NALC Value Plan	PPO-FEE	2680	2480	4200	8060	10370	15880
315	GEHA-Std	PPO-FEE	4040	4040	4790	8140	10340	17040
415	MHBP Value Plan	PPO-FEE	3290	3290	5190	8300	10560	16490
382	Rural Carrier	PPO-FEE	4880	4880	5820	8300	10230	14880
N62	Aetna Direct CDHP	CDHP	4640	2840	5240	8610	10780	16640
445	SAMBA-Std	PPO-FEE	4660	4660	5760	8720	10790	18660
422	Compass Rose	PPO-FEE	6850	6850	7680	9130	10290	13850
225	Aetna HealthFund HDHP	HDHP	5080	3480	5530	9450	11900	18880
472	APWU-Hi	PPO-FEE	6710	6710	8000	10100	11690	19710
312	GEHA-Hi	PPO-FEE	7910	7910	8560	10880	12500	17910
105	Blue Cross-Std	PPO-FEE	7460	7460	8790	11100	12720	17460
Z25	Aetna Advantage	PPO-FEE	3690	3690	6090	11620	15440	18690
442	SAMBA-Hi	PPO-FEE	11760	11760	12780	15290	17020	23760

* These are the premiums after tax savings, offset by savings accounts for plans that offer them. If you have no or low health-care costs with these plans, it can result in actual saving to you, which we indicate with a negative number.

Continued from page 69

Enrollment in Part B gives you some "insurance" against the possibility that the Congress would enact some major adverse change to the FEHB program.

Finally, for many the value of "peace of mind" that you get from coverage under both programs exceeds the increase in premium costs.

There is an important innovation under way that reduces the cost of enrolling under both programs that will be attractive so many. The national Aetna Direct plan not only has a Medicare wraparound, but also lets you use your $900 a year per spouse personal care account to reimburse most of your Medicare Part B premium, or to offset dental and other expenses not covered by FEHB plans or Medicare. This gives you the advantage of wraparound coverage at a significantly lower cost than you would otherwise pay. Since the plan also waives its deductible and other cost sharing if you have parts A and B, this plan winds up costing less with Medicare than without Medicare for those who pay normal Part B premiums. Likewise, the Blue Cross Basic plan now provides both a wraparound benefit and an $800 yearly reimbursement for each spouse with Part B, and GEHA High has a $600 reimbursement for each. Some HDHP and CDHP plans, including the national MHBP HDHP plan, and the CareFirst HDHP plan in the DC metro area, offer similar premium and/or personal account advantages, including the wraparound benefit. In fact, in the MHBP High Deductible and Aetna Direct plans, most enrollees will actually come out ahead by enrolling in Part B.

If you do decide to drop (or not start) Part B you can join it later. But there is a 10 percent a year penalty if you later decide to join or rejoin. As a financial matter, however many years you elect to do without Part B, you will be money ahead for approximately the first five or six years after joining or rejoining. After that, the penalty will outweigh your earlier savings (except for those who were once above, but now fall below, the income-tested premium). If you never join or rejoin, you will (on average) save annually roughly the amounts indicated in our tables showing costs with and without Parts B—generally about half the cost of the Part B premium, though this varies somewhat from plan to plan. Thus, either not joining or dropping Part B is not an irrevocable decision, and later rejoining Part need not be highly costly.

There are some circumstances to which the conclusions above do not apply:

- **Working employees over age 65** with Medicare Parts A and B coverage face a different situation. The special waivers of deductibles and coinsurance do not apply, because Medicare is by law the secondary rather than primary payer (except for firms with fewer than 20 employees). Your best choice is to stay in your preferred FEHB plan, and **postpone joining Medicare Part B until you actually retire. There is no penalty** for joining after age 65 if you were working and covered by employer insurance (subject to the same exception for small firms).
- **A few people over age 65 did not earn Medicare Part A and can join by paying** a very substantial premium—about $5,000 a year. We recommend strongly against this purchase. Almost all FEHB plans charge you at most a few hundred dollars for hospital admissions, far less than the Part A premium.

Income-Related Part B Premiums

Historically, the taxpayer has funded three-fourths of the Medicare Part B premium and the enrollee has paid only one fourth of the cost. Under current law, however, some higher income enrollees pay more than the traditional one-fourth share.

This only affects individuals with Adjusted Gross Income (AGI) of $85,000 or more, and married couples filing jointly with income of $170,000 or more. These thresholds are not adjusted for inflation. The actual calculation includes adding some forms of income, such as tax-exempt interest income, to AGI. In 2020 the resulting annual Part B premium will range from about $2,400 for individual AGI of $85,000 to $107,000 and increase in steps to almost $6,000 for income of more than $500,000. The corresponding amounts for married couples filing jointly are twice as high.

There are additional factors that may determine whether this affects you. For example, if you marry or divorce or suffer a casualty loss you may become exempt. If your income fluctuates from year to year you may be subject to the increase one year but not the next (generally, the calculation is based on your AGI two years previously). If you have just retired with previous income above these thresholds, it is very important to apply to the Social Security Administration to use your lower retirement income to reduce or eliminate the higher premium. The premium calculation is made based on your income two years ago, which for many is a much higher pre-retirement amount, unless you apply for an adjustment. The "bottom line" is that if your income is above these thresholds and likely to remain there, the case for enrolling in Medicare Part B becomes far weaker. Dropping Part B will not affect your continued premium-free enrollment in Part A. The sensible solution for many high income annuitants will be to drop out of Medicare Part B and rely on your FEHB plan. Why pay more than $2,000 annually for a Part B benefit that rarely results in reduced cost sharing of more than a third of that amount?

Medicare Advantage Basics

Almost a third of Medicare beneficiaries now enroll in a Medicare Advantage plan, rather than sticking with Original Medicare. Medicare Advantage (MA) is a program designed to be very similar in operation to the FEHB program. Retirees can choose from a wide range of PPO and HMO plans in an annual Open Season. These plans' premiums are paid mainly through the Medicare Part A and B payments (with some adjustments) that the government would otherwise have paid in direct benefits. The enrollees continue to pay their Part B premium. Almost all of these plans include prescription drug coverage and various improvements over the original Medicare structure. For example, most eliminate most of the hospital deductible. In some cases, these plans charge no extra premium for drug coverage and other benefits. Very importantly, all of these plans now provide protection against catastrophic costs. The MA program is thoroughly described in the *Medicare & You* brochure mailed to all Medicare participants. The Medicare web site at *www.medicare.gov* contains additional information and provides an MA plan comparison tool that includes many of the same features as the online *Guide*, with a comparison of total costs including both premium and out-of-pocket expenses.

This is important to Federal retirees because if you join an MA plan you are allowed to temporarily suspend your FEHB enrollment and stop paying two sets of premiums. Under this "suspend" option you pay only the Part B premium and sometimes an extra premium charge (usually only a few hundred dollars per year and often nothing at all) that the Medicare Advantage plan charges Medicare enrollees for additional benefits such as prescription drug coverage. You can later switch out of Medicare Advantage and rejoin the FEHB program as if you had never left during any future Open Season. This works equally well for a couple when both spouses are enrolled in Medicare, or if they are willing to pursue separate health insurance options.

Suspending your FEHB enrollment generates substantial savings because you will pay one premium instead of two. How much you will save depends on the precise benefits the MA plan offers to Medicare enrollees and whether or how much it charges in extra premium. Most MA plans are comparable to FEHB plans in hospital and medical benefits, but the prescription drug benefits will not be as good because the plans have a "coverage gap" where you are responsible for all or most drug costs until you reach a catastrophic limit. Assuming you join a plan with no extra premium, you would pay only the Part B premium, at a cost in 2020 of about $1,700 (for those who do not pay a higher income-tested premium).

New Medicare Advantage and FEHB Cost-Saving Options

There is an additional option previously available through some West Coast Kaiser plans and now available in most parts of the country through UnitedHealthcare plans. Under these "Senior Advantage 2" and "Retiree Advantage" options, you enroll in these carriers' local Medicare Advantage plan while remaining fully enrolled in their local FEHB plan rather than suspending FEHB enrollment. You nominally pay both premiums but obtain a large Part B premium reimbursement equal to most of the cost of the regular Part B premium. In effect, you can enroll in both programs at not much more than the cost of one premium. You get much-reduced cost-sharing—close to zero cost to you for hospital and doctor services—if you use network providers. You can also use your FEHB plan outside the Medicare Advantage network. To find out more about these options, these carriers have more information on their websites (*www.uhcfeds.com* and *www.kp.org/feds*) and provide phone access to

Extra Cost of Enrolling in Both an FEHB Plan and Medicare Part B

Plan code	Plan name	Average cost for self only			Average cost for self plus one		
		With Medicare A only	With Medicare A & B	Extra cost of Part B	With Medicare A only	With Medicare A & B	Extra cost of Part B
D.C. Area Plans When You Use Preferred Providers							
B61-3	CareFirst HDHP	2570	3170	600	5010	6130	1120
E34-6	Kaiser-Std	3010	4290	1280	6400	8820	2420
B64-6	CareFirst Blue Value	3530	4390	860	6540	7980	1440
T71-3	Kaiser Basic	2990	4430	1440	6230	8730	2500
E31-3	Kaiser-Hi	3390	4710	1320	8400	10990	2590
L91-3	United Choice Plus Advanced	3360	4960	1600	6690	9840	3150
V41-3	United HDHP	3380	4970	1590	7290	10350	3060
Y81-3	United Choice Primary	3600	5230	1630	7170	10430	3260
AS1-3	United Choice Plus Primary	3660	5280	1620	7290	10550	3260
LR1-3	United Choice Open Access	4280	5780	1500	8640	11570	2930
JN4-6	Aetna Open Access Basic	4430	6050	1620	8310	11570	3260
2G4-6	CareFirst-Std POS	5210	6060	850	9490	10930	1440
QQ4-6	Aetna Saver	4690	6280	1590	9530	12610	3080
JP1-3	MD-IPA	6040	6850	810	10340	12050	1710
F51-3	Aetna HealthFund CDHP	5810	7440	1630	13350	16610	3260
F54-6	Aetna Value Plan	5980	7610	1630	13400	16630	3230
JN1-3	Aetna Open Access-Hi	8840	10460	1620	19550	22780	3230
National Plans When You Use Preferred Providers							
481-3	MHBP HDHP	3520	3380	-140	7050	6590	-460
111-3	Blue Cross Basic	3770	3740	-30	7690	7810	120
131-3	FEP Blue Focus	3430	3760	330	7140	7690	550
N61-3	Aetna Direct CDHP	3940	3820	-120	8000	7470	-530
Z24-6	Aetna Advantage	5080	4220	-860	10990	8200	-2790
401-3	Foreign Service	3400	4410	1010	7260	9240	1980
454-6	MHBP-Std	3710	4410	700	7450	8840	1390
341-3	GEHA HDHP	2860	4480	1620	5780	9020	3240
324-6	NALC CDHP	2970	4550	1580	6160	9320	3160
314-6	GEHA-Std	3790	4580	790	7480	8830	1350
251-3	GEHA Elevate Plus	3610	4590	980	7250	9230	1980
311-3	GEHA-Hi	4410	4600	190	9380	9680	300
421-3	Compass Rose	3960	4670	710	8470	9960	1490
321-3	NALC-Hi	4020	4790	770	8580	10210	1630
254-6	GEHA Elevate	3270	4900	1630	6670	9770	3100
444-6	SAMBA-Std	4320	4950	630	8530	9740	1210
471-3	APWU-Hi	4510	5160	650	8580	10000	1420
KM1-3	NALC Value Plan	3780	5360	1580	7800	10950	3150
474-6	APWU CDHP	3810	5440	1630	7690	10950	3260
381-3	Rural Carrier	4840	5700	860	8180	10070	1890
414-6	MHBP Value Plan	4080	5710	1630	8190	11440	3250
104-6	Blue Cross-Std	5080	5750	670	10590	11890	1300
224-6	Aetna HealthFund HDHP	4930	6520	1590	10180	13370	3190
441-3	SAMBA-Hi	6710	7500	790	14230	15790	1560

* The comparisons use the standard Part B premium. Higher "income-tested" premium levels would raise the extra costs identically for each plan.

specialized teams of advisors. The nationwide UnitedHealthcare contact number is 844-481-8821. The Kaiser number for Kaiser Northwest is 877-221-8221, for Kaiser Washington is 855-366-9013, for Kaiser Northern and Southern California is 800-443-0815, and for Kaiser Colorado is 800-476-2167. The Kaiser DC plan does not reimburse Medicare premiums, but does offer improved benefits for those who enroll in its Medicare Advantage and FEHB plans (301-816-6143).

Your Final Decision on Medicare Part B and the FEHB Program

Throughout our advice we have highlighted specific advantages and disadvantages of enrolling in Medicare Part B in addition to your FEHB enrollment. On the minus side, there is one large factor—paying two costly sets of premiums instead of one. For those who pay the higher part B income-tested premiums, this is a very considerable cost, at least $2,400 and for some almost $6,000 extra to join Part B, depending on exact income level. On the plus side there are several factors, including avoiding network restrictions, better coverage for a few services, and having the option to join Medicare Advantage plans and paying only one premium without losing FEHB eligibility.

By now, you should realize that you have many options, each with advantages and disadvantages. Taking into account dollar costs only, there are five good sets of options.

- One option is to enroll in a Medicare Advantage plan and suspend FEHB enrollment. This is the lowest-cost option for many. Many MA plans have benefits as good as many FEHB plans and charge nothing beyond the regular Part B premium.
- A second option is to enroll in a plan that contributes a substantial amount toward your Medicare premium, such as Aetna Direct CDHP or Blue Cross Basic. In both CDHP and HDHP plans your special account will pay towards the Part B premium (or in the Aetna Direct plan for drug or dental costs not otherwise covered), and you also get a Medicare wraparound. Several HDHP plans give you an equivalent value through their Health Reimbursement Account. We rate MHBP HDHP and CareFirst HDHP as particularly good buys.
- A third option is to enroll simultaneously in a UnitedHealthcare or Kaiser FEHB plan and the corresponding local Medicare Advantage plan to obtain a "Senior Advantage" or "Retiree Advantage" option that pays most of the Part B premium while dramatically lowering your cost-sharing for medical expenses.
- A fourth cost-saving choice is to enroll in an FEHB plan with good benefits such as APWU, NALC, Kaiser Standard option, or a number of HMO, HDHP, and CDHP plans, and bypass Medicare Part B enrollment.
- As a fifth choice, you can enroll in a relatively low-premium plan like FEP Blue Focus, Aetna Advantage, Blue Cross Basic, CareFirst Blue Value, Aetna Direct or MHBP HDHP, along with Part B, and get either a rich Medicare wraparound benefit or simply the ability to use Medicare to go outside the plan's network should you choose to do so.

All of these options and the plans that save the most money within each option vary in details that you can only assess after studying the brochure of several plans. All of them can provide most annuitants substantial annual savings.

What you should generally not do is stay in a high premium FEHB plan to get the Part B wraparound benefit when you can join a less costly FEHB plan with an equally good wraparound benefit. If your medical costs are close to zero in a number of plans, in or out of network, why pay a higher rather than lower premium? Of course, there are always cases where even the most expensive combination provides a benefit essential to you. And differences in prescription drug formularies or cost sharing can make a seemingly more expensive option actually a less expensive option. So there is no simple "one size fits all" answer. What you should do, regardless, is at least be aware of the dollar costs or gains of whatever decision you reach.

Our table on the extra cost of enrolling in both an FEHB plan and Medicare Part B shows which plans are likely to cost you the least or save you the most by enrolling in Part B. We present the plans in national and local groups, and within each list the plans in order of the lowest cost for self only enrollment in both FEHB and Part B. Some plans cost very little extra for Part B, taking into account both premium and enhanced benefits. These are sometimes the plans that offer the best premium reimbursements, and sometimes not. The table does not include estimates for the options involving enrollment in Medicare Advantage as your primary plan, but these are generally better buys than those shown in the table, provided that you are willing to consider such a major change.

Medicare Part D

The Medicare Part D prescription drug program benefits millions of low-income elderly. It fills a major hole in Medicare that lasted fifty years. But it will rarely benefit those, like Federal retirees, who have good drug coverage from their former employer.

Few Federal retirees should join a Part D plan. A typical plan will cost four or five hundred dollars in premium and provide little improved benefit for most. Also, there is no penalty for joining Part D at a later time if you have current "creditable" coverage. This test is met by all FEHB plans. There are three exceptions. First, a few Federal annuitants have incomes and liquid assets low enough to qualify for special help. For example, a divorced former spouse may receive so little in pension that he or she qualifies for low-income assistance (the income cutoff is approximately $18,000, depending on state of residence). In such a case, the annuitant may be able to reduce drug costs to almost nothing. You apply to the Social Security Administration to obtain an official decision. Second, the Part D benefit can offer savings to annuitants in plans with relatively weak prescription drug coverage, like GEHA Standard option. This GEHA plan only reimburses half the cost of name brand drugs. An enrollee with a name brand drug costing at retail $2,000 a year would be out of pocket $1,000 under GEHA. Many Part D plans would pay most of this cost for a premium of $500 a year or less, and GEHA would pay half the rest. Third, a Part D plan will let enrollees in High Deductible and Consumer-Driven plans such as Aetna Direct, NALC CDHP, or MHBP HDHP avoid using their personal account for routine drug expenses.

Unfortunately, the national plans are not offering extra benefits such as copay waivers to those who join Part D, unlike their improved coverage for those with Parts A or B. They simply promise to "consider" paying part of your Part D costs, whatever that means. And having two drug plans involves a lot of paperwork. Hence, only if you can achieve substantial savings for your particular drugs is it worthwhile to join Part D. Also, before enrolling in Part D check whether or not you are subject to income-related premiums. The law now subjects Part D enrollees to the same income-tested levels as under Part B. If your adjusted gross income is $85,000 or more for single people, or $170,000 or more for couples, you would have to pay a premium surcharge for Part D.

Chapter 5

Cost Sharing

Health insurance plans never pay 100 percent of all health-related expenses. Every plan limits coverages in various ways. For example, no plan pays for elective cosmetic surgery. Most plans pay little or nothing towards expensive dental procedures. Almost all plans charge something—usually $20 to $40—for physician visits. Almost all plans charge much more for name brand drugs than for generic drugs. Many plans charge deductibles, either before reimbursing any expenses or before reimbursing particular categories of expenses, such as hospital or prescription drugs. These and other payment limitations are complicated and vary from plan to plan. Taken together, they dictate what you will pay out-of-pocket at various levels and mixes of health care expenses. We estimate these out-of-pocket costs for you using a complex computer model that takes into account all these various interactions, but in some cases you may want to focus on particular coverages and copayments of concern to you.

Deductibles, Copayments, and Coinsurance

You can use cost sharing details to assist you in choosing a plan by pinpointing strengths and weaknesses for cost items of particular concern to you. If you are especially concerned about a broad area of coverage, such as reimbursement for prescription drugs, copayment information can identify plans that are most acceptable to you for that feature, and be used together with the cost rankings to narrow your choice. Our comparisons of deductibles, coinsurance, and copays display many—but by no means all—of the cost sharing provisions taken into account in our overall cost comparisons. (In the printed *Guide*, we present a cost-sharing table for national plans and DC area local plans, but not for the local plans in other parts of the country that we are able to display online.)

In recent years prescription drug copayments have become increasingly complex. Plans require you to pay more for "name brand" drugs than for "generic" drugs. Name brand drugs, once past their patent protection period, are usually met with competition from generic drugs that the Food and Drug Administration has determined to be therapeutically identical. As a result, generic drugs tend to be much less expensive, and it is in the financial interest of both you and the plan that you select them. Most plans now use at least a six-tier reimbursement structure for prescription drugs: generic, preferred name brand, and non-formulary name brand at the local pharmacy for a one-month supply; and the same three categories for a three-month supply by mail order (multi-thousand dollar "specialty drugs" are often yet another tier). Our overall cost comparisons reflect these differences, but if you have unusually high (or low) name brand drug costs, you can use our cost sharing tables to identify plans most likely to match your needs.

You should not rely primarily on cost sharing information to select a plan. Choosing a plan with the best rate for a particular benefit without taking into account its premium and all its other benefits would be a mistake. You could try to compare key factors two or three at a time, but this approach necessarily either omits other key factors or requires so many oversimplified comparisons as to become meaningless. For example, whether or not and how much a separate hospital deductible matters compared to premium dollars depends on a key unknown: your likelihood of one or more hospital stays. With few exceptions (e.g., routine visits and maintenance prescription drugs, and some planned operations if you avoid complications that lead to readmissions) you cannot forecast just what medical expenses of each type you will incur next year, and even if you could it is very complex to make all the interactive calculations involved. Furthermore, cost sharing can be and often is expressed in annual, monthly, biweekly, per dollar spent, and per service unit for different benefits in the same plan. It can be expressed as the dollar amount you pay, the dollar amount the plan pays, the percent you pay, or the percent the plan pays. Converting all these disparate measures to the common metric of annual cost is essential to making comparisons. Otherwise, you are comparing apples to oranges—how much biweekly premium equals how many annual physician visit copayments or what coinsurance percent for name brand prescriptions? We not only handle these messy computations for you, but also use actuarial information on the probability of different kinds and amounts of costs. **Most importantly, you cannot sensibly compare plans based only or primarily on expenses you already expect—that misses the main purpose of insurance: to protect you against unknown and potentially devastating future expenses.**

Each of the table entries for costs of various types shows the dollar copayment or coinsurance percentage you must pay for bills of each type. In some cases a plan uses both methods of payment for the same benefit, or a different amount depending on which type of provider or prescription drug is involved. These amounts and percentages do not take into account deductibles, and can be very misleading. A plan that pays all expenses in excess of a deductible of $300 pays none of your bills in a year when your costs are less than $300, and only half in a year in which your costs reach $600.

In most cases, our entries are the same as those given in the plan brochures. Unfortunately, the reimbursement structure for many plans is so complicated that there is no simple way to present or compare these payments, even organized by type of expense. For example, some plans vary your hospital copayment based on how many days you stay as a patient, and while some use dollar copayments others use percentage coinsurance. Therefore, unless you are quite confident as to a high level of spending in a particular category, and are willing to compare several plan brochures carefully, do not rely on cost sharing details to inform your decision.

Dealing with a Known High Expense

There is an exception to our general advice about focusing on overall plan costs, not just one benefit category. If you know for sure that you will need a particular expensive service, you should look for the answer to "Which plans pay best?" If several plans pay equally well, then you can choose whichever of these is an overall better buy.

The High Deductible and Consumer-Driven plans' copayments are particularly subject to confusion because they change by expenditure level. You start the year with a savings account you can use for any physician, dental, drug, or other expense. In addition, just as in all other plans you get complete coverage of a physical exam that will cost hundreds of dollars. Your copayment for these expenses is zero. If and when you exhaust the savings account, you pay a substantial deductible. After that, you pay a small proportion of hospital and physician costs until you reach the catastrophic limit. Your coinsurance ranges from zero, to 100 percent, to 10 or 15 percent and, once you reach the catastrophic limit, back to zero. The purpose of this is to give you incentives for careful decisions on medical spending. However, these plans' designs make it very difficult to estimate your costs.

We recommend great caution in comparing the details of these plans' deductibles with each other or with traditional insurance plans. HDHP plans show as a deductible the entire amount that must be spent before regular insurance cost sharing kicks in, regardless of whether the enrollee chooses to spend the Health Savings Account, since whether or not that Account is spent is an enrollee decision. In contrast, CDHP plans require that their accounts be spent on medical expense and used up before the deductible starts, and show as a deductible the amount between that spending level and where insurance cost sharing kicks in. As a result, a CDHP plan will invariably show a much smaller deductible than an HDHP plan even if the spending level at which the insurance coverage kicks in is the same. Our estimates of out-of-pocket costs take these variations into account, but the calculations can be complex.

Cost Sharing for National Plans & D.C. Area Plans		Savings account for self	Savings account for family	Deductibles			
Plan code	Plan name (listed in alphabetical order within group)			Single	Family	Extra for drugs (self)	Extra for 2-day hospital stay
D.C. Area Plans When You Use Preferred Providers							
F51-3	Aetna HealthFund CDHP	$1,000	$2,000	$1,000	$2,000	None	None
JN1-3	Aetna Open Access-Hi	None	None	None	None	None	$300
JN4-6	Aetna Open Access Basic	None	None	None	None	None	None
QQ4-6	Aetna Saver	None	None	$1,000	$2,000	None	None
F54-6	Aetna Value Plan	None	None	$700	$1,400	None	None
B64-6	CareFirst Blue Value Plus	None	None	None	None	$100	None
B51-3	CareFirst HDHP*	$900	$1,800	$1,400	$2,800	None	None
2G4-6	CareFirst-Std POS*	None	None	None	None	None	None
T71-3	Kaiser Basic*	None	None	$100	$200	None	$750
E31-3	Kaiser-Hi*	None	None	None	None	None	$100
E34-6	Kaiser-Std*	None	None	None	None	None	$500
JP1-3	MD-IPA*	None	None	None	None	None	$300
LR1-3	United Choice Open Access	None	None	None	None	None	$300
L91-3	United Choice Plus Advanced	None	None	$500	$1,000	None	None
AS1-3	United Choice Plus Primary	None	None	$500	$1,000	Varies	Varies
Y81-3	United Choice Primary	None	None	$500	$1,000	Varies	Varies
V41-3	United HDHP	$750	$1,500	$1,500	$3,000	None	$500
National Plans When You Use Preferred Providers							
Z24-6	Aetna Advantage*	None	None	$2,000	$4,000	None	None
N61-3	Aetna Direct CDHP*	$900	$1,800	$1,600	$3,200	None	None
224-6	Aetna HealthFund HDHP	$800	$1,600	$1,800	$3,600	None	None
474-6	APWU CDHP	$1,200	$2,400	$1,000	$2,000	None	None
471-3	APWU-Hi*	None	None	$400	$800	None	None
111-3	Blue Cross Basic*†	None+	None	None	None	None	$350
104-6	Blue Cross-Std*	None	None	$350	$700	None	$350
421-3	Compass Rose*	None	None	$350	$700	None	$200
131-3	FEP Blue Focus**	None	None	$500	$1,000	None	None
401-3	Foreign Service*	None	None	$300	$600	None	None
254-6	GEHA Elevate	None	None	$500	$1,000	None	None
251-3	GEHA Elevate Plus	None	None	None	None	None	$400
341-3	GEHA HDHP	$900	$1,800	$1,500	$3,000	None	None
311-3	GEHA-Hi*†	None	None	$350	$700	None	$100
314-6	GEHA-Std*	None	None	$350	$700	None	None
481-3	MHBP HDHP*	$1,200	$2,400	$2,000	$4,000	None	$150
414-6	MHBP Value	None	None	$500	$1,000	None	None
454-6	MHBP-Std*	None	None	$350	$700	None	$200
324-6	NALC CDHP	$1,200	$2,400	$2,000	$4,000	None	None
KM1-3	NALC Value	$100	$200	$2,000	$4,000	None	None
321-3	NALC-Hi*	None	None	$300	$600	None	$350
381-3	Rural Carrier*	None	None	$350	$700	$200	$100
441-3	SAMBA-Hi*	None	None	$300	$600	None	$200
444-6	SAMBA-Std*	None	None	$350	$700	None	$200

* If you have Medicare parts A and B, most or all deductibles and hospital and physician cost sharing are waived.

You pay after deductible and after using savings account:							
				Prescription drugs ($) or (%)			
Hospital room & board (%)	Other hospital inpatient (%)	Visit to primary care ($ or %)	Visit to specialist ($ or %)	Generic local pharmacy	Name brand local pharmacy	Generic mail order 90 day	Name brand mail order 90 day
15%	15%	15%	15%	$10	50%	$20	50%
None	None	$15	$30	$3	$35	$6	$70
20%	20%	$25	$55	$10	50%	$20	50%
30%	30%	30%	30%	$10	50%	$30	50%
20%	20%	$25	$40	$10	30%	$20	30%
25%	25%	$10	$50	$10	$50	$20	$100
20%	20%	None	$35	None	$30	None	$60
20%	20%	None	$40	None	$35	None	$70
None	None	$30	$40	$10	$45	$24	$129
None	None	$10	$20	$7	$30	$15	$84
None	None	$20	$30	$10	$40	$24	$114
None	None	$25	$40	$7	$35	$21	$105
None	None	$25	$35	$10	$40	$25	$100
20%	20%	$25	$50	$10	$35	$25	$88
20%	20%	$0	$60	$5	$50	$12	$125
20%	20%	$0	$60	$5	$50	$12	$125
None	None	$15	$30	$10	$40	$25	$100
30%	30%	30%	30%	$10	45%	$20	45%
20%	20%	20%	20%	$6	30%	$2	30%
15%	15%	15%	15%	$10	50%	$20	50%
15%	15%	15%	15%	25%	25%	25%	25%
15%	15%	$25	$25	$10	25%	$20	25%
None	None	$30	$40	$10	$55	NA	NA
None	None	$25	$35	$7.50	30%	$15	$90
None	None	$15	$25	$5	$35	$10	$70
30%	30%	$10/30%**	$10/30%**	$5	40%	NA	NA
None	None	10%	10%	$10	25%	$15	$60
25%	25%	$10	$25	$4	50%	NA	NA
None	None	$20	$35	$5	up to $80	$12	up to $200
5%	5%	5%	5%	25%	25%	25%	25%
None	10%	$20	$20	$10	25%	$20	25%
15%	15%	$15	$30	$10	50%	$20	50%
None	None	$15	$15	$10	30%	$20	$80
20%	20%	$30	$50	$10	45%	$30	45%
None	10%	$10-20	$30	$5	30%	$10	$80
20%	20%	$20	$20	$10	$40	$20	$90
20%	20%	$20	$20	$10	$40	$20	$90
None	None	$20	$20	20%	30%	$15	$90
None	None	$20	$20	30%	30%	$10	$50
None	15%	$15	$25	$10	30%	$15	30%
None	20%	$20	$30	$12	35%	$20	35%

** Plan provides 10 visits for $10 each with no deductible, then regular cost sharing applies.
† For those who pay Medicare Part B premiums, these plans reimburse about half the cost.

Non-Preferred Providers

You face far higher costs if you use non-preferred providers. Plans not only charge you more for deductibles, copayments, and coinsurance, but also require you to pay the entire cost above the rate the plan sets as its allowance used in its network for a particular procedure. That rate is bargained with health care providers and usually varies by zip code and is not available to the public or to plan enrollees in advance. In general, we advise you to stay with preferred providers whenever possible. Remember that out-of-network cost-sharing percentages are valid ONLY if the non-preferred provider accepts the plan's allowance. In most cases this will not be true unless you bargain, and the plan will likely pay less than half the bill. Half is better than nothing, but you should plan your health care to stay in network wherever possible. There is almost always a wide range of high quality preferred providers in network.

Chapter 6

Coverage Features

Using the *Guide*'s cost comparisons, you should first select several plans for which your costs are likely to be relatively low. The second step in selecting a plan is to focus on any special needs or circumstances that the cost tables do not fully reflect. The third step is to consider how important it is to you to retain a particular doctor(s) and, if necessary, to find out whether your doctor belongs to particular plans. The best way to do this is simply to call the doctor's office and ask. You can also go to the plan's Web site, or get a provider list at a health fair, but those provider lists are sometimes out of date. You can reverse the order of these steps, but it never makes sense to pay an extra $1,000 in premium if the most you will spend on a particular physician or service is a few hundred dollars. You should save the "for sure" premium cost and if necessary pay for a particular visit directly, without using your insurance.

Even if you know you are going to use a particular service, you can enroll in a plan that costs less overall but doesn't necessarily have a particularly good benefit in that area. You can use the savings to establish a Flexible Spending Account and focus that spending on that special need. Flexible Spending Accounts give employees (but not retirees) a way to reduce foreseeable costs substantially. If you anticipate, for example, having substantial dental or talk therapy expenses even after your coverage by health or dental insurance, in 2020 you can set aside up to $2,750 in a health care FSA account ($5,500 for a couple) and that income will not be subject of Federal and State income taxes, or to Social Security taxes. For most, this has the effect of reducing the amount you actually pay by about one third. You estimate your likely spending and set up this account during the same Open Season used for selecting health plans. An FSA is perfect way to get about a one-third discount on a benefit for which your plan restricts coverage. FSA accounts are no longer "use or lose" and you can carry over up to $500 into the next without penalty.

Still, it is best to choose the low-cost plan that best covers an expense you can predict. Our Coverage Features analysis and tables focus on benefit categories that vary widely across plans, such as non-network psychiatric care. Online our tables show Coverage Features for all plans in the program, nationwide. In the printed *Guide,* we present these detailed tables only for national plans and DC area local plans, and very selectively for plans in other States in the "Cost and Coverage Features of Local Plans" table at the end of the "Key Tips and Final Plan Selection" section.

We have worded the comparison headings to allow standard entries, such as "Yes," "Some," or "No." A "Yes" always means broader coverage and a "No" always means narrower coverage. However, even though a number of plans are rated "Yes," this does not mean that the benefits are identical. You need to compare brochures.

Very importantly, if you know that you will need some specific and expensive type of care, whether or not it is in our tables, and whether or not the brochure seems clear, it is always a sensible strategy to talk to at least one potential provider and ask the simple question "Which plans pay best for the care I need?" You can also talk to a plan representative, but the information you get is not always reliable and carries no guarantee. The actual providers (or their office staff) know which plans pay best in the real world. Explore especially carefully if the service is near some boundary of coverage. For example, some hospitals provide regular hospital care, skilled nursing care, and custodial care in the same facility. You need to be sure that whichever level of service you get will be billed and paid under a category paid by your plan.

Coverage Features of National Plans and D.C. Area Plans

Plan code	Plan name (listed in alphabetical order within group)	Pays for (in most cases only if medically necessary): Day limit in skilled nursing facility	Maximum non-network mental outpatient	Routine dental care	Dental accident	Adult vision care
D.C. Area Plans When You Use Preferred Providers						
F51-3	Aetna HealthFund CDHP	60	Unlim	Yes	Some	Exam
JN1-3	Aetna Open Access-Hi	60	None	Some	Some	Yes
JN4-6	Aetna Open Access Basic	60	None	Some	Some	Yes
QQ4-6	Aetna Saver	60	None	No	Some	Exam
F54-6	Aetna Value Plan	60	Unlim	No	No	Yes
B64-6	CareFirst Blue Value Plus	Unlim	Unlim	Some	Yes	Exam
B61-3	CareFirst HDHP	Unlim	Unlim	Some	Yes	Exam
2G4-6	CareFirst-Std POS	Unlim	Unlim	Some	Yes	Exam
T71-3	Kaiser Basic	100	None	No	Yes	Exam
E31-3	Kaiser-Hi	100	None	Yes	Yes	Exam
E34-6	Kaiser-Std	100	None	Yes	Yes	Exam
JP1-3	MD-IPA	60	None	Yes	Yes	Yes
LR1-3	United Choice Open Access	60	None	Some	Yes	Exam
L91-3	United Choice Plus Advanced	60	Unlim	Some	Yes	Exam
AS1-3	United Choice Plus Primary	60	Unlim	Some	Yes	Exam
Y81-3	United Choice Primary	60	Unlim	Some	Yes	Exam
V41-3	UnitedHealthcare HDHP	60	Unlim	Some	Yes	Exam
National Plans When You Use Preferred Providers						
Z24-6	Aetna Advantage	60	Unlim	No	Yes	Exam
N61-3	Aetna Direct CDHP	60	Unlim	No	Yes	Exam
224-6	Aetna HealthFund HDHP	60	Unlim	Yes	Some	Exam
474-6	APWU CDHP	30	Unlim	Yes	Yes	Some
471-3	APWU-Hi	30	Unlim	Yes	Yes	No
111-3	Blue Cross Basic	0	None	Some	Yes	No
104-6	Blue Cross-Std	30	Unlim	Some	Yes	No
421-3	Compass Rose	90	Unlim	Yes	Yes	Exam
131-3	FEP Blue Focus	0	None	No	Yes	Exam
401-3	Foreign Service	90	Unlim	Some	Yes	No
254-6	GEHA Elevate	0	Unlim	Yes	Yes	No
251-3	GEHA Elevate Plus	21	Unlim	Yes	Yes	No
341-3	GEHA HDHP	21	Unlim	Yes	Yes	Yes
311-3	GEHA-Hi	21	Unlim	Yes	Yes	No
314-6	GEHA-Std	21	Unlim	Yes	Yes	No
481-3	MHBP HDHP	28	Unlim	No	Yes	No
414-6	MHBP Value	40	Unlim	No	Yes	No
454-6	MHBP-Std	40	Unlim	No	Yes	No
324-6	NALC CDHP	0	Unlim	Yes	Some	No
KM1-3	NALC Value	0	Unlim	Yes	Some	No
321-3	NALC-Hi	0	Unlim	Yes	Some	No
381-3	Rural Carrier	60	Unlim	Yes	Yes	No
441-3	SAMBA-Hi	45	Unlim	No	Yes	No
444-6	SAMBA-Std	30	Unlim	No	Yes	No

Note: Your savings accounts in CDHP and HDHP plans, or your FSA account, pay for ALL of these benefits, in addition to what the plans pay.

Pays for (in most cases only if medically necessary):							
Chiropractic	Acupuncture	Hearing aids	Infertility treatment	Prostheses (artificial limbs)	Diabetic supplies	Durable medical equipment	Nurse advice by phone
Yes	Some	No	Some	Yes	Some	Yes	800-556-1555
Yes	Some	Yes	Little	Yes	Yes	Yes	800-556-1555
Some	Some	Yes	Little	Yes	Yes	Yes	800-556-1555
Some	Some	No	Little	Some	Some	Some	800-556-1555
No	Some	No	Some	Yes	Some	Yes	800-556-1555
Some	Some	Some	Little	Some	Some	Some	800-535-9700
Some	Some	Yes	Little	Some	Yes	Some	800-535-9700
Some	Some	Yes	Little	Some	Yes	Some	800-535-9700
Some	Some	Child	Little	Yes	Yes	Some	703-359-7878
Yes	Yes	Child	Little	Yes	Yes	Some	703-359-7878
Some	Some	Child	Little	Yes	Yes	Some	703-359-7878
Some	Some	Child	Yes	Some	Yes	Some	888-887-4114
Some	Some	No	Some	Yes	Yes	Yes	877-835-9861
Some	Some	Child	Some	Yes	Yes	Yes	877-835-9861
Some	Some	Yes	Little	Yes	Yes	Yes	877-835-9861
Some	Some	Yes	Little	Yes	Yes	Yes	877-835-9861
Yes	Some	Yes	Some	Yes	Yes	Yes	877-835-9861
No	Little	No	Little	Yes	Some	Yes	800-556-1555
No	No	Some	Little	Yes	Some	Yes	800-556-1555
No	No	No	Little	Yes	Some	Yes	800-556-1555
Yes	Yes	Yes	Little	Yes	Yes	Yes	800-718-1299
Some	Some	Yes	Some	Yes	Yes	Yes	800-582-1314
Some	Some	Yes	Some	Some	Yes	Some	888-258-3432
Some	Yes	Yes	Some	Yes	Yes	Yes	888-258-3432
Yes	Yes	Yes	Some	Yes	Yes	Yes	None
Some	Some	No	Little	Some	Some	Some	888-258-3432
Yes	Yes	Yes	Some	Yes	Yes	Yes	855-482-5750
Some	Yes	No	Little	Some	Yes	Some	888-257-4342
Some	Yes	Some	Little	Some	Yes	Some	888-257-4342
Some	Yes	No	Little	Yes	Some	Yes	888-257-4342
Some	Yes	Yes	Little	Yes	Yes	Yes	888-257-4342
Some	Yes	Some	Little	Yes	Yes	Yes	888-257-4342
Yes	Yes	Some	Little	Yes	Yes	Yes	800-694-9901
Yes	Yes	Some	Little	Yes	Yes	Yes	800-410-7778
Yes	Yes	Yes	Little	Yes	Yes	Yes	800-410-7778
Some	Some	Some	Some	Yes	Yes	Yes	877-220-6252
Some	Some	Some	Some	Yes	Yes	Yes	877-220-6252
Yes	Some	Some	Some	Yes	Yes	Yes	877-220-6252
Yes	Yes	Some	Some	Yes	Yes	Yes	800-638-8432
Yes	Yes	Some	Little	Yes	Yes	Yes	800-887-9735
Some	Yes	Some	Little	Yes	Yes	Yes	800-887-9735

Nursing Care

There are four kinds of nursing care: skilled care while in a hospital, skilled care in a special "extended" or "skilled" care facility, care in your own home provided by visiting nurses, and "custodial" care either in your own home or in a "nursing home." No health insurance plan will pay for custodial care, the kind where your principal needs are to be fed, bathed, and clothed and where you need help with ordinary life tasks rather than to recover. At the other extreme, all plans pay for necessary care by nurses while you are in the hospital. Similarly, all plans cover some form of home health care, usually with at least 90 days or visits.

Plans differ in their coverage of care in an "extended" or "skilled" nursing care facility. Most national plans offer no coverage; but a few cover 60 or 90 days per confinement, usually at the same cost to you as hospital treatment. Most HMOs, however, cover skilled nursing care, usually 90 or 100 days.

We did not reflect the value of skilled care in a facility in our cost tables. Since very few younger persons ever need such care, the plan rankings would not have changed much if we had taken into account the statistical probabilities. Virtually all retirees over age 65 have a substantial Medicare Part A benefit for skilled nursing care. Accordingly, they will rarely if ever need any FEHB plan benefit for this care.

Nonetheless, stays in skilled nursing care facilities cost about half as much as in hospitals. This is one of the potentially substantial expenses to which some plans leave you exposed. If you think you are likely to need more than a month of this care, we recommend careful attention to brochure language in relation to your particular needs. Remember, moreover, that these stays are subject to plan approval and must involve rehabilitative needs, not simply help with daily living.

For custodial care, either in your own home or a nursing home, OPM sponsors a Long Term Care insurance program, separate from the FEHB program. This program pays for long term care services if you can't take care of yourself because of an extended illness, such as Alzheimer's disease. The program covers both institutional and home care. Premiums are substantial, and there is no government contribution. You can find out more about it at *www.opm.gov/insure/ltc*. Similar insurance can be purchased individually from the same companies that underwrite the OPM program. If your retirement income and assets are relatively low, and you otherwise cannot afford needed custodial care, you can ultimately rely on the Federal/State Medicaid program.

Value of Outpatient Mental Benefits

OPM has long required that plans pay the same benefits for physician visits or hospital stays whether due to either physical or mental illness. This requirement is called "parity," and, at face value, seems to eliminate any distinction between physical and mental health benefits. It represented a significant advance in covering clinically necessary hospital stays for mental illness. In 2010 the government issued regulations requiring all employer-sponsored health plans to meet an even stricter version of parity. Under these regulations, plans are no longer allowed even to charge separate deductibles for physical and mental health or substance abuse services. In theory, all FEHB plans will now pay for unlimited mental health services without even such a small difference in cost sharing.

The catch is that all plans select the providers for their networks, and will rarely if ever use providers whose practices emphasize weekly sessions of "talk therapy." Nor will plans reimburse full costs for services provided by a psychiatrist of your choosing. Instead, they provide a limited number of plan-affiliated psychiatrists, and often rely mainly on the services of clinical psychologists, clinical social workers, and other non-M.D. staff.

Few of the HMO plans offer any mental health services outside of the plan network, or outside of pre-approved treatment plans. The major exceptions are the HMOs with an Opt-Out or "Point of Service" provision. In contrast, all of the national fee-for-service plans except Blue Cross Basic offer a relatively unconstrained out-of-network benefit, as do Consumer-Driven and High Deductible plans. If you expect to use an out of network provider, consider setting up a Flexible Spending Account during Open Season.

Other Coverage Features

Most plans limit reimbursement for most of the following services. Current employees can cover any of them through a Flexible Spending Account.

- *Dental care*—We indicate which health insurance plans pay for routine and accidental dental expenses, and show the better benefits with a "Yes." Our separate chapter on "Dental, Vision and Hearing" provides dollar ratings of these plans along with the standalone dental plans (we have even more detailed comparisons online). Those standalone plans charge a premium, but offer stronger benefits. Nonetheless, our ratings show that for most people joining an FEHB plan with modest dental benefits is a low-cost option.
- *Vision care*—All plans pay for medically necessary care of your eyes, such as cataract surgery. No national plans pay for eyeglasses or contact lenses, although several of them have arranged for discounts at some chains. A few pay for examinations to determine the prescription you need. Among HMOs, many pay just for an "Exam," and some for most of the cost of glasses or contact lenses ("Yes" in our tables). You may want to join one of the vision plans described in our chapter on "Dental, Vision and Hearing," but a combination of prudent shopping and Flexible Spending Account will often match the value of the standalone vision plans.
- *Chiropractic services*—Most plans reimburse some chiropractic services. The medical establishment has traditionally viewed chiropractors unfavorably because chiropractors are not trained as medical doctors. However, chiropractic services have been proven useful in treating some problems of the muscles, back, and joints. We label "Yes" plans that pay for 20 or more visits at a cost of no more than $20 a visit.
- *Acupuncture*—Another non-traditional treatment that an increasing number of plans reimburse, often for a dozen or more visits.
- *Hearing aids*—Most plans pay for diagnostic hearing tests performed by a physician or audiologist, and all pay for medically necessary treatment for hearing problems. At OPM urging, most plans now pay for hearing aids for both adults and children, and others for hearing aids for children only. In our table, a "Yes" indicates both a relatively generous allowance, and coverage of both children and adults. The "Dental, Vision and Hearing" chapter provides detailed comparisons.
- *Infertility treatment*—Very few plans pay for the costs of in vitro fertilization or for the most advanced and expensive infertility treatments such as assisted reproductive technology procedures. Few plans pay for fertility drugs or for treatments such as artificial insemination. Generosity varies so you should compare brochures or consult providers before choosing a plan. Fertility physicians and clinics are likely to know which plans best cover their services.
- *Diabetic supplies*—Some plans cover drugs but do not cover the cost of syringes and/or special testing supplies and kits needed by diabetics. Even for the plans listed as "Yes," a diabetic should check brochures to determine the precise coverage the plans provide.
- *Durable medical equipment*—All national plans pay for prostheses, or artificial limbs. Some plans limit such coverage. Some plans also fail to pay for the purchase or rental costs of hospital beds, walkers, and other equipment you may need while recuperating from surgery or illness. Others pay only a limited benefit, such as 50 percent of the cost. This is another area to compare brochures and consult providers.
- *Nurse advice*—Most plans let you call a service to discuss medical problems that confuse you. Nurse advisors can greatly assist you in deciding, for example, whether to call a doctor and, if so, which specialty you need. Nurses can also advise you on handling minor medical problems of all kinds, on compliance with your medication needs, and diet and health, and on other issues. For plans that offer this, we enter the telephone number of the advisory service.

Chapter 7

Dental, Vision and Hearing

The Federal government offers standalone "FEDVIP" dental and vision plans, separate and distinct from the FEHB program. These plans share the same Open Season dates as the health insurance plans, but you join them separately. To enroll, you can use the special OPM Web site at *www.benefeds.com*, or call 1-877-888-3337. In sharp contrast to regular health insurance benefits, there is no direct Federal government contribution to the cost of the premium. You pay it all, though with substantial tax savings to employees (but not annuitants).

While these plans do have an element of insurance, in that they protect you against some unforeseen dental or vision expenses, they are best thought of as primarily pre-paid care. Most people enroll in these kinds of plans because they know roughly what kinds of expenses to expect, and plan to do a little better than breaking even. In effect, you pay for those new contact lenses or your recurring dental expenses on the biweekly or monthly installment plan, with protection against some unanticipated expense.

The dental and vision plans save you money in two ways. First, they use affiliated providers who provide discounts because of the increased business the plans attract. Second, because employees (but not retirees) pay the premiums with "pre-tax" dollars, you save approximately one-third of the premium cost. As explained in our analysis of "Costs and Taxes" almost all Federal employees face a marginal tax rate close to or above 33 percent, taking into account Federal income tax, State income tax, the Medicare tax and, for FERS employees, the Social Security tax. Any money an employee spends on dental or vision insurance is not subject to these taxes and employees get what amounts to a one-third discount on the premium, depending on their tax bracket.

On the other hand, these plans charge a premium, ranging from about $200 to $400 a year for self-only dental and about $80 to $150 a year for self-only vision, with family premiums about three times as high. Also, the companies that underwrite these plans know that they will attract persons who are heavy users of these services. This means that the premiums have to be higher than would otherwise be the case.

Virtually all FEHB health insurance plans provide insurance coverage for accidental dental or vision injuries. Typical brochure language says, "We cover services and supplies necessary to promptly repair sound natural teeth" when services are needed due to an "accidental injury." For vision services, typical brochure language says the plan will cover testing and evaluation and fitting for implanted ocular lenses or contact lenses when the impairment is "caused by accident or illness." Most FEHB plans also have some routine dental and vision benefits. These are often substantial benefits (though never as good as in FEDVIP plans). By joining a health insurance plan with better than average dental or vision benefits, you can eliminate much of the need for a supplemental plan. As an example, the Aetna Consumer-Driven plan offers a special $300 fund for self-only enrollees (and double that for families) that covers dental costs.

You can also use a Flexible Spending Account to provide prepaid dental or vision care. By earmarking several hundred or even several thousand dollars of your salary, you avoid paying taxes on that income and effectively gain the same one-third discount that the FEDVIP plans provide. To set up an FSA, you estimate your likely spending for dental, vision, or other anticipated out of pocket expenses. You create an FSA during the same Open Season used for selecting health plans and FEDVIP plans.

You can use all three approaches simultaneously. For example, suppose you enroll in a health insurance plan that pays for preventive dental care and an annual eye exam. You can also enroll in a supplemental vision or dental plan, or both. The health insurance plan will be "primary" and pay first, and the FEDVIP plan pay second. You can then use your FSA account to pay the residual that the first two sources do not cover. This three-part approach may, of course, require more planning and more paperwork than you are willing to tolerate. There is the further complication that your favorite provider may not be a plan participant under either the FEHB or FEDVIP plan. But it does give you maximum wrap-around coverage.

Annuitants do not get the same tax advantages as employees. They may sign up for supplemental dental or vision plans, but do not get the pre-tax "discount." They are not allowed to create FSAs. However, annuitants do get the government contribution towards their FEHB plans, which averages about 70 percent. A health insurance plan with a good dental benefit may be an excellent choice for retirees with low to moderate dental or vision expenses, and with heavy anticipated expenses a FEDVIP plan is a sensible choice even without the taxpayer subsidy.

Consumer-Driven and High Deductible health plans are particularly flexible and comprehensive options for funding dental and vision expenses. These plans allow you to shelter from taxes a personal savings account that you can use for dental and vision expenses, and carry over from year to year. Several of them have special dental funds, and all of them allow employees (but not annuitants) to augment savings accounts during the year if unanticipated expenses arise. These accounts may be used for dental or vision expenses quite apart from those expenses that the plan normally covers, and without restrictions on provider choice (though you may lose discounts if you use non-plan providers). If you already know your dental expenses will be high next year, you can even set up a special account called a Limited Expense Health Care FSA (LEX HCFSA) during Open Season. This will provide dental and vision funding over and above the normal limits on your tax-free contributions to personal savings accounts.

Dental and vision benefits are areas in which you can plan, and in which it pays to plan. Unlike true insurance, where your main need is to guard against large and unpredictable expenses, you probably have a pretty good idea what you are likely to spend on dental and eye care expenses. You can structure your decision around those predictable costs, keeping in mind of course that a tooth, crown, or bridge can break unexpectedly, or some other dental emergency arise. Be careful to read the fine print of the plan brochures carefully, however. The plan may be unlikely to pay for a denture if the need arose before you joined the plan, for example.

The dental and vision plans offer a three-part premium structure—self only, self plus one, and family of three or more. The premiums for families of two or three are almost always about double or triple the self-only premium. If you have a family of three (or more) you may enroll as self plus one and designate which two persons will be eligible for benefits.

Dental Care

Plans' dental benefits differ widely in details, and many of the brochures use technical terminology such as "gingival" (gum, in English), "alveolar" (the part of the jawbone that holds teeth in place), and "amalgam restorations" (filling cavities). Moreover, many plans use schedules of allowances so you don't know if the full charge will be paid (usually not). Since most of the plans limit coverage to the items listed in the schedule of allowances, the particular problem you have may not be covered at all. Worst of all, no plans offer a catastrophic dental benefit that would cover you if, for example, you developed a chronic infection of the jaw and required dental procedures costing thousands of dollars. If you are not sure that a plan adequately covers the particular dental problems of your family, or to be sure you get the network discount, you should talk to your dentist before choosing that plan. For example, most dental plans now cover dental implants, a very expensive procedure. But exactly which parts of the procedure are covered for sure, which options are best, which of these parts or options require plan approval, and how likely a case like yours is to get plan approval, varies from plan to plan. You can call the plan to discuss your case, but the best way to find out which dental plan will cover your implant at least cost to you is to ask your dental surgeon what his patients' experience has been.

In recent years OPM has not allowed most health plans to expand dental benefits. However, OPM has allowed plans to offer "non-FEHB" benefits to plan members, as shown on a special page in brochures. In many cases, extra dental benefits are offered, usually through a network of dentists

Dental Plan Ratings for Employees—Single Person*							
Plan code	Plan name	Plan type	Extra yearly premium	Approximate yearly cost to you if your dental usage is:			Maximum benefit per person
				Low	Average	High	
D.C. Area Plans When You Use Preferred Providers							
E31	Kaiser-Hi	Both	$0	$90	$400	$1,400	None
E34	Kaiser-Std	Both	$0	$90	$400	$1,400	None
B64	CareFirst-Std POS	Unofficial	$0	$140	$480	$1,480	None
2G4	CareFirst-Std POS	Unofficial	$0	$140	$480	$1,480	None
B61	CareFirst HDHP	Unofficial	$0	$140	$480	$1,480	None
F51	Aetna HealthFund CDHP	Official	$0	$120	$600	$2,200	$300+prev
JP1	MD-IPA	Both	$0	$120	$600	$2,200	$500
JN1	Aetna Open Access-Hi	Official	$0	$140	$630	$2,230	None
JN4	Aetna Open Access Basic	Official	$0	$140	$630	$2,230	None
QQ4	Aetna Saver	Official	$0	$140	$630	$2,230	None
AS1	United Choice Plus Primary	Unofficial	$0	$150	$750	$2,750	$500
Y81	United Choice Primary	Unofficial	$0	$150	$750	$2,750	$500
LR1	United Choice Open Access	Unofficial	$0	$150	$750	$2,750	$500
L91	United Choice Plus Advanced	Unofficial	$0	$150	$750	$2,750	$500
V41	United HDHP	Unofficial	$0	$150	$750	$2,750	$500
National Plans When You Use Preferred Providers							
471	APWU-Hi	Both	$0	$140	$530	$1,730	None
421	Compass Rose	Unofficial	$0	$170	$580	$1,780	None
321	NALC-Hi	Unofficial	$0	$210	$700	$2,100	None
KM1	NALC Value Plan	Unofficial	$0	$210	$700	$2,100	None
324	NALC CDHP	Unofficial	$0	$210	$700	$2,100	None
341	GEHA HDHP	Both	$0	$140	$680	$2,480	None
254	GEHA Elevate	Both	$0	$210	$800	$2,600	None
251	GEHA Elevate Plus	Both	$0	$210	$800	$2,600	None
314	GEHA-Std	Both	$0	$210	$800	$2,600	None
311	GEHA-Hi	Both	$0	$260	$880	$2,680	None
401	Foreign Service	Official	$0	$270	$900	$2,700	None
381	Rural Carrier	Official	$0	$310	$930	$2,730	None
224	Aetna HealthFund HDHP	Official	$0	$150	$750	$2,750	None
111	Blue Cross Basic	Official	$0	$170	$780	$2,780	None
104	Blue Cross-Std	Official	$0	$270	$950	$2,950	None
Supplemental Dental Plans When You Use Preferred Providers							
	Dominion Dental High	FEDVIP	$190	$230	$390	$930	Unlim
	Humana Dental	FEDVIP	$210	$250	$410	$950	$15,000
	Dominion Dental Std	FEDVIP	$130	$180	$400	$1,120	Unlim
	United Concordia Dental	FEDVIP	$370	$420	$640	$1,360	Unlim
	Aetna Dental	FEDVIP	$310	$380	$650	$1,550	$30,000
	FEP BlueDental High	FEDVIP	$370	$440	$710	$1,610	Unlim
	GEHA Dental High	FEDVIP	$400	$480	$750	$1,650	$35,000
	Metlife Dental High	FEDVIP	$440	$510	$780	$1,680	Unlim
	FEP BlueDental Std	FEDVIP	$200	$280	$610	$1,690	$1,500
	Delta Dental High	FEDVIP	$470	$540	$810	$1,710	$30,000
	Delta Dental Std	FEDVIP	$230	$310	$640	$1,720	$1,500
	GEHA Dental Std	FEDVIP	$230	$310	$640	$1,720	$2,500
	Metlife Dental Std	FEDVIP	$240	$320	$650	$1,730	$1,500

* Plans are listed in order of lowest cost to you for a high cost year for self only in each group of plans.

Dental Plan Ratings for Employees—Family of Three or More*

Plan code	Plan name	Extra yearly premium	Approximate yearly cost to you if your dental usage is: Low	Average	High	Maximum benefit per person	Child orth-odontic
D.C. Area Plans When You Use Preferred Providers							
E32	Kaiser-Hi	$0	$220	$1,200	$3,200	None	Some
E35	Kaiser-Std	$0	$220	$1,200	$3,200	None	Some
B65	CareFirst-Std POS	$0	$360	$1,410	$3,410	None	No
2G5	CareFirst-Std POS	$0	$360	$1,410	$3,410	None	No
B62	CareFirst HDHP	$0	$360	$1,410	$3,410	None	No
F52	Aetna HealthFund CDHP	$0	$280	$1,680	$4,880	$300+prev	No
JP2	MD-IPA	$0	$280	$1,840	$5,040	$500	No
JN2	Aetna Open Access-Hi	$0	$330	$1,750	$4,950	None	Some
JN5	Aetna Open Access Basic	$0	$330	$1,750	$4,950	None	Some
QQ5	Aetna Saver	$0	$330	$1,750	$4,950	None	No
AS2	United Choice Plus Primary	$0	$350	$2,300	$6,300	$500	No
Y82	United Choice Primary	$0	$350	$2,300	$6,300	$500	No
LR2	United Choice Open Access	$0	$350	$2,300	$6,300	$500	No
L92	United Choice Plus Advanced	$0	$350	$2,300	$6,300	$500	No
V42	United HDHP	$0	$350	$2,300	$6,300	$500	No
National Plans When You Use Preferred Providers							
472	APWU-Hi	$0	$350	$1,530	$3,930	None	No
422	Compass Rose	$0	$440	$1,730	$4,130	None	No
322	NALC-Hi	$0	$560	$2,100	$4,900	None	No
KM2	NALC Value Plan	$0	$560	$2,100	$4,900	None	No
325	NALC CDHP	$0	$560	$2,100	$4,900	None	No
342	GEHA HDHP	$0	$320	$2,070	$5,670	None	No
255	GEHA Elevate	$0	$540	$2,420	$6,020	None	No
252	GEHA Elevate Plus	$0	$540	$2,420	$6,020	None	No
315	GEHA-Std	$0	$540	$2,420	$6,020	None	No
312	GEHA-Hi	$0	$680	$2,630	$6,230	None	No
402	Foreign Service	$0	$710	$2,700	$6,300	None	Yes
382	Rural Carrier	$0	$830	$2,780	$6,380	None	No
225	Aetna HealthFund HDHP	$0	$350	$2,300	$6,300	None	No
112	Blue Cross Basic	$0	$400	$2,370	$6,370	None	No
105	Blue Cross-Std	$0	$700	$2,840	$6,840	None	No
Supplemental Dental Plans When You Use Preferred Providers							
	Dominion Dental High	$560	$640	$1,140	$2,220	Unlim	Wait
	Humana Dental	$630	$720	$1,230	$2,310	$15,000	Yes
	Dominion Dental Std	$380	$510	$1,190	$2,630	Unlim	Yes
	United Concordia Dental	$1,100	$1,230	$1,890	$3,330	Unlim	Wait
	Aetna Dental	$920	$1,080	$1,920	$3,720	$30,000	Yes
	FEP BlueDental High	$1,100	$1,260	$2,100	$3,900	Unlim	Yes
	GEHA Dental High	$1,210	$1,370	$2,190	$3,990	$35,000	Yes
	Metlife Dental High	$1,310	$1,470	$2,310	$4,110	Unlim	Yes
	FEP BlueDental Std	$590	$780	$1,810	$3,970	$1,500	Wait
	Delta Dental High	$1,410	$1,570	$2,410	$4,210	$30,000	Wait
	Delta Dental Std	$690	$880	$1,910	$4,070	$1,500	Wait
	GEHA Dental Std	$700	$900	$1,930	$4,090	$2,500	Wait
	Metlife Dental Std	$720	$900	$1,930	$4,090	$1,500	Yes

* Plans are listed in order of lowest cost to you for a high cost year for self only in each group of plans.

Dental Plan Ratings for Annuitants—Single Person*

Plan code	Plan name	Plan type	Extra yearly premium	Approximate yearly cost to you if your dental usage is: Low	Average	High	Maximum benefit per person
D.C. Area Plans When You Use Preferred Providers							
E33	Kaiser-Hi	Both	$0	$90	$400	$1,400	None
E36	Kaiser-Std	Both	$0	$90	$400	$1,400	None
B66	CareFirst-Std POS	Unofficial	$0	$140	$480	$1,480	None
2G6	CareFirst-Std POS	Unofficial	$0	$140	$480	$1,480	None
B63	CareFirst HDHP	Unofficial	$0	$140	$480	$1,480	None
F53	Aetna HealthFund CDHP	Official	$0	$120	$600	$2,200	$300+prev
JP3	MD-IPA	Both	$0	$120	$600	$2,200	$500
JN3	Aetna Open Access-Hi	Official	$0	$140	$630	$2,230	None
JN6	Aetna Open Access Basic	Official	$0	$140	$630	$2,230	None
QQ6	Aetna Saver	Official	$0	$140	$630	$2,230	None
AS3	United Choice Plus Primary	Unofficial	$0	$150	$750	$2,750	$500
Y83	United Choice Primary	Unofficial	$0	$150	$750	$2,750	$500
LR3	United Choice Open Access	Unofficial	$0	$150	$750	$2,750	$500
L93	United Choice Plus Advanced	Unofficial	$0	$150	$750	$2,750	$500
V43	United HDHP	Unofficial	$0	$150	$750	$2,750	$500
National Plans When You Use Preferred Providers							
473	APWU-Hi	Both	$0	$140	$530	$1,730	None
423	Compass Rose	Unofficial	$0	$170	$580	$1,780	None
323	NALC-Hi	Unofficial	$0	$210	$700	$2,100	None
KM3	NALC Value Plan	Unofficial	$0	$210	$700	$2,100	None
326	NALC CDHP	Unofficial	$0	$210	$700	$2,100	None
343	GEHA HDHP	Both	$0	$140	$680	$2,480	None
256	GEHA Elevate	Both	$0	$210	$800	$2,600	None
253	GEHA Elevate Plus	Both	$0	$210	$800	$2,600	None
316	GEHA-Std	Both	$0	$210	$800	$2,600	None
313	GEHA-Hi	Both	$0	$260	$880	$2,680	None
403	Foreign Service	Official	$0	$270	$900	$2,700	None
383	Rural Carrier	Official	$0	$310	$930	$2,730	None
226	Aetna HealthFund HDHP	Official	$0	$150	$750	$2,750	None
113	Blue Cross Basic	Official	$0	$170	$780	$2,780	None
106	Blue Cross-Std	Official	$0	$270	$950	$2,950	None
Supplemental Dental Plans When You Use Preferred Providers							
	Dominion Dental High	FEDVIP	$280	$320	$480	$1,020	Unlim
	Humana Dental	FEDVIP	$320	$360	$520	$1,060	$15,000
	Dominion Dental Std	FEDVIP	$190	$240	$460	$1,180	Unlim
	United Concordia Dental	FEDVIP	$550	$600	$820	$1,540	Unlim
	Aetna Dental	FEDVIP	$460	$530	$800	$1,700	$30,000
	FEP BlueDental High	FEDVIP	$550	$620	$890	$1,790	Unlim
	GEHA Dental High	FEDVIP	$610	$680	$950	$1,850	$35,000
	Metlife Dental High	FEDVIP	$660	$730	$1,000	$1,900	Unlim
	FEP BlueDental Std	FEDVIP	$300	$380	$710	$1,790	$1,500
	Delta Dental High	FEDVIP	$700	$770	$1,040	$1,940	$30,000
	Delta Dental Std	FEDVIP	$350	$430	$760	$1,840	$1,500
	GEHA Dental Std	FEDVIP	$350	$430	$760	$1,840	$2,500
	Metlife Dental Std	FEDVIP	$360	$440	$770	$1,850	$1,500

* Plans are listed in order of lowest cost to you for a high cost year for self only in each group of plans.

Dental Plan Ratings for Annuitants—Self Plus One*

Plan code	Plan name	Extra yearly premium	Approximate yearly cost to you if your dental usage is: Low	Average	High	Maximum benefit per person	Child orth-odontic
D.C. Area Plans When You Use Preferred Providers							
E33	Kaiser-Hi	$0	$150	$800	$2,300	None	Some
E36	Kaiser-Std	$0	$150	$800	$2,300	None	Some
B66	CareFirst-Std POS	$0	$230	$950	$2,450	None	No
2G6	CareFirst-Std POS	$0	$230	$950	$2,450	None	No
B63	CareFirst HDHP	$0	$230	$950	$2,450	None	No
F53	Aetna HealthFund CDHP	$0	$200	$1,200	$3,600	$300+prev	No
JP3	MD-IPA	$0	$200	$1,200	$3,600	$500	No
JN3	Aetna Open Access-Hi	$0	$230	$1,250	$3,650	None	Some
JN6	Aetna Open Access Basic	$0	$230	$1,250	$3,650	None	Some
QQ6	Aetna Saver	$0	$230	$1,250	$3,650	None	No
AS3	United Choice Plus Primary	$0	$250	$1,500	$4,500	$500	No
Y83	United Choice Primary	$0	$250	$1,500	$4,500	$500	No
LR3	United Choice Open Access	$0	$250	$1,500	$4,500	$500	No
L93	United Choice Plus Advanced	$0	$250	$1,500	$4,500	$500	No
V43	United HDHP	$0	$250	$1,500	$4,500	$500	No
National Plans When You Use Preferred Providers							
473	APWU-Hi	$0	$230	$1,050	$2,850	None	No
423	Compass Rose	$0	$280	$1,150	$2,950	None	No
323	NALC-Hi	$0	$350	$1,400	$3,500	None	No
KM3	NALC Value Plan	$0	$350	$1,400	$3,500	None	No
326	NALC CDHP	$0	$350	$1,400	$3,500	None	No
343	GEHA HDHP	$0	$230	$1,350	$4,050	None	No
256	GEHA Elevate	$0	$350	$1,600	$4,300	None	No
253	GEHA Elevate Plus	$0	$350	$1,600	$4,300	None	No
316	GEHA-Std	$0	$350	$1,600	$4,300	None	No
313	GEHA-Hi	$0	$430	$1,750	$4,450	None	No
403	Foreign Service	$0	$450	$1,800	$4,500	None	Yes
383	Rural Carrier	$0	$530	$1,850	$4,550	None	No
226	Aetna HealthFund HDHP	$0	$250	$1,500	$4,500	None	No
113	Blue Cross Basic	$0	$280	$1,550	$4,550	None	No
106	Blue Cross-Std	$0	$450	$1,900	$4,900	None	No
Supplemental Dental Plans When You Use Preferred Providers							
	Dominion Dental High	$560	$630	$970	$1,780	Unlim	Wait
	Humana Dental	$630	$700	$1,040	$1,850	$15,000	Yes
	Dominion Dental Std	$380	$470	$920	$2,000	Unlim	Yes
	United Concordia Dental	$1,100	$1,190	$1,640	$2,720	Unlim	Wait
	Aetna Dental	$920	$1,030	$1,600	$2,950	$30,000	Yes
	FEP BlueDental High	$1,100	$1,210	$1,780	$3,130	Unlim	Yes
	GEHA Dental High	$1,210	$1,320	$1,890	$3,240	$35,000	Yes
	Metlife Dental High	$1,310	$1,420	$1,990	$3,340	Unlim	Yes
	FEP BlueDental Std	$590	$730	$1,400	$3,020	$1,500	Wait
	Delta Dental High	$1,410	$1,520	$2,090	$3,440	$30,000	Wait
	Delta Dental Std	$690	$830	$1,500	$3,120	$1,500	Wait
	GEHA Dental Std	$700	$840	$1,510	$3,130	$2,500	Wait
	Metlife Dental Std	$720	$860	$1,530	$3,150	$1,500	Yes

* Plans are listed in order of lowest cost to you for a high cost year for self only in each group of plans.

National Vision Plans

Plan name	Aetna Vision		FEP Blue Vision		UnitedHealthcare		VSP	
	High	Std.	High	Std.	High	Std.	High	Std.
Website	aetnafeds.com		fepbluevision.com		fedvip.myuhcvision.com		choosevsp.com	
Telephone	855-347-6899		888-550-2583		866-249-1999		800-807-0764	
Annual Cost for Employees (with tax savings of one-third)								
Self only	$100	$60	$100	$60	$90	$60	$120	$60
Self plus one	$200	$110	$190	$120	$170	$110	$230	$120
Self and family	$300	$170	$290	$180	$250	$160	$350	$180
Annual Cost for Annuitants (published premium without tax savings)								
Self Only	$150	$80	$140	$90	$130	$90	$170	$90
Self Plus One	$300	$170	$290	$180	$250	$170	$350	$180
Self and Family	$450	$250	$430	$270	$370	$250	$520	$270
Copayments								
Deductible	None	None	None	None	None	None	None	None
Annual eye exam	$0	$0	$0	$0	$10	$10	$10	$10
Eyeglass lenses	$0	$10	$0	$0	$10	$25	$0	$20
Inexpensive frames	$0	$0	$0	$0	$0	$0	$0	$0
Contact lenses	$0	$0	$0	$0	$10	$25	$0	$0
Lens and Frame Benefits								
Replace lost/broken lenses?	No	No	No	No	No	No	No	No
Frequency of lenses	Annual	Annual	Annual	Annual	Annual	Annual	Annual	Annual
Frequency of frames	Annual	Annual	Annual	Biannual	Annual	Annual	Annual	Annual
Frame allowance	$230	$140	$150	$130	$200	$200	$150	$120
Premium frames allowance/discount	$230/20%	$140/20%	$150/20%	$130/20%	$150/none	$150/none	$150/20%	$120/20%
Anti-reflective coating cost	$20	$45	$20	$35	Included	$40	$21	$41
UV coating cost	Included	$15	Included	Included	Included	$16	Included	$16
Progressive lens cost	$0	$75	$0	$50	$25	$70	$0	$0
Other Benefits								
Laser surgery discount	15%	15%	40%	40%	40%	40%	15%	15%
Out of network	Reduced	Reduced	Reduced	None	Reduced	Reduced	Reduced	Reduced
International	Reduced	Reduced	Reduced	Reduced	Reduced	Reduced	Reduced	Reduced

who provide discounts for the extra business the plan brings. When these do not involve an extra premium, and represent a significant benefit that can be determined from the brochure, we have included their value in our ratings and tables. While they are not part of the OPM contract and will not be enforced by OPM, they are nonetheless plan commitments to you.

The new standalone dental plans give you a good deal more advance assurance about what is covered and how much you are likely to pay than most of the health plans. However, how much each plan will cover depends importantly on whether your expenses are mainly for children or for adults, and whether for preventive and diagnostic services, or for more expensive restorative services (including surgical, endodontic, prosthodontic, etc.).

Our dental benefit tables help you sort this out. First, we provide estimates of the cost to you under each plan that provides dental benefits, organized by type of plan. There are no extra premiums under the health plans, but there are for the standalone dental plans and we show the annual premium cost together with the likely out of pocket cost under low, average, and high usage scenarios. Because the premium cost is a "for sure" expense we include it in each column.

We also show which plans cover roughly how much on average for child preventive, child restorative, adult preventive, and adult restorative services. These estimates are based on a market basket of dental procedures that are among the most common in each category. For example, we assume that children receive the following preventive and diagnostic services through an annual visit: periodic examination, prophylaxis, bitewing x-rays, and fluoride treatment. For adult restorative services, our index includes fillings, extractions, crowns, root canal treatment, periodontal treatment, and dentures. Although the tables show specific percentages, these are rough estimates, based on national average prices. Your dentist may charge more or less. Also, we had to translate varied plan reimbursement approaches into the "percent you pay," and sometimes this is only an approximation. However, these data can steer you towards particular plans' brochures if there are particular benefits you want to check out in detail for the best coverage.

Is Your Dentist in the Network?

Dental plans use network rates that may reduce your costs by more than the cost saving shown in the plan. It pays to choose a dentist first, and then a plan with a network he has joined.

We also show you the maximum benefit levels (if any) of each plan. Most health plans do not have maximums because their benefits are low enough that they do not face substantial cost exposure. However, most of the standalone plans impose maximum ceilings on what they will pay. If you expect very high expenses, consider a plan with a high or even unlimited maximum, but expect to pay more in premium.

Orthodontic coverage is important to some. All of the standalone FEDVIP dental plans have a substantial orthodontic benefit, as does the Foreign Service plan. The coverage terms vary, so you should compare them carefully. Especially importantly, some dental plans try to discourage you from joining at the last minute to take advantage of these benefits, often by imposing 12 month waiting periods on eligibility. Many plans, however, impose no waiting periods. Orthodontics is the perfect dental expense for combining a dental plan with an FSA account for expenses the plan doesn't cover. It is also an area where it makes sense to talk to providers about getting the lowest cost, taking into account which networks and plans they have joined.

In sum, even if you and your family do not need substantial dental work, one of the health plans may be worth several hundred dollars per year, or more, a benefit that costs you no additional premium. The standalone dental plans provide a distinctly better benefit than almost all health plans, but at a premium cost that largely offsets their better benefits. The dental plans make the most sense for persons who are sure they will have moderately or very high dental expenses, want some protection against an unexpected expense, and like the predictability of paying a regular premium and reducing wide fluctuations from month to month in what they may pay.

Before selecting a dental plan, be sure to check with your family dentist as to which plan(s) he or she affiliates with. Our estimates are based on the assumption that you use network providers. But

Hearing Aid Benefits—Adults

Plan code	Plan name	Hearing aids coverage for adults?	Frequency of replacement	Most plan will pay for one ear	Most plan will pay for two ears
D.C. Area Plans When You Use Preferred Providers					
F51-3	Aetna HealthFund CDHP	No	NA	NA	NA
JN1-3	Aetna Open Access-Hi	Some	3 years	1400	2800
JN4-6	Aetna Open Access Basic	Some	3 years	1400	2800
QQ4-6	Aetna Saver	No	NA	NA	NA
F54-6	Aetna Value Plan	No	NA	NA	NA
B64-6	CareFirst Blue Value Plus	Some	3 years	1000	1000
B61-3	CareFirst HDHP	Yes	No limit	No limit	No limit
2G4-6	CareFirst-Std POS	Yes	3 years	No limit	No limit
T71-3	Kaiser Basic	No	NA	NA	NA
E31-3	Kaiser-Hi	No	NA	NA	NA
E34-6	Kaiser-Std	No	NA	NA	NA
JP1-3	MD-IPA	No	NA	NA	NA
LR1-3	United Choice	No	NA	NA	NA
L91-3	United Choice Plus	No	NA	NA	NA
AS1-3	United Choice Plus Primary	Yes	3 years	2500	5000
Y81-3	United Choice Primary	Yes	3 years	2500	5000
V41-3	United HDHP	Yes	No limit	No limit	No limit
National Plans When You Use Preferred Providers					
Z24-6	Aetna Advantage	No	NA	NA	NA
N61-3	Aetna Direct CDHP	Yes	3 years	3000	3000
224-6	Aetna HealthFund HDHP	No	NA	NA	NA
474-6	APWU CDHP	Some	3 years	1500	1500
471-3	APWU-Hi	Some	3 years	1500	1500
111-3	Blue Cross Basic	Yes	3 years	2500	2500
104-6	Blue Cross-Std	Yes	3 years	2500	2500
421-3	Compass Rose	Some	5 years	1200	2400
131-3	FEP Blue Focus	No	NA	NA	NA
401-3	Foreign Service	Yes	5 years	4000	4000
254-6	GEHA Elevate	No	NA	NA	NA
251-3	GEHA Elevate Plus	Yes	3 years	1500	1500
341-3	GEHA HDHP	No	NA	NA	NA
311-3	GEHA-Hi	Yes	3 years	2500	2500
314-6	GEHA-Std	Yes	3 years	2500	2500
481-3	MHBP HDHP	Some	5 years	1500	1500
414-6	MHBP Value	Some	5 years	1500	1500
454-6	MHBP-Std	Some	5 years	2000	2000
324-6	NALC CDHP	Some	3 years	500	1000
KM1-3	NALC Value	Some	3 years	500	1000
321-3	NALC-Hi	Some	3 years	500	1000
381-3	Rural Carrier	Yes	5 years	3000	3000
441-3	SAMBA-Hi	Some	3 years	500	1000
444-6	SAMBA-Std	Some	3 years	500	1000

Hearing Aid Benefits—Children

Plan code	Plan name	Hearing aids coverage for children?	Age limit for child	Frequency of replacement	Most plan will pay for one ear	Most plan will pay for two ears
D.C. Area Plans When You Use Preferred Providers						
F51-2	Aetna HealthFund CDHP	No	NA	NA	NA	NA
JN1-2	Aetna Open Access-Hi	Some	None	3 years	1400	2800
JN4-5	Aetna Open Access Basic	Some	None	3 years	1400	2800
QQ4-6	Aetna Saver	No	NA	NA	NA	NA
F54-5	Aetna Value Plan	No	NA	NA	NA	NA
B64-6	CareFirst Blue Value Plus	Some	No limit	3 years	1000	1000
B61-2	CareFirst HealthyBlue-HDHP	Yes	18	No limit	No limit	No limit
2G4-5	CareFirst BlueChoice-Std POS	Yes	18	3 years	No limit	No limit
E31-2	Kaiser-Hi	Yes	19	3 years	No limit	No limit
E31-2	Kaiser-Hi	Yes	19	3 years	No limit	No limit
E34-5	Kaiser-Std	Yes	19	3 years	No limit	No limit
JP1-2	M.D. IPA	Some	19	3 years	700	1400
LR1-3	United Choice	No	NA	NA	NA	NA
L91-2	United Choice Plus	Yes	18	3 years	2500	5000
AS1-3	United Choice Plus Primary	Yes	No limit	3 years	2500	5000
Y81-3	United Choice Primary	Yes	No limit	3 years	2500	5000
V41-3	United HDHP	Yes	No limit	No limit	No limit	No limit
National Plans When You Use Preferred Providers						
Z24-6	Aetna Advantage	No	NA	NA	NA	NA
N61-2	Aetna Direct CDHP	Yes	None	3 years	3000	3000
224-5	Aetna HealthFund HDHP	No	NA	NA	NA	NA
474-5	APWU CDHP	Some	None	3 years	1500	1500
471-2	APWU-Hi	Some	None	3 years	1500	1500
111-2	Blue Cross Basic	Yes	22	1 year	2500	2500
104-5	Blue Cross-Std	Yes	22	1 year	2500	2500
421-2	Compass Rose	Yes	22	No limit	No limit	No limit
131-2	FEP Blue Focus	No	NA	NA	NA	NA
401-2	Foreign Service	Yes	22	No limit	No limit	No limit
254-6	GEHA Elevate	No	NA	NA	NA	NA
251-3	GEHA Elevate Plus	Yes	22	3 years	1500	1500
341-2	GEHA HDHP	No	NA	NA	NA	NA
311-2	GEHA-Hi	Yes	22	1 year	2500	2500
314-5	GEHA-Std	Yes	22	1 year	2500	2500
481-2	MHBP HDHP	Some	None	5 years	1500	1500
414-5	MHBP Value Plan	Some	None	5 years	1500	1500
454-5	MHBP-Std	Some	None	5 years	2000	2000
324-5	NALC CDHP	Some	None	3 years	500	1000
KM1-2	NALC Value	Some	None	3 years	500	1000
321-2	NALC-Hi	Some	None	3 years	500	1000
381-2	Rural Carrier	No	NA	NA	NA	NA
441-2	SAMBA-Hi	Some	18	3 years	1000	2000
444-5	SAMBA-Std	Some	18	3 years	1000	2000

plan coverage out of network loses you the network discount. These plans are good buys only when you use network providers.

Vision Care

All FEHB plans pay for medically necessary care of your eyes, such as cataract surgery. Many pay for annual refractive examinations to determine your prescription for eye glasses or contact lens, and some pay for part of the cost for the lens and frame, or arrange for a discount at plan-affiliated providers (this is often stated as an unofficial non-FEHB benefit in brochures.) Our coverage tables show which health plans pay the most toward vision services.

The nation-wide standalone FEDVIP vision plans provide tax-advantaged premiums for employees (but not retirees), and use the purchasing power of their enrollees to obtain discounts for all enrollees. They are not true insurance plans, and will pay neither for lost or broken glasses nor for medical or surgical care. Instead, they are a way to prepay your anticipated and routine costs for refractive eye examination, glasses and frames, contact lenses, and related services and supplies. If you plan to purchase unusually expensive frames, or multiple pairs of glasses, you will need to rely on discounts rather than direct plan benefits.

Unfortunately, the vision plan brochures do not present benefits in a consistent format, making them very hard to compare. We have attempted to capture most of the important features of the plans in our table on national vision plans to help you decide whether, and which, plans you may want to examine in depth. In general, their benefits and premiums are similar, but most offer both high and standard options with differences in both premiums and cost sharing. If you have a preferred optician or eyewear outlet you should ask which plan(s) if any it affiliates with in order to inform your decision.

You have several alternatives to enrolling in these plans. You can simply decide to pay for your predictable dental and vision expenses without the bother of using a plan, or being restricted to its providers. If you combine this with prudent shopping, you can achieve substantial savings. For example, *Washington Consumers' Checkbook* magazine has rated dozens of DC area providers for optical services and found that prices one-fourth or more below (or above) the average for glasses or contact lenses are not uncommon. Also, most FEHB health insurance plans have unofficial plan benefits and discounts for eyewear from particular chains, without paying any extra premium.

You have two other major alternatives for vision care. As for other categories of expense, employees (but not retirees) can establish a Flexible Spending Account that covers vision along with other expenses. Or you can join a Consumer-Driven or High Deductible plan and use its savings account feature to pay for vision costs. You can even supplement a High Deductible plan's savings account with a LEX HCFSA. Either of these options gives employees the same tax advantage—about a one third saving—as a separate vision plan. If you use any FEHB plan, of course, the government pays most of the premium.

The primary advantages of joining a vision plan are that it enables you to lock in a provider discount as well as a tax saving while budgeting for your eye wear. You pay roughly $10, $20, or $30 a month (depending on your family size and which plan you select) knowing that each covered family member will be able to get a good deal on a refractive examination and one good set of eyewear equipment.

Hearing Aids

All plans cover medical problems, such as infections, that affect any part of your body, including your ears. All plans cover routine hearing testing for children. Almost all will pay most of the cost for hearing-related medical procedures, such as cochlear implants. But only in recent years have plans begun to cover the cost of hearing aids to compensate for deafness. Coverages vary widely, with some plans covering only children, ages of child coverage varying, frequency of replacement varying, and big differences in the cost amount the plan will cover. We compare these coverages in our table on hearing aid benefits. Before selecting a plan on this basis, it is worth checking with providers for special discounts, some tailored to specific plans. Publications read by Federal employees or annuitants, such as the magazine of the National Active and Retired Federal Employees Association, often carry ads that promise high quality hearing aids at no cost to enrollees in specific plans.

Chapter 8

Plan Types and Flexibility

All FEHB plans impose restraints on provider choice, using networks as a key strategy to reduce payments and hold down premium costs. The only significant exception to this pattern is for retirees with Medicare Parts A and B, who in most national plans and some HMOs can go to almost any hospital or physician at no cost. This flexibility is allowed because Medicare pays first for these enrollees, and the Federal government uses its legal power to force Medicare-participating providers to accept government fee limitations regardless of their actual costs.

Although all plans, not just HMOs, now provide significantly reduced benefits if you do not use "preferred" or "network" providers, there remain significant differences between PPO plans, PPO plans with fee-for-service (FFS) benefits for using out-of-network providers, local HMOs, and the Consumer-Driven (CDHP) and High Deductible (HDHP) plans. All national plans use PPO networks and no HMOs are national, but each type of plan can be found in local offerings in most large cities.

Type of Plan

In national plans—whether PPO/FFS, HDHP, or CDHP—you generally get a much larger selection of preferred providers, national as well as local. In addition, in all national plans except for Blue Cross Basic you can go to virtually any doctor or hospital you choose—provided you are willing to pay much more (often half or more) of the bill. Under this FFS coverage of providers outside the network, you are covered if you choose to use a world-famous facility, such as the Mayo Clinic, even if it is not a preferred provider. This flexibility gives you maximum freedom of choice, but imposes higher costs on you. The national plans offering broad PPO networks and out of network coverage usually but not always charge higher premiums than most local HMOs, although the gap has narrowed in recent years. HDHP and CDHP plans also provide this flexibility, usually at lower premiums than traditional plans.

Most HMO plans are quite different. They operate through a relatively limited group or network of physicians who share your fees, regardless of which doctor you use. Our analysis below on "Joining an HMO" presents their important advantages and disadvantages in detail. Although cost and benefit comparisons are the key considerations in assessing most plans, other factors are important in deciding whether to enroll in an HMO plan and, if so, which one. Most HMOs will not cover you at all outside of their provider network except in emergencies, but some offer fee-for-service coverage for non-network providers, similar to the national plan (see the point-of-service discussion that follows). Others offer non-emergency out of area benefits to students or, in some cases, to your whole family.

HDHP and CDHP present yet another dimension of choice. These plans provide incentives to you to hold costs down by prudent shopping. The plans provide savings accounts, which, if not fully used, roll over their balances so they can be used in future years. In fact, in some of these plans the amount in your savings account at the end of the year will exceed what you paid in premium (after Premium Conversion savings), if your usage is low. However, once the savings account is used up, you face a high deductible before complete health insurance kicks in. Thus, these plans seemingly present more risk than traditional PPO or HMO plans, as described below in "Joining a High Deductible Plan." However, they have significant tax advantages that largely negate their seemingly higher risk, and their catastrophic cost protection is generally as good or better than in other plans.

Plan Flexibility: National Plans and D.C. Area Plans

Plan code	Plan name (listed in alphabetical order within group)	Get regular benefits anywhere?	Payment for out of network providers (non-emergency)?		Specialist visits covered without referral?		Open formulary?	Company offers a Medicare Advantage plan?	Medicare premium rebate available?
			Without Medicare Part B?	Cost-free with Part B?	Gynecologist	Other specialists			
D.C. Area Plans When You Use Preferred Providers									
F51-3	Aetna HealthFund CDHP	Many Areas	Reduced	No	Yes	Yes	Pay More	Many Areas	No
JN1-3	Aetna Open Access-Hi	Many Areas	No	No	Yes	Yes	Pay More	Yes	No
JN4-6	Aetna Open Access Basic	Many Areas	No	No	Yes	Yes	Pay More	Yes	No
QQ4-6	Aetna Saver	Some Areas	No	No	Yes	Yes	Pay More	Yes	No
F54-6	Aetna Value Plan	Many Areas	Reduced	No	Yes	Yes	Pay More	Yes	No
B64-6	CareFirst Blue Value Plus	Some Areas	No	Yes	Yes	Yes	Pay More	Yes	No
B61-3	CareFirst HDHP	Some Areas	Reduced	Yes	Yes	Yes	Pay More	No	No
2G4-6	CareFirst-Std POS	Some Areas	Reduced	Yes	Yes	Yes	Pay More	No	No
T71-3	Kaiser Basic	Some Areas	No	No	Yes	Some	Pay More	Yes	No
E31-3	Kaiser-Hi	Some Areas	No	No	Yes	Some	Pay More	Yes	No
E34-6	Kaiser-Std	Some Areas	No	No	Yes	Some	Pay More	Yes	No
JP1-3	MD-IPA	No	No	Yes	Yes	No	Pay More	No	No
LR1-3	United Choice Open Access	Some Areas	Reduced	No	Yes	Yes	Pay More	Yes	Yes
L91-3	United Choice Plus Advanced	Some Areas	Reduced	No	Yes	Yes	Pay More	Yes	Yes
AS1-3	United Choice Plus Primary	Many Areas	Reduced	No	Yes	Yes	Pay More	Yes	Yes
Y81-3	United Choice Primary	No	No	No	Yes	Yes	Pay More	Yes	Yes
V41-3	United HDHP	Some Areas	Reduced	No	Yes	Yes	Pay More	Yes	No
National Plans When You Use Preferred Providers									
Z24-6	Aetna Advantage	Many Areas	Reduced	No	Yes	Yes	Pay More	Many Areas	No
N61-3	Aetna Direct CDHP	Many Areas	Reduced	Yes	Yes	Yes	Pay More	Many Areas	Yes
224-6	Aetna HealthFund HDHP	Many Areas	Reduced	No	Yes	Yes	Pay More	Many Areas	No
474-6	APWU CDHP	Nationwide	Reduced	No	Yes	Yes	Yes	No	No
471-3	APWU-Hi	Nationwide	Reduced	Yes	Yes	Yes	Yes	No	No
111-3	Blue Cross Basic	Nationwide	No	No	Yes	Yes	Pay More	Many Areas	Yes
104-6	Blue Cross-Std	Nationwide	Reduced	Yes	Yes	Yes	Pay More	Many Areas	No
421-3	Compass Rose	Nationwide	Reduced	Yes	Yes	Yes	Pay More	No	No
131-3	FEP Blue Focus	Nationwide	No	No	Yes	Yes	Pay More	Many Areas	No
401-3	Foreign Service	Nationwide	Reduced	Yes	Yes	Yes	Pay More	No	No
254-6	GEHA Elevate	Many Areas	Reduced	No	Yes	Yes	Pay More	No	No
251-3	GEHA Elevate Plus	Many Areas	Reduced	Yes	Yes	Yes	Pay More	No	No
341-3	GEHA HDHP	Nationwide	Reduced	No	Yes	Yes	Yes	No	No
311-3	GEHA-Hi	Nationwide	Reduced	Yes	Yes	Yes	Pay More	No	Yes
314-6	GEHA-Std	Nationwide	Reduced	Yes	Yes	Yes	Pay More	No	No
481-3	MHBP HDHP	Nationwide	Reduced	Yes	Yes	Yes	Pay More	No	No
454-6	MHBP Value	Nationwide	Reduced	No	Yes	Yes	Pay More	No	No
454-6	MHBP-Std	Nationwide	Reduced	Yes	Yes	Yes	Pay More	No	No
324-6	NALC CDHP	Nationwide	Reduced	No	Yes	Yes	Pay More	No	No
KM1-3	NALC Value	Nationwide	Reduced	No	Yes	Yes	Pay More	No	No
321-3	NALC-Hi	Nationwide	Reduced	Yes	Yes	Yes	Pay More	No	No
381-3	Rural Carrier	Nationwide	Reduced	Yes	Yes	Yes	Yes	No	No
441-3	SAMBA-Hi	Nationwide	Reduced	Yes	Yes	Yes	Pay More	No	No
444-6	SAMBA-Std	Nationwide	Reduced	Yes	Yes	Yes	Pay More	No	No

Cost Controls

Plans engage in many forms of cost control. All plans now use networks of preferred providers, who agree to accept lower fees and avoid unnecessary utilization. All plans also engage in other measures, such as second opinions before surgery, penalties for non-emergency hospital admissions without a "preadmission certification," prior approval of expensive services or products, case management, or a combination. Some cost control measures, such as second opinions before elective surgery, are good for both you and the plan since neither wants you to have an unnecessary operation. Another "win-win" measure is high discounts on generic drugs that are therapeutically equivalent to name brand drugs. Others pose problems if you are not careful.

In the national PPO and FFS plans, there is a $500 penalty for any non-emergency hospital admission without a "preadmission certification." HMOs normally refuse to pay for unauthorized non-emergency admissions. This means that **you must obtain permission from the plan, not just your doctor, before you enter a hospital**. Likewise, with the major exceptions of routine visits and emergencies, many plans do not pay for expensive care that is not approved in advance by the plan. Such requirements have often been expanded to "specialty" drugs for cancer or other diseases. Plans also use "case management" to reduce expenses in costly cases. For example, if you have a stroke, the plan may authorize extra home health benefits in lieu of prolonged hospitalization. This can benefit you as well as the plan, but you must use the procedure specified by the plan.

Preferred Providers

All national plans obtain reduced rates from "preferred providers," operating through PPO networks. You share in these savings through elimination of deductibles or lower copayments if you use one of these preferred providers. These providers also guarantee that their fee will be accepted by the plan. Such PPO plans are similar in some ways to HMOs. The main difference is that the number of preferred providers in each community is often much larger. At any time, you can switch to a provider of your choice rather than a preferred provider. However, you get the low copayments only from preferred providers, and the plans will not recognize costs above their fee schedule.

Each national plan, except Blue Cross Basic and FEP Blue Focus, allows you to use non-preferred providers on a fee-for-service basis, but limits reimbursement for doctors who are not in the network to a schedule of charges. These schedules often reflect usual rates (or less), but never allow higher rates. The problem is that your doctor may be one who charges much more than the plan will allow. Moreover, in recent years most plans have reduced the generosity of the fee schedules they use with non-participating doctors. **You should never use a non-preferred provider without first checking to be sure that the provider will accept the plan's payment level, including your coinsurance or copayment, as payment in full**. The way to find out is simple: **BEFORE** incurring an expensive procedure, ask the provider point blank if he or she will accept your plan's payment level. Do not accept an equivocal answer—they know roughly what the plans pay and can offer in advance to accept that amount. Moreover, you can bargain for a network or Medicare rate. (Retirees over age 65 face little such risk, since by law almost all physicians must give them a Medicare rate.)

For provider choice, the value of the PPO benefit depends in part on how many doctors and hospitals participate. Blue Cross has agreements with about half of all physicians and most hospitals to be preferred providers. Most other plans also offer you a wide choice. For example, GEHA, APWU, NALC, and other national plans use UnitedHealthcare, Aetna, and other insurance firms to provide an almost equally broad selection of providers. However, it is prudent to check provider lists, particularly if you live in a rural area. The best way to check for overall choices is to use plan Web sites. For a specific provider, simply call the office and check not only whether he or she is currently participating, but also whether he or she intends to continue with the plan.

Point of Service

Some HMOs provide a Point of Service (POS) option under which you may, by paying a deductible and coinsurance, use any doctor or hospital. This benefit is essentially identical to the fee-for-service benefit in national plans. In effect, these HMOs operate as dual plans, in which you can go to any doctor of your choice if you pay a deductible and coinsurance. In most cases the deductible is

$250 or $300 and you pay coinsurance of 25 or 30 percent. These arrangements allow you to join an HMO, get most of your health care with little out-of-pocket cost, but preserve the ability to go out of plan "just in case" you want a doctor not participating in the plan. In other words, if you join an HMO with a POS benefit, you get essentially the same choices as if you join a national plan with both PPO and FFS benefits. Some HMOs offer this benefit limited to college students while away from home.

Joining a Traditional HMO

HMO plans provide not just insurance, but also a different approach to health care delivery from traditional fee-for-service medicine. Therefore, although cost and benefit comparisons are the key considerations in assessing most plans, other factors are important in deciding whether to enroll in an HMO plan and, if so, which one.

There are two main types of HMO plans. One is the facility-based group practice where enrollees agree to receive their health care from a group of doctors working together at the plan's facilities and at hospitals chosen by the plan. The doctors usually are on salary or in a form of partnership. They generally are paid no more if their patients receive more extensive surgery or other medical treatment, thus, their incentives are different from those of doctors working in the traditional fee-for-service system, who can increase their incomes by increasing the amount of care. The Kaiser plans are the largest of this type.

A much more common type of HMO plan is the individual practice association (IPA). In IPAs, physicians agree to share costs and premium income. Each physician continues to practice in his or her own office and continues to serve some patients who are not plan members. All IPAs have a system to assure that physicians do not give costly, excessive service. In a typical system, each physician negotiates a fee schedule with the plan. After seeing a patient, the physician bills the plan for the agreed fee, but the plan pays only part of the bill, such as 80 percent. The remaining 20 percent is kept in a reserve. If costs are held down, the plan will later distribute the reserve to the physicians. To protect against physicians who might deliver excessive services, a committee of physicians regularly reviews treatment practices of each physician. Joining an individual practice association plan is a more modest departure from the fee-for-service system than joining a group practice plan. Some have both groups and individual physicians. Each HMO brochure describes which of these models it uses, and how you get service.

Some features of HMO plans considered desirable by many consumers are:

- They generally have systems for doctors to review each other's practices.
- They eliminate the inconvenience of submitting claims for costs of services.
- They assure you access to a group of doctors.
- They prevent a doctor from charging more than the plan will reimburse.

Some features of HMO plans considered undesirable by many consumers are:

- The IPA plans often have many participating physicians and hospitals, but rarely a majority of those in the community, and rarely prestigious facilities in other states, such as the Lombardi Center or Mayo Clinic. In contrast, the preferred provider panels offered by the national plans are generally far broader, and cover many facilities around the country.
- The group plans require you to go to one of their office locations except in emergencies. Some group plans have only a few locations. They limit your choice of doctor even further: to those who work for the plan. You will have to give up your existing doctors when you join a group plan. In contrast, IPA plans use doctors in private practice and your physician may well participate in one or more IPA HMOs.
- Both types of plan impose barriers to obtaining care as rapidly as you might like, such as waits for the next available appointment for "non-urgent" visits or, rarely nowadays, obtaining the approval of a "gatekeeper" primary care physician in order to see a specialist.

Some features that you may or may not like are:

- Some HMOs rely very heavily on mid-level professionals such as nurse practitioners and physician assistants.
- HMOs generally put patients in hospitals less frequently and keep them there for a shorter time than fee-for-service physicians. This is the major reason HMOs usually have lower costs. A number of studies have found no overall difference in medical outcomes between HMOs and traditional practice. On the other hand, if you want quick surgery to relieve a painful but not life-threatening problem, you may not want to wait while an HMO tries more conservative therapies.
- Few HMOs offer the extra benefits to Medicare enrollees that are found in most national plans, although the number that do so is increasing.

Joining a High Deductible Plan

Several national companies and some local HMO organizations now offer High Deductible or Consumer-Driven plans. Aetna offers such plans in almost all parts of the country, and United-Healthcare in many places. These plans differ in details, but all share two main features. First, they provide some form of savings account for health care expenses, financed on a tax-free basis through the premium paid to the plan and, in some cases, through additional contributions by enrollees. This account is typically about $1,000 for a self-only enrollment, and twice as much for a family enrollment. During the year, you can use this account to pay for any of your qualified health care expenses, including expenses that the plan does not otherwise cover, such as a hearing aid. Second, if you use up the account on other expenses (or decide to save it rather than use it), you face a high deductible, often almost twice as much as the savings account. Thereafter, you typically pay 10 or 15 percent of expenses, up to an out-of-pocket spending limit, though some plans pay everything above the deductible. The main focus of these plans is to encourage you to be a prudent purchaser. If you are relatively healthy and spend wisely, you may avoid any out of pocket expenses. Furthermore, your unused account balances "roll over" and you can build up a substantial cushion that even earns interest. Your total cost under these plans can be LESS than your tax-preferred premium share.

Because of this design, there is no simple answer to "what is my copayment" or "what is my deductible." If you stay within your spending account both are zero. After your account is used up you pay 100 percent, until you pass your deductible amount. In our tables, we provide the percentage that applies after your deductible and until you hit the catastrophic limit.

Two other important features that these plans share is that routine preventive care does not count against either the spending account or the deductible, and you have good catastrophic expense protection. Most of these plans' limits have none of the loopholes found in other plans.

The High Deductible plans offer two kinds of spending accounts. Which one you get depends on your eligibility. A "Health Savings Account" (HSA) not only lets you accumulate funds, but also lets you retain the savings account when you change plans or retire. Moreover, you can earn interest or capital gains, tax-free, for decades to come. The HSA is your property. In contrast, a "Health Reimbursement Arrangement" (HRA), or "Personal Care Account" as it is called in some plans, works almost the same but terminates when you change plans. In that case, the unspent balance remains with the plan. The Consumer-Driven plans offer only HRAs. Unlike HSAs, HRAs do not let you grow the account through interest. You can use an HRA, but not an HSA, if you are covered by other health insurance, such as TRICARE, a spouse's plan, or Medicare. In the HDHP plans, annuitants with Medicare get an HRA in the same amount as the HSA received by other enrollees. To fully understand these complex plans, you should read the explanations in their brochures carefully, and you may want to consult material on the OPM Web site.

The other important characteristic of an HSA account (in contrast to an HRA) is that you can make voluntary contributions to it during the year. This feature comes into play if your expenses are much higher than you expected, but you can make contributions regardless of your expected expenses. In an HSA you can make voluntary contributions up to the amount of the deductible, less the personal account amount funded by the plan. Your contributions are tax preferred. Thus, if you need to spend an extra thousand dollars, rather than pay it directly to providers you can contribute it to the HSA account, lower your taxable income by a thousand dollars, and pay providers from the HSA account. If you are in a 33 percent tax bracket, this saves you over three hundred dollars compared to traditional health insurance plans. This is a better arrangement for you than under Flexible Spending Accounts, because there is no "use or lose" penalty. **HSA accounts are sometimes described as "Trifecta" benefits because the contribution is tax-free, the account grows tax-free, and disbursements from the account are tax-free when spent for health care.**

Annuitants are eligible for these plans, but most of these plans do not provide extra benefits for having Medicare Parts A and B (significant exceptions are the Aetna Direct CDHP and MHBP HDHP national plans, and in the Washington DC area the CareFirst HDHP plan). However, these spending accounts cover many expenses that Medicare does not, and Medicare protects you from substantial copayment expense. For hospital expenses, you will almost always get the zero percent Medicare rate (after deductible) rather than the plan's rate of cost sharing. Therefore, they work well for retirees with Medicare. Once you have Medicare the law allows you to contribute only to an HRA, not to an HSA, and the HDHP plans all allow for that.

Plan Flexibility

Our comparisons of flexibility capture as best as we can the features of each plan that affect your ability to select the providers of your preference. We would like to display the number of affiliated providers in each local area, but such data are not available for many plans. Of course, staff model HMOs would always show a relatively low number, because they ordinarily limit you to primary care providers on their staff.

In our comparisons, we show first which HMOs allow you to get regular plan benefits from providers located outside the plan's main service area. For example, the Kaiser plans allow you to use Kaiser facilities and providers anywhere they are located. Of course, national plans all cover the entire nation. All plans cover emergencies throughout the world (not shown). Second, we show how plans deal with providers who are not preferred. National plans and some HMOs let you use non-preferred providers with a significantly higher cost sharing. Third, we show which plans provide annuitants with Medicare Parts A and B wrap around benefits to make all hospital and doctor care cost-free, in or out of network.

We show which plans allow women to visit a gynecologist without having to be referred by a primary care provider. Almost all HMOs now allow self-referral, at least for an annual exam (those which allow only an examination without referral are marked "Exam"). Unfortunately, some HMOs do not allow self-referral to other specialists, though the number that do so is growing.

Our entry for "open formulary" indicates whether the plan will pay for any name brand drug that your physician prescribes, or just for those that are on the plan's list of approved drugs (commonly called a "formulary"). Most plans will pay for any drug but require higher copays for non-formulary drugs. We indicate these with a "Pay More" entry.

We indicate whether each company sponsors a Medicare Advantage (MA) plan, so that Medicare participants can elect to stay with their health plan while paying only one premium. However, even though we enter "Yes" you have to check further to see if the Medicare Advantage plan covers the exact area where you live. Not shown, all Medicare Parts A and B enrollees have access to at least some MA plans, and most have access to dozens.

Finally, we show which plans will reimburse much or most of your Medicare Part B premium either as a separate contribution or as an allowed use of your savings account.

Chapter 9

Quality and Service

For traditional fee-for-service insurance plans, service quality used to be a minor issue. The main service concerns were how easily you could get help from plan representatives regarding coverage questions and how fairly and promptly claims were paid.

Now even fee-for-service plans now have some involvement in the quality of your health care. All plans require you to get authorization before hospitalization or surgery. And almost all have assembled networks of preferred providers and have prescription drug formularies. Because you save money by using providers from these networks and preferred drugs in these formularies, the availability and quality of preferred providers and the lists of preferred drugs are important.

Meanwhile, many prepaid (HMO) plans are available and now substantial numbers of Federal employees have selected these plans. Your choice of HMO can have a big effect on the quality of medical care and service you receive. Not only does an HMO offer you a selected list of providers to choose among; your HMO may be set up so that your primary care doctor is a "gatekeeper" who decides whether to authorize you to get specialist, hospital, and other types of services. In addition, an HMO may be able to manage care so that members get better service than they would get in a less structured system. For example, some HMOs have succeeded in reducing asthma problems by having doctors, nurses, pharmacists, and other HMO staff work together to train patients and families in self-medication and other self-care techniques.

Customer Satisfaction Ratings

The table beginning on page 113 reports plan-by-plan customer satisfaction ratings reported by OPM. These ratings come from a 2019 survey in which a standardized questionnaire was sent to a sample of each plan's members. The table tells you how plans compare for several categories of service, based on answers given to various questions asked on the survey. OPM reports scores for:

- Overall quality of the plan
- Overall rating of personal doctors
- Getting needed care
- Getting care quickly
- Coordination of care
- Claims processing
- Plan's customer service
- Information on costs

For each of these aspects of care, the table reports how OPM scored the survey results for each plan. OPM used the following scale:

● = Outstanding (plan's score was in the 90th percentile)
◕ = Excellent (plan's score was in the 75th-89th percentile)
◑ = Good (plan's score was in the 50th-74th percentile)
◔ = Fair (plan's score was in the 25th to 49th percentile)
○ = Poor (plan's score was worse than the 25th percentile)
N/A = Blanks indicate no data was reported for the measure

We advise that you keep several points in mind when using the customer ratings:

- Some of the ratings are based on opinions. Your opinions might not be the same as those of survey respondents.
- The way enrollees rate their plans can be affected by their age, education level, state of health, and other characteristics. For example, older individuals tend to rate their plans relatively high. If one plan has attracted a large proportion of members over age 65, its ratings might be high for that reason. The scores reported here have not been adjusted for member characteristics. Within the group of HMO and POS plans, it does not appear that such differences in member characteristics had much effect on scores; very few plans' overall scores would change by more than two percentage points if the scores were adjusted for member differences. But the effects might be greater among fee-for-service plans.
- Since the survey included only a sample of plan members, it is possible that a plan's ratings were affected by "the luck of the draw": a disproportionately large number of satisfied or dissatisfied members happened to respond.
- Some enrollees did not return the questionnaire. It is possible that those who responded are more satisfied or less satisfied than those who did not. Our analysis of these and similar survey data has indicated that younger members and men are less likely to respond than women and older members. Young male members also tend to give somewhat lower ratings than older members of either gender. Fortunately, with roughly 40 percent of surveyed members responding for most plans, the respondents do at least represent a substantial portion of members. And we have some evidence from follow-up survey tests we have done that scores would not have changed much even if an additional 10 or 15 percent of surveyed members had responded.

In interpreting member ratings, also keep in mind that comparing across different *types* of plans is at best imperfect. First, it is not possible directly to compare regional plans (primarily HMO and POS plans) to national plans. For example, high or low ratings of "personal doctors" by enrollees in a national plan don't tell you how that plan's members in a particular region rate their doctors, and yet it is the national plan's doctors in that region who should be compared to the doctors of members of regional plans serving only that region. Second, for the national plans (and the ratings we report for Blue Cross and Blue Shield by state), the ratings are only from FEHBP enrollees, while the ratings for the regional HMO and POS plans include ratings from non-FEHBP enrollees.

Even among HMO and POS plans, the ratings given by non-federal members may have been given for a different variant of the plan. We have found, for example, that among members of the same plan, POS users are about two to three percentage points less likely than basic HMO users to give high ratings to the overall plan.

It should also be noted that differences in the way the survey was administered might explain small differences in plan scores. All of the plans are required to use an independent firm to conduct their surveys under the supervision of the nonprofit National Committee for Quality Assurance (NCQA) using standardized survey procedures. But there is some room for variation in procedures. For example, some plans allow members to respond by the Internet in addition to mail and phone calls, and Internet responders tend to give somewhat lower ratings. Also, some plans get a relatively high percentage of their responses by phone (as opposed to mail), and phone responders tend to give higher ratings than mail responders.

Disputed Claims

Along with the customer satisfaction survey results, we have another indicator of service quality for the fee-for-service plans. We checked "disputed claims" on file at OPM. A "disputed claim" is a case in which a plan member has been denied benefits and has followed the required procedure to appeal the denial to OPM.

The Disputed Claims table on page 128 shows disputed claims per 10,000 Federal enrollees for the period from October 2018 through September 2019. The table also shows in how many cases

Continues on page 127

Plan Quality

See chapter text for discussion of these data

Plan	Enrollment code	Ratings from plan members: Overall rating of plan	Overall rating of personal doctors	Getting needed care	Getting care quickly	Coordination of care	Claims processing	Customer service	Information on costs
National Plans									
APWU (PPO)	47	◕	◕	◑	◑	●	◔	○	◑
APWU CDHP (PPO)	47	◕	○	◑	◔	○	◔	N/A	◑
Aetna HealthFund HDHP/Aetna Direct (PPO)	N6	◕	◔	◑	◔	○	◔	N/A	◔
Blue Cross-Basic (PPO)	11	●	◑	◑	◕	◑	◕	◕	●
Blue Cross-Std (PPO)	10	●	◑	◕	◕	◑	◕	◕	◕
Compass Rose (PPO)	42	●	◑	◑	◕	○	◑	◑	◕
Foreign Service (PPO)	40	◕	○	○	◔	○	○	○	◑
GEHA HDHP (PPO)	34	◕	◑	◔	◔	○	◔	◔	○
GEHA-Hi (PPO)	31	●	◕	◕	●	◑	◑	◕	◑
GEHA-Std (PPO)	31	◑	◕	◑	◑	○	○	○	◕
MHBP HDHP (PPO)	48	◑	◔	◕	◕	◕	◔	○	○
MHBP Value Plan (PPO)	41	◕	◑	◑	◕	◔	◑	◔	◑
MHBP-Std (PPO)	45	●	◑	●	◕	◔	◑	◕	●
NALC CDHP (PPO)	32	●	◔	◑	◑	◔	◕	◔	◕
NALC Value Plan (PPO)	KM	○	○	◔	○	N/A	N/A	N/A	N/A
NALC-Hi (PPO)	32	○	○	◔	○	N/A	N/A	N/A	N/A
Panama Canal (All lines)	43	●	●	●	●	◕	N/A	○	◔
Rural Carrier (PPO)	38	●	◑	◑	◑	◑	◕	◕	◕
SAMBA-Hi (PPO)	44	●	◕	●	●	●	●	◕	◕
SAMBA-Std (PPO)	44	●	◔	◔	◔	◔	◔	◑	◑
Local Plans and National Plans with Scores from Members in Specific States									
Alabama									
Blue Cross-Basic (PPO)	11	●	○	◕	◔	○	●	N/A	N/A
Blue Cross-Std (PPO)	10	●	◑	●	●	◔	●	N/A	◕
United Choice Open Access (PPO)	KK	◑	◕	●	◔	N/A	N/A	N/A	◔

● = Outstanding (plan's score was in the 90th percentile)
◕ = Excellent (plan's score was in the 75th-89th percentile)
◑ = Good (plan's score was in the 50th-74th percentile)
◔ = Fair (plan's score was in the 25th to 49th percentile)
○ = Poor (plan's score was worse than the 25th percentile)
N/A = Blanks indicate no data was reported for the measure

Plan Quality See chapter text for discussion of these data	Enrollment code	Ratings from plan members: Overall rating of plan	Overall rating of personal doctors	Getting needed care	Getting care quickly	Coordination of care	Claims processing	Customer service	Information on costs
United HDHP (PPO)	LS	◑	◕	●	◔	N/A	N/A	N/A	◔
Alaska									
Blue Cross-Basic (PPO)	11	●	○	◔	◑	◕	●	N/A	N/A
Blue Cross-Std (PPO)	10	◕	◔	◔	◑	○	◕	N/A	◑
Arizona									
Aetna Open Access (HMO/POS)	WQ	◑	○	◕	◑	○	N/A	N/A	N/A
Blue Cross-Basic (PPO)	11	●	○	◕	◑	○	●	N/A	N/A
Blue Cross-Std (PPO)	10	●	○	◔	◕	○	●	◔	◕
GEHA (PPO)	31	◕	◔	◔	◔	○	◔	N/A	◑
Humana CoverageFirst (HMO/POS) (Phoenix)	R6	○	○	◑	N/A	N/A	N/A	N/A	N/A
Humana CoverageFirst (HMO/POS) (Tuscon)	R9	○	○	◑	N/A	N/A	N/A	N/A	N/A
Humana Health (HMO/POS) (Phoenix)	BF	○	○	◑	N/A	N/A	N/A	N/A	N/A
Humana Health (HMO/POS) (Tuscon)	C7	○	○	◑	N/A	N/A	N/A	N/A	N/A
United Choice (PPO)	KT	◑	○	○	◑	○	N/A	N/A	N/A
United HDHP (PPO)	LU	◑	○	○	◑	○	N/A	N/A	N/A
Arkansas									
Blue Cross-Basic (PPO)	11	●	◑	◑	◑	○	●	◔	◕
Blue Cross-Std (PPO)	10	●	●	●	●	◑	●	●	●
QualChoice (HMO/POS)	DH	○	◔	◔	◔	○	◔	N/A	○
United Choice Open Access (PPO)	KK	◔	○	○	◔	○	○	N/A	N/A
United HDHP (PPO)	LS	◔	○	○	◔	○	○	N/A	N/A
California									
Aetna HealthFund (PPO)	JS	◔	○	○	○	N/A	N/A	N/A	N/A
Aetna Open Access (HMO/POS)	2X	◔	○	○	○	N/A	N/A	N/A	N/A
Anthem Blue Cross (HMO/POS)	B3	◕	◔	○	○	◔	◔	◔	N/A
Blue Cross-Basic (PPO)	11	●	○	◔	○	N/A	N/A	N/A	N/A
Blue Cross-Std (PPO)	10	●	◔	◑	◔	◔	◔	N/A	◔

Plan Quality

See chapter text for discussion of these data

Plan	Enrollment code	Ratings from plan members: Overall rating of plan	Overall rating of personal doctors	Getting needed care	Getting care quickly	Coordination of care	Claims processing	Customer service	Information on costs
Blue Shield Access (HMO/POS)	SI	◕	◔	○	○	◔	N/A	◔	◔
GEHA (PPO)	31	◕	◔	◔	◔	○	◔	N/A	◑
Health Net (HMO/POS) (Northern CA)	LB	◑	◔	○	○	◔	○	○	◔
Health Net (HMO/POS) (Southern CA)	LP	◑	◔	○	○	◔	○	○	◔
Health Net Basic (HMO/POS) (Northern CA)	T4	◑	◔	○	○	◔	○	○	◔
Health Net Basic (HMO/POS) (Southern CA)	P6	◑	◔	○	○	◔	○	○	◔
Kaiser (HMO) (Fresno)	NZ	◑	◔	◑	◔	◔	○	◔	◔
Kaiser (HMO) (Northern CA)	59	◑	◔	◑	◔	◔	○	◔	◔
Kaiser (HMO) (Southern CA)	62	◕	◔	◔	◔	◔	○	◔	◑
Kaiser-Basic (HMO) (Northern CA)	KC	◑	◔	◑	◔	◔	○	◔	◔
Colorado									
Aetna HealthFund (PPO)	G5	◑	◔	◑	◑	◔	◑	N/A	○
Blue Cross-Basic (PPO)	11	●	◔	◔	◑	○	●	N/A	◔
Blue Cross-Std (PPO)	10	●	○	●	◑	◔	◕	◕	◕
Humana Health (HMO/POS) (CO Springs)	NR	○	○	N/A	N/A	N/A	N/A	N/A	N/A
Humana Health (HMO/POS) (Denver)	NT	○	○	N/A	N/A	N/A	N/A	N/A	N/A
Humana Health Basic (HMO/POS) (CO Springs)	R2	○	○	N/A	N/A	N/A	N/A	N/A	N/A
Humana Health Basic (HMO/POS) (Denver)	RZ	○	○	N/A	N/A	N/A	N/A	N/A	N/A
Kaiser (HMO)	65	◔	○	◔	◑	○	N/A	○	○
Kaiser Basic (HMO)	N4	◔	○	◔	◑	○	N/A	○	○
United Choice Open Access (PPO)	KT	◔	◔	○	N/A	N/A	N/A	N/A	N/A
United HDHP (PPO)	LU	◔	◔	○	N/A	N/A	N/A	N/A	N/A
Connecticut									
Blue Cross-Basic (PPO)	11	●	◑	◕	◔	◑	◕	N/A	N/A
Blue Cross-Std (PPO)	10	●	●	●	◕	●	●	N/A	◕

● = Outstanding (plan's score was in the 90th percentile)
◕ = Excellent (plan's score was in the 75th-89th percentile)
◑ = Good (plan's score was in the 50th-74th percentile)
◔ = Fair (plan's score was in the 25th to 49th percentile)
○ = Poor (plan's score was worse than the 25th percentile)
N/A = Blanks indicate no data was reported for the measure

Plan Quality

See chapter text for discussion of these data

	Enrollment code	Ratings from plan members							
		Overall rating of plan	Overall rating of personal doctors	Getting needed care	Getting care quickly	Coordination of care	Claims processing	Customer service	Information on costs
Delaware									
Aetna Open Access (HMO/POS)	P3	◑	◔	◑	◔	◔	◔	◕	◕
District of Columbia									
Aetna HealthFund (PPO)	F5	◕	◔	◑	◔	○	◔	N/A	◔
Aetna HealthFund HDHP (PPO)	22	◕	◔	◑	◔	○	◔	N/A	◔
Aetna Open Access (HMO/POS)	JN	◕	◕	◑	◕	◔	N/A	N/A	◔
Blue Cross-Basic (PPO)	11	◕	○	○	◔	○	N/A	N/A	◔
Blue Cross-Std (PPO)	10	◕	◔	◑	○	○	◑	N/A	○
CareFirst (HMO/POS)	2G	◑	◑	◕	◔	○	◕	◕	●
CareFirst Blue Value (HMO/POS)	B6	◑	◑	◕	◔	○	◕	◕	●
GEHA-Hi (PPO)	31	◑	○	◔	◑	○	○	N/A	◔
Kaiser (HMO)	E3	◕	◔	◔	◑	◑	N/A	◔	N/A
Kaiser Basic (HMO)	T7	◕	◔	◔	◑	◑	N/A	◔	N/A
MD-IPA (HMO/POS)	JP	◕	◕	◕	●	◑	◔	●	●
United Choice Open Access (PPO)	LR	○	◑	○	◑	N/A	N/A	N/A	N/A
United Choice Plus (PPO)	L9	○	◑	○	◑	N/A	N/A	N/A	N/A
United HDHP (PPO)	V4	○	◑	○	◑	N/A	N/A	N/A	N/A
Florida									
AvMed (HMO/POS)	ML	●	◑	◑	◑	◑	N/A	N/A	N/A
AvMed HDHP (HMO/POS)	WZ	●	◑	◑	◑	◑	N/A	N/A	N/A
Blue Cross-Basic (PPO)	11	●	◕	◑	◕	◔	N/A	N/A	N/A
Blue Cross-Std (PPO)	10	●	◑	◕	◑	◕	◑	◕	◕
Capital Health (HMO)	EA	●	◑	◕	◕	◔	●	◑	◕
GEHA-Hi (PPO)	31	●	◑	◔	○	○	◑	◕	◕
Humana CoverageFirst (HMO/POS) (Daytona)	W9	◔	●	○	N/A	N/A	N/A	N/A	N/A
Humana CoverageFirst (HMO/POS) (Orlando)	X2	◔	●	○	N/A	N/A	N/A	N/A	N/A
Humana CoverageFirst (HMO/POS) (South FL)	QP	◔	●	○	N/A	N/A	N/A	N/A	N/A

Plan Quality

See chapter text for discussion of these data

Plan	Enrollment code	Ratings from plan members: Overall rating of plan	Overall rating of personal doctors	Getting needed care	Getting care quickly	Coordination of care	Claims processing	Customer service	Information on costs
Humana CoverageFirst (HMO/POS) (Tampa)	MJ	◔	●	○	N/A	N/A	N/A	N/A	N/A
Humana Medical (HMO/POS) (Daytona)	EX	◔	●	○	N/A	N/A	N/A	N/A	N/A
Humana Medical (HMO/POS) (Orlando)	E2	◔	●	○	N/A	N/A	N/A	N/A	N/A
Humana Medical (HMO/POS) (South FL)	EE	◔	●	○	N/A	N/A	N/A	N/A	N/A
Humana Medical (HMO/POS) (Tampa)	LL	◔	●	○	N/A	N/A	N/A	N/A	N/A
United Choice Open Access (PPO)	KK	◑	○	◑	N/A	N/A	N/A	N/A	N/A
United Choice Plus Advanced (PPO)	LV	◑	○	◑	N/A	N/A	N/A	N/A	N/A
United HDHP (PPO)	LS	◑	○	◑	N/A	N/A	N/A	N/A	N/A
Georgia									
Aetna Open Access (HMO/POS)	2U	◔	●	◔	○	N/A	N/A	N/A	N/A
Blue Cross-Basic (PPO)	11	●	◑	◔	◕	○	◕	N/A	N/A
Blue Cross-Std (PPO)	10	●	◑	◕	◑	○	●	N/A	◕
Blue Open Access (HMO/POS)	QM	◑	◑	◕	N/A	N/A	N/A	N/A	N/A
GEHA (PPO)	31	●	◑	◔	○	○	◑	◕	◕
Humana CoverageFirst (HMO/POS)	AD	◔	◑	N/A	N/A	N/A	N/A	N/A	N/A
Humana Employers (HMO/POS) (Atlanta)	DG	◔	◑	N/A	N/A	N/A	N/A	N/A	N/A
Humana Employers (HMO/POS) (Columbus)	CB	◔	◑	N/A	N/A	N/A	N/A	N/A	N/A
Humana Employers (HMO/POS) (Macon)	DN	◔	◑	N/A	N/A	N/A	N/A	N/A	N/A
Humana Employers Basic (HMO/POS) (Atlanta)	Q7	◔	◑	N/A	N/A	N/A	N/A	N/A	N/A
Humana Employers Basic (HMO/POS) (Columbus)	RM	◔	◑	N/A	N/A	N/A	N/A	N/A	N/A
Humana Employers Basic (HMO/POS) (Macon)	RJ	◔	◑	N/A	N/A	N/A	N/A	N/A	N/A
Kaiser (HMO)	F8	◑	○	○	○	○	N/A	○	◔
United Choice Plus Advanced (PPO)	LV	◑	◕	◕	◔	N/A	N/A	N/A	N/A
Guam									
Calvo's Selectcare (HMO)	B4	◔	○	○	○	N/A	N/A	N/A	N/A
TakeCare (HMO)	JK	○	○	○	○	N/A	N/A	N/A	N/A

● = Outstanding (plan's score was in the 90th percentile)
◕ = Excellent (plan's score was in the 75th-89th percentile)
◑ = Good (plan's score was in the 50th-74th percentile)
◔ = Fair (plan's score was in the 25th to 49th percentile)
○ = Poor (plan's score was worse than the 25th percentile)
N/A = Blanks indicate no data was reported for the measure

Plan Quality

See chapter text for discussion of these data

Plan	Enrollment code	Ratings from plan members: Overall rating of plan	Overall rating of personal doctors	Getting needed care	Getting care quickly	Coordination of care	Claims processing	Customer service	Information on costs
TakeCare HDHP (HMO)	KX	○	○	○	○	N/A	N/A	N/A	N/A
Hawaii									
HMSA (HMO/POS)	87	●	◕	●	◕	◕	●	N/A	●
Kaiser (HMO)	63	◕	◑	◔	◔	◑	N/A	N/A	◑
Idaho									
Aetna Health/Altius-Hi (HMO/POS)	9K	◑	◕	●	●	◑	◑	◑	◑
Aetna Health/Altius-Std (HMO/POS)	DK	◑	◕	●	●	◑	◑	◑	◑
Blue Cross-Basic (PPO)	11	●	○	◑	◑	○	●	◑	◔
Kaiser Washington (HMO)	54	○	○	○	○	○	N/A	○	○
Illinois									
Aetna HealthFund (PPO)	H4	◕	◑	◑	◔	◑	○	N/A	N/A
Blue Cross-Basic (PPO)	11	●	◔	◔	○	◔	●	N/A	◑
Blue Cross-Std (PPO)	10	●	●	◑	◕	◕	◑	N/A	●
Blue Preferred (HMO/POS)	9G	◑	○	◑	◕	◔	N/A	N/A	◑
Health Alliance (HMO/POS)	K8	◕	◔	◔	◑	◑	◑	N/A	◕
Humana CoverageFirst (HMO/POS) (Central IL)	GB	◑	◑	◔	○	◕	N/A	N/A	N/A
Humana CoverageFirst (HMO/POS) (Chicago)	MW	◑	◑	◔	○	◕	N/A	N/A	N/A
Humana Health Basic (HMO/POS) (Chicago)	RW	◑	◑	◔	○	◕	N/A	N/A	N/A
Humana Health-Hi (HMO/POS) (Chicago area)	75	◑	◑	◔	○	◕	N/A	N/A	N/A
Humana Health-Hi (HMO/POS) (Rockford/NW IL)	9F	◑	◑	◔	○	◕	N/A	N/A	N/A
Humana Health-Std (HMO/POS) (Rockford/NW IL)	AB	◑	◑	◔	○	◕	N/A	N/A	N/A
Union Health (HMO)	76	◑	◔	○	○	◑	N/A	N/A	N/A
United Choice Plus (PPO)	L9	◔	◑	◔	◔	N/A	N/A	N/A	N/A
Indiana									
Blue Cross-Basic (PPO)	11	●	◑	◑	◕	◔	●	◕	◕
Blue Cross-Std (PPO)	10	●	◕	◕	◑	◑	●	N/A	●
Health Alliance (HMO/POS)	K8	◕	◔	◔	◑	◑	◑	N/A	◕

Plan Quality

See chapter text for discussion of these data

Plan	Enrollment code	Ratings from plan members: Overall rating of plan	Overall rating of personal doctors	Getting needed care	Getting care quickly	Coordination of care	Claims processing	Customer service	Information on costs
Humana CoverageFirst (HMO/POS)	MW	◑	◑	◔	○	◕	N/A	N/A	N/A
Humana Health (HMO/POS) (Chicago)	75	◑	◑	◔	○	◕	N/A	N/A	N/A
Humana Health (HMO/POS) (Louisville)	MH	◑	●	◔	◑	◑	◕	N/A	◕
Humana Health Basic (HMO/POS)	RW	◑	◑	◔	○	◕	N/A	N/A	N/A
Humana Health-Std (HMO/POS)	AB	◑	◑	◔	○	◕	N/A	N/A	N/A
Iowa									
Blue Cross-Basic (PPO)	11	●	●	●	●	◕	●	N/A	◕
Blue Cross-Std (PPO)	10	●	◕	●	●	●	◕	◔	●
Health Alliance (HMO/POS)	K8	◕	◔	◔	◑	◑	◑	N/A	◕
HealthPartners (HMO/POS)	V3	◑	●	◑	●	◕	●	◕	◔
United Choice Open Access (PPO)	LJ	◔	◔	◔	◔	◔	◑	N/A	N/A
United HDHP (PPO)	N7	◔	◔	◔	◔	◔	◑	N/A	N/A
Kansas									
Aetna Open Access (HMO/POS)	HA	◑	◔	◔	◔	◔	◑	N/A	◑
Blue Cross-Basic (PPO)	11	●	◑	◕	◔	◑	◕	◔	◑
Blue Cross-Std (PPO)	10	●	◑	●	●	●	●	◔	●
Humana CoverageFirst (HMO/POS)	PH	◕	◑	●	◕	◔	N/A	N/A	●
Humana Health (HMO/POS)	MS	◕	◑	●	◕	◔	N/A	N/A	●
Kentucky									
Blue Cross-Basic (PPO)	11	●	●	●	◑	◔	●	N/A	◕
Blue Cross-Std (PPO)	10	●	◕	●	●	◔	●	◕	●
Humana CoverageFirst (PPO) (Lexington)	6N	◔	◑	N/A	N/A	N/A	N/A	N/A	N/A
Humana CoverageFirst (PPO) (Louisville)	TC	◔	◑	N/A	N/A	N/A	N/A	N/A	N/A
Humana Health (HMO/POS) (Lexington/Central)	MI	◑	●	◔	◑	◑	◕	N/A	◕
Humana Health (HMO/POS) (Louisville)	MH	◑	●	◔	◑	◑	◕	N/A	◕

● = Outstanding (plan's score was in the 90th percentile)
◕ = Excellent (plan's score was in the 75th-89th percentile)
◑ = Good (plan's score was in the 50th-74th percentile)
◔ = Fair (plan's score was in the 25th to 49th percentile)
○ = Poor (plan's score was worse than the 25th percentile)
N/A = Blanks indicate no data was reported for the measure

Plan Quality

See chapter text for discussion of these data

Plan	Enrollment code	Ratings from plan members: Overall rating of plan	Overall rating of personal doctors	Getting needed care	Getting care quickly	Coordination of care	Claims processing	Customer service	Information on costs
United Choice Open Access (PPO)	LJ	◔	◔	○	◑	○	◕	N/A	N/A
United HDHP (PPO)	N7	◔	◔	○	◑	○	◕	N/A	N/A
Louisiana									
Blue Cross-Basic (PPO)	11	●	◕	◕	◕	◔	●	N/A	N/A
Blue Cross-Std (PPO)	10	●	●	●	●	◕	●	N/A	◕
Humana Health (HMO/POS) (Baton Rouge)	AE	◑	◑	◑	N/A	N/A	N/A	N/A	N/A
Humana Health (HMO/POS) (New Orleans)	BC	◑	◑	◑	N/A	N/A	N/A	N/A	N/A
United Choice Open Access (PPO)	KK	◑	◑	◔	◔	◑	N/A	N/A	N/A
United HDHP (PPO)	LS	◑	◑	◔	◔	◑	N/A	N/A	N/A
Maine									
Blue Cross-Basic (PPO)	11	◕	○	◑	◑	◑	●	N/A	N/A
Maryland									
Aetna HealthFund (PPO)	F5	◕	◔	◑	◔	○	◔	N/A	◔
Aetna HealthFund HDHP (PPO)	22	◕	◔	◑	◔	○	◔	N/A	◔
Aetna Open Access (HMO/POS)	JN	◕	◕	◑	◕	◔	N/A	N/A	◔
Blue Cross-Basic (PPO)	11	●	◔	◔	◔	○	N/A	N/A	N/A
Blue Cross-Std (PPO)	10	●	●	◕	◕	◑	●	N/A	◔
CareFirst Blue Value (HMO/POS)	B6	◑	◑	◕	◔	○	◕	◕	●
CareFirst-Std (HMO/POS)	2G	◑	◑	◕	◔	○	◕	◕	●
GEHA-Hi (PPO)	31	◑	○	◔	◑	○	○	N/A	◔
Kaiser (HMO)	E3	◕	◔	◔	◑	◑	N/A	◔	N/A
Kaiser Basic (HMO)	T7	◕	◔	◔	◑	◑	N/A	◔	N/A
MD-IPA (HMO/POS)	JP	◕	◕	◕	●	◑	◔	●	●
United Choice Open Access (PPO)	LR	◕	●	●	◔	N/A	N/A	N/A	N/A
United Choice Plus (PPO)	L9	◕	●	●	◔	N/A	N/A	N/A	N/A
United HDHP (PPO)	V4	◕	●	●	◔	N/A	N/A	N/A	N/A

Plan Quality

See chapter text for discussion of these data

Plan	Enrollment code	Ratings from plan members							
		Overall rating of plan	Overall rating of personal doctors	Getting needed care	Getting care quickly	Coordination of care	Claims processing	Customer service	Information on costs
Massachusetts									
Blue Cross-Basic (PPO)	11	●	◑	●	◑	◑	◕	N/A	N/A
Blue Cross-Std (PPO)	10	●	◕	◑	◑	●	●	◔	◕
Michigan									
Blue Care Network (HMO) (Detroit)	LX	◔	◑	◑	◑	◔	◑	N/A	◔
Blue Care Network (HMO) (Flint/Saginaw)	K5	◔	◑	◑	◑	◔	◑	N/A	◔
Blue Cross-Basic (PPO)	11	◕	◔	◔	◔	◔	●	N/A	○
Blue Cross-Std (PPO)	10	●	◕	●	●	●	●	N/A	◕
Health Alliance-Hi (HMO/POS)	52	◑	◔	◕	◑	◑	◔	○	◕
Health Alliance-Std (HMO/POS)	GY	◑	◔	◕	◑	◑	◔	○	◕
Priority Health (HMO/POS)	LE	○	◑	◔	○	◔	◕	◔	◕
Minnesota									
Blue Cross-Basic (PPO)	11	●	◕	●	●	◑	●	N/A	◑
Blue Cross-Std (PPO)	10	◕	◕	●	◕	◑	◕	◑	◕
HealthPartners (HMO/POS)	V3	◑	●	◑	●	◕	●	◕	◔
Mississippi									
Blue Cross-Basic (PPO)	11	●	◕	◕	◕	◑	◕	N/A	N/A
Blue Cross-Std (PPO)	10	●	●	●	◕	◑	●	N/A	◕
United Choice Open Access (PPO)	KK	◑	●	◑	○	N/A	N/A	N/A	N/A
United HDHP (PPO)	LS	◑	●	◑	○	N/A	N/A	N/A	N/A
Missouri									
Aetna Open Access (HMO/POS)	HA	◑	◔	◔	◔	◔	◑	N/A	◑
Blue Cross-Basic (PPO)	11	●	◑	◔	◕	◔	◕	N/A	N/A
Blue Cross-Std (PPO)	10	●	●	●	◕	◑	●	◕	◕
Blue Preferred (HMO/POS)	9G	◑	○	◑	◕	◔	N/A	N/A	◑

● = Outstanding (plan's score was in the 90th percentile)
◕ = Excellent (plan's score was in the 75th-89th percentile)
◑ = Good (plan's score was in the 50th-74th percentile)
◔ = Fair (plan's score was in the 25th to 49th percentile)
○ = Poor (plan's score was worse than the 25th percentile)
N/A = Blanks indicate no data was reported for the measure

Plan Quality

See chapter text for discussion of these data

Plan	Enrollment code	Ratings from plan members: Overall rating of plan	Overall rating of personal doctors	Getting needed care	Getting care quickly	Coordination of care	Claims processing	Customer service	Information on costs
GEHA (PPO)	31	◕	◔	◑	◕	◑	◑	◕	◕
Humana CoverageFirst (HMO/POS)	PH	◕	◑	●	◕	◔	N/A	N/A	●
Humana Health (HMO/POS)	MS	◕	◑	●	◕	◔	N/A	N/A	●
Humana Health Basic (HMO/POS)	QY	◔	◔	N/A	N/A	N/A	N/A	N/A	N/A
Montana									
Blue Cross-Basic (PPO)	11	◕	◔	◔	◕	◔	◑	◕	◕
Nebraska									
Blue Cross-Basic (PPO)	11	●	◑	◕	◑	◑	◕	N/A	◑
Nevada									
Blue Cross-Basic (PPO)	11	●	○	○	○	○	◑	N/A	N/A
Health Plan of Nevada (HMO/POS)	NM	◔	○	○	N/A	N/A	N/A	N/A	N/A
United Choice Open Access (PPO)	KT	◑	○	○	○	○	◔	N/A	N/A
United HDHP (PPO)	LU	◑	○	○	○	○	◔	N/A	N/A
New Hampshire									
Blue Cross-Basic (PPO)	11	●	◕	●	●	●	●	N/A	N/A
New Jersey									
Aetna HealthFund (PPO)	EP	◑	◔	◔	○	○	N/A	N/A	N/A
Aetna Open Access (HMO/POS) (Northern NJ)	JR	●	◔	◕	◑	◑	N/A	N/A	N/A
Aetna Open Access (HMO/POS) (Southern NJ)	P3	●	◔	◕	◑	◑	N/A	N/A	N/A
Blue Cross-Basic (PPO)	11	◕	◑	◔	◔	◑	◕	○	◑
Blue Cross-Std (PPO)	10	◕	◕	◔	◑	◔	◕	N/A	◑
GHI Health (PPO)	80	◕	◑	◑	●	N/A	N/A	N/A	N/A
New Mexico									
Blue Cross-Basic (PPO)	11	●	○	○	○	○	◕	N/A	◕
Blue Cross-Std (PPO)	10	●	○	○	◔	◔	◕	◑	◕
Presbyterian-Hi (HMO/POS)	P2	◔	○	○	○	○	○	○	○
Presbyterian-Std (HMO/POS)	PS	◔	○	○	○	○	○	○	○

Plan Quality

See chapter text for discussion of these data

Plan	Enrollment code	Ratings from plan members: Overall rating of plan	Overall rating of personal doctors	Getting needed care	Getting care quickly	Coordination of care	Claims processing	Customer service	Information on costs
New York									
Aetna HealthFund (PPO)	EP	◕	◕	◔	○	◕	N/A	N/A	N/A
Aetna Open Access (PPO)	JC	◕	◕	◔	○	◕	N/A	N/A	N/A
Blue Cross-Basic (PPO)	11	●	◔	◕	◑	○	◕	N/A	N/A
Blue Cross-Std (PPO)	10	◕	◑	◑	◑	◔	◑	◑	◕
CDPHP (PPO)	SG	●	◕	●	●	◕	N/A	N/A	N/A
GHI Health (PPO)	80	◕	◑	◑	●	N/A	N/A	N/A	N/A
HIP HMO-Hi (HMO/POS)	51	◔	◔	○	○	N/A	N/A	N/A	N/A
HIP HMO-Std (HMO/POS)	YL	◔	◔	○	○	N/A	N/A	N/A	N/A
Independent Health-Hi (HMO/POS)	QA	◕	◑	●	◕	●	N/A	N/A	N/A
Independent Health-Std (HMO/POS)	C5	◕	◑	●	◕	●	N/A	N/A	N/A
North Carolina									
Blue Cross-Basic (PPO)	11	●	◕	●	●	◑	◑	N/A	◕
Blue Cross-Std (PPO)	10	●	◑	◑	●	◑	◑	○	◑
United Choice Open Access (PPO)	KK	◔	◕	◑	◔	◔	◔	N/A	N/A
United HDHP (PPO)	LS	◔	◕	◑	◔	◔	◔	N/A	N/A
North Dakota									
HealthPartners (HMO/POS)	V3	◑	●	◑	●	◕	●	◕	◔
Ohio									
AultCare (HMO)	3A	◕	◕	●	●	●	N/A	●	◕
Blue Cross-Basic (PPO)	11	●	◑	◑	◑	◑	●	N/A	N/A
Blue Cross-Std (PPO)	10	●	◑	◕	◕	◑	●	◔	●
GEHA-Hi (PPO)	31	◕	◑	◕	◕	◔	◔	◕	◑
Medical Mutual (HMO/POS)	X6	◑	◑	●	◔	●	◔	N/A	◑
Medical Mutual Basic (HMO/POS)	UX	◑	◑	●	◔	●	◔	N/A	◑
Medical Mutual-Std (HMO/POS)	64	◑	◑	●	◔	●	◔	N/A	◑

● = Outstanding (plan's score was in the 90th percentile)
◕ = Excellent (plan's score was in the 75th-89th percentile)
◑ = Good (plan's score was in the 50th-74th percentile)
◔ = Fair (plan's score was in the 25th to 49th percentile)
○ = Poor (plan's score was worse than the 25th percentile)
N/A = Blanks indicate no data was reported for the measure

Plan Quality

See chapter text for discussion of these data

Plan	Enrollment code	Ratings from plan members: Overall rating of plan	Overall rating of personal doctors	Getting needed care	Getting care quickly	Coordination of care	Claims processing	Customer service	Information on costs
Oklahoma									
Blue Cross-Basic (PPO)	11	●	●	●	●	◑	◑	N/A	N/A
Blue Cross-Std (PPO)	10	●	◕	◕	●	◑	●	N/A	●
GlobalHealth (HMO)	IM	◑	◑	◑	◑	◔	○	◑	◕
Oregon									
Blue Cross-Basic (PPO)	11	●	○	◔	◑	○	◑	N/A	◕
Blue Cross-Std (PPO)	10	◕	○	◑	◑	◑	◕	◑	◕
Kaiser Northwest (HMO)	57	◑	○	○	◔	◔	N/A	○	○
United Choice Open Access (PPO)	KT	○	○	◔	◑	○	○	N/A	N/A
United HDHP (PPO)	LU	○	○	◔	◑	○	○	N/A	N/A
Pennsylvania									
Aetna HealthFund (PPO)	H4	◔	◔	●	◑	◑	N/A	N/A	N/A
Aetna Open Access (HMO/POS) (Philadelphia)	P3	◔	○	◔	◔	◔	N/A	N/A	◑
Aetna Open Access (HMO/POS) (Western PA)	YE	◔	○	◔	◔	◔	N/A	N/A	◑
Blue Cross-Basic (PPO)	11	◕	◑	◕	◕	◕	◑	N/A	◕
Blue Cross-Std (PPO)	10	◕	◕	◕	◕	●	◕	◑	●
Geisinger (HMO/POS)	GG	◔	◔	◔	◔	◑	N/A	N/A	N/A
UPMC (PPO)	8W	○	◔	◔	◔	◔	◑	N/A	N/A
UPMC-Hi (HMO)	8W	◑	●	◑	◕	◕	◑	◑	◑
UPMC-Std (HMO/POS)	UW	◑	●	◑	◕	◕	◑	◑	◑
United Choice Open Access (PPO)	LR	○	◑	◑	N/A	N/A	N/A	N/A	N/A
United HDHP (PPO)	V4	○	◑	◑	N/A	N/A	N/A	N/A	N/A
Puerto Rico									
Humana Health (POS)	ZJ	●	●	◔	◔	○	N/A	◔	○
Triple-S Salud (PPO)	89	◕	◕	○	N/A	N/A	N/A	N/A	N/A
Rhode Island									
Blue Cross-Basic (PPO)	11	◕	◕	◕	◕	◔	N/A	N/A	N/A

Plan Quality See chapter text for discussion of these data	Enrollment code	Ratings from plan members							
		Overall rating of plan	Overall rating of personal doctors	Getting needed care	Getting care quickly	Coordination of care	Claims processing	Customer service	Information on costs
South Carolina									
Blue Cross-Basic (PPO)	11	●	○	◔	◑	○	◕	N/A	◕
Blue Cross-Std (PPO)	10	●	●	◕	◕	◑	◕	N/A	◑
South Dakota									
HealthPartners (HMO/POS)	V3	◑	●	◑	●	◕	●	◕	◔
Tennessee									
Aetna Open Access (HMO/POS)	UB	●	●	N/A	N/A	N/A	N/A	N/A	N/A
Blue Cross-Basic (PPO)	11	●	◕	●	●	◑	●	N/A	N/A
Blue Cross-Std (PPO)	10	●	◑	●	●	◔	●	◕	●
United Choice Open Access (PPO)	KK	◔	◔	○	○	N/A	N/A	N/A	N/A
United HDHP (PPO)	LS	◔	◔	○	○	N/A	N/A	N/A	N/A
Texas									
Aetna HealthFund (PPO)	JS	◔	◔	◔	◔	N/A	N/A	N/A	N/A
Aetna HealthFund HDHP (PPO)	22	◔	◔	◔	◔	N/A	N/A	N/A	N/A
Blue Cross-Basic (PPO)	11	●	○	◔	◔	○	N/A	N/A	N/A
Blue Cross-Std (PPO)	10	●	●	◕	◑	◔	◑	N/A	◑
GEHA-Hi (PPO)	31	●	◑	◔	○	○	◔	N/A	◕
Humana CoverageFirst (HMO/POS) (Austin)	TV	◔	◔	N/A	N/A	N/A	N/A	N/A	N/A
Humana CoverageFirst (HMO/POS) (C Christi)	TP	◔	N/A	N/A	N/A	N/A	N/A	N/A	N/A
Humana CoverageFirst (HMO/POS) (Houston)	T3	◔	◕	N/A	N/A	N/A	N/A	N/A	N/A
Humana CoverageFirst (HMO/POS) (San Ant)	TU	◔	N/A	N/A	N/A	N/A	N/A	N/A	N/A
Humana Health (HMO/POS) (Austin)	UU	◔	◔	N/A	N/A	N/A	N/A	N/A	N/A
Humana Health (HMO/POS) (Corpus Christi)	UC	◔	N/A	N/A	N/A	N/A	N/A	N/A	N/A
Humana Health (HMO/POS) (Houston)	EW	◔	◕	N/A	N/A	N/A	N/A	N/A	N/A
Humana Health (HMO/POS) (San Antonio)	UR	◔	N/A	N/A	N/A	N/A	N/A	N/A	N/A
Humana Health Basic (HMO/POS) (C Christi)	Q2	◔	N/A	N/A	N/A	N/A	N/A	N/A	N/A

● = Outstanding (plan's score was in the 90th percentile)
◕ = Excellent (plan's score was in the 75th-89th percentile)
◑ = Good (plan's score was in the 50th-74th percentile)
◔ = Fair (plan's score was in the 25th to 49th percentile)
○ = Poor (plan's score was worse than the 25th percentile)
N/A = Blanks indicate no data was reported for the measure

Plan Quality

See chapter text for discussion of these data

		Ratings from plan members							
	Enrollment code	Overall rating of plan	Overall rating of personal doctors	Getting needed care	Getting care quickly	Coordination of care	Claims processing	Customer service	Information on costs
Humana Health Basic (HMO/POS) (Houston)	Q6	◔	◕	N/A	N/A	N/A	N/A	N/A	N/A
Humana Health Basic (HMO/POS) (San Ant)	QX	◔	N/A	N/A	N/A	N/A	N/A	N/A	N/A
Scott & White (HMO/POS) (Austin/Central TX)	A8	◑	●	◔	●	◕	N/A	N/A	○
Scott & White (HMO/POS) (Dallas/Ft Worth)	P8	◑	●	◔	●	◕	N/A	N/A	○
United Choice Plus (PPO)	L9	◑	◑	◔	◔	○	◔	N/A	N/A
Utah									
Aetna Health/Altius-Hi (HMO/POS)	9K	◑	◕	●	●	◑	◑	◑	◑
Aetna Health/Altius-Std (HMO/POS)	DK	◑	◕	●	●	◑	◑	◑	◑
Blue Cross-Basic (PPO)	11	◕	◑	◑	◑	◔	◑	◔	◑
Blue Cross-Std (PPO)	10	●	◕	◕	●	◔	◑	◑	◕
SelectHealth (HMO/POS)	SF	◔	◕	◔	◔	N/A	◔	N/A	N/A
SelectHealth HDHP (HMO/POS)	WX	◔	◕	◔	◔	N/A	◔	N/A	N/A
Virgin Islands									
Triple-S Salud POS (PPO)	85	◕	◕	○	N/A	N/A	N/A	N/A	N/A
Virginia									
Aetna HealthFund (PPO)	F5	◑	◔	◔	◑	◔	◔	N/A	N/A
Aetna Open Access (HMO/POS)	JN	◕	◕	◑	◕	◔	N/A	N/A	◔
Blue Cross-Basic (PPO)	11	●	◑	◑	◕	○	◕	N/A	N/A
Blue Cross-Std (PPO)	10	●	◔	◕	●	◔	◑	N/A	◑
CareFirst Blue Value (HMO/POS)	B6	◑	◑	◕	◔	○	◕	◕	●
CareFirst-Std (HMO/POS)	2G	◑	◑	◕	◔	○	◕	◕	●
GEHA-Hi (PPO)	31	◑	○	◔	◑	○	○	N/A	◔
Kaiser (HMO)	E3	◕	◔	◔	◑	◑	N/A	◔	N/A
Kaiser Basic (HMO)	T7	◕	◔	◔	◑	◑	N/A	◔	N/A
MD-IPA (HMO/POS)	JP	◕	◕	◕	●	◑	◔	●	●
Optima Health (HMO/POS)	PG	◔	◔	◑	◑	◑	◔	N/A	◔
United Choice Open Access (PPO)	LR	◔	●	○	◕	N/A	N/A	N/A	N/A

Plan Quality

See chapter text for discussion of these data

Plan	Enrollment code	Overall rating of plan	Overall rating of personal doctors	Getting needed care	Getting care quickly	Coordination of care	Claims processing	Customer service	Information on costs
		Ratings from plan members							
United Choice Plus (PPO)	L9	◔	●	○	◕	N/A	N/A	N/A	N/A
United HDHP (PPO)	V4	◔	●	○	◕	N/A	N/A	N/A	N/A
Washington									
Aetna HealthFund (PPO)	G5	◔	◔	◑	◕	●	○	N/A	N/A
Blue Cross-Basic (PPO)	11	◕	○	○	◑	○	◑	N/A	N/A
Blue Cross-Std (PPO)	10	◕	○	◔	◔	◔	●	●	◔
GEHA-Hi (PPO)	31	◔	○	○	◔	○	◔	N/A	◔
Kaiser Northwest (HMO)	57	◑	○	○	◔	◔	N/A	○	○
Kaiser Washington (HMO)	54	○	○	○	○	○	N/A	○	○
Kaiser Washington Options (PPO)	L1	○	○	○	○	○	N/A	N/A	○
United Choice Open Access (PPO)	KT	○	○	◔	N/A	N/A	N/A	N/A	N/A
United HDHP (PPO)	LU	○	○	◔	N/A	N/A	N/A	N/A	N/A
West Virginia									
Blue Cross-Basic (PPO)	11	●	◑	◕	◔	◔	●	N/A	N/A
Blue Cross-Std (PPO)	10	●	◔	◑	●	●	◕	N/A	●
Wisconsin									
Blue Cross-Basic (PPO)	11	●	◑	●	◕	◑	●	N/A	◑
Blue Cross-Std (PPO)	10	●	◕	●	●	◕	●	◔	◕
Dean Health (HMO)	WD	◔	◑	◕	◑	◕	N/A	N/A	N/A
Group Health Coop (HMO)	WJ	◕	◑	◑	◕	◑	N/A	◑	◑
HealthPartners (HMO/POS)	V3	◑	●	◑	●	◕	●	◕	◔
MercyCare (HMO)	EY	◔	◑	◔	◑	◑	N/A	N/A	○
Wyoming									
Aetna Health/Altius-Hi (HMO/POS)	9K	◑	◕	●	●	◑	◑	◑	◑
Aetna Health/Altius-Std (HMO/POS)	DK	◑	◕	●	●	◑	◑	◑	◑

● = Outstanding (plan's score was in the 90th percentile)
◕ = Excellent (plan's score was in the 75th-89th percentile)
◑ = Good (plan's score was in the 50th-74th percentile)
◔ = Fair (plan's score was in the 25th to 49th percentile)
○ = Poor (plan's score was worse than the 25th percentile)
N/A = Blanks indicate no data was reported for the measure

Continued from page 112
per 10,000 enrollees a plan's initial decision in a disputed claim was changed or reversed. The disputed claim information is shown for national plans.

There are several possible explanations for differences in incidence of disputed claims. For example, some plans may have an unusually large share of hypercritical members, be more aggressive than others in enforcing their policy limitations to prevent benefit abuses, or have benefit limits that enrollees tend not to notice or not to understand. Most of the disputed claims are resolved in favor of the plans on the grounds that they involve matters that are not within the plans' coverage. But do you want to be in a plan where you will feel the need to file a disputed claim? Everything else equal, it seems preferable to join a plan where the coverage limits are easily understood, communication is good, benefit limitations are interpreted broadly—and disputed claims are rare.

Disputed Claims Per 10,000 Federal Enrollees Filed with the Office of Personnel Management

Plan name	Disputed claims	Disputed claims in which plan's decision was changed or reversed
Blue Cross Blue Shield	3.14	0.43
Rural Carrier*	5.95	1.25
Foreign Service*	9.19	3.98
NALC	9.47	1.98
APWU	9.67	3.51
MHBP	9.74	2.56
Aetna HealthFund	14.81	2.47
GEHA	15.36	5.82
SAMBA	22.6	7.94
Compass Rose*	28.26	9.8

* These plans not open to all.

Clinical Quality of Care

At GuideToHealthPlans.org, we report additional ratings from OPM on how plans compared for clinical quality of care. These ratings indicate how well plans performed for prevention measures (immunizations, breast cancer screenings, etc.) and how well plans performed for treating chronic conditions (asthma, diabetes, etc.). OPM used the same scale to report these results as it did for the customer satisfaction survey results.

Accreditation

At GuideToHealthPlans.org, we also report whether or not plans are accredited by NCQA or by URAC or AAAHC, two smaller accrediting organizations. These organizations have procedures to determine whether plans meet the organization's accreditation standards. The standards cover many areas of performance, such as whether the plan takes appropriate steps to check the credentials of its physicians, whether the plan has appropriate health promotion and disease prevention programs, and whether the plan has appropriate protections of patients' rights. NCQA includes in its accreditation process assessments of plan performance on member satisfaction survey measures and effectiveness of care measures, such as the percentage of two-year-olds who have had all recommended immunizations and the percentage of heart attack patients who are given a specific type of recommended medication.

Chapter 10

Premiums and Taxes

There are major tax advantages for health insurance. The "employer share" of health insurance—paid by agencies for employees and by OPM for annuitants—is part of employee compensation but by law is exempted from being counted as taxable income. For Federal employees and annuitants, the non-taxable premium share paid by employing agencies and OPM averages about $6,000 for self-only enrollments, about $13,000 for self plus one, and about $14,000 for families. The tax laws also allow employers to make the "employee share" of the premium tax-free to employees, and to set up tax advantaged Flexible Spending Accounts for employees. The average tax-sheltered employee share of premium for Federal self-only enrollees is about $2,000 and for families about $5,000. In total, employees in family plans shelter about $19,000 in employee compensation for health insurance from Federal, State, and local income taxes, as well as from OASDI taxes. This saves employees a tidy sum, about $6,000 per family on average. By law, only the tax benefits for the employer share, but not the annuitant share, are available to retirees in either the public or private sectors. But annuitants in Medicare Parts A and B also get over $9,000 per person of untaxed insurance benefits on top of their FEHB savings, for a total tax shelter of about $22,000 for a retired couple.

Tax Savings for Employee Premium Share

Federal employees shelter their share of the FEHB plan premium from income taxes through what is called "Premium Conversion." Employees have the right to opt out of this program. This increases very slightly future Social Security benefits. However, that offsetting amount is a very small fraction—a few pennies on the dollar—of the gains from the Premium Conversion program. We strongly advise all employees NOT to opt out of Premium Conversion tax savings.

How much employees gain from this tax subsidy varies depending on employee salary, spousal salary, other income, state income tax rate, number of dependents, amount of deductions, whether or not they file jointly, and whether or not they are in FERS (and hence paying Social Security taxes). The overall marginal tax rate can often reach 40 percent, or even more in some high tax states.

At income ranges typical of Federal employees, whether in single- or dual-earner families, and whether in the FERS or CSRS retirement systems, almost everyone will save at least 25 percent, and very few will save much more than 40 percent, from tax-sheltered health care premiums or other expenses.

How Much Tax-Sheltered Premiums Are Reduced

Because the effects of different marginal tax rates are relatively small in comparing plans, and never change our relative rankings or the general magnitude of plan-to-plan differences, we use a 33 percent premium savings estimate in all Guide tables for employees, who are eligible for Premium Conversion. This simplifies presentation and gives you the essential information you need to compare plans. You can, of course, make your own calculation of marginal tax rate, but this is complicated and will not affect most plan comparisons substantially.

Flexible Spending Accounts

Health Care Flexible Spending Accounts (FSAs) provide a way to shelter even more health care spending from taxes. FSAs allow you to shelter the out-of-pocket costs that you incur for copayments, coinsurance, deductibles, charges above customary and reasonable, and uncovered health care expenses. Under health reform, you can no longer use an FSA account to pay for over-the-counter drugs without a physician prescription (insulin is an exception) but all other categories of expense are unchanged. For most people, the favored categories for using FSAs are dental expenses, vision expenses, and your share of costs for services covered by the plan—for example, the coinsurance you pay for mental health services, or the annual deductible.

Under IRS rules, you have to set up your FSA account and amount in advance. OPM allows you to use the regular Open Season period for setting up your account. For health care, in 2020 you can elect to choose any amount from a minimum of $100 to a maximum of $2,750. (You can also elect to set aside additional amounts for "Dependent Care.") You establish the account by enrolling online at *www.fsafeds.com* or by calling 1-877-372-3337. Unlike Premium Conversion, you have to elect this benefit and will NOT be enrolled automatically. Until recently, enrollees in Consumer-Driven and High Deductible plans were not allowed to create FSAs. However, they may now set up "Limited Expense" FSAs that cover only dental and vision expenses that are not reimbursed by insurance.

You can carry up to $500 in unused FSA accounts into the next year. But any amount over $500 that you elect to set aside for an FSA must be spent by the end of the year, or it will be forfeited (a "grace period" of 2 1/2 months is no longer allowed). You should plan carefully based on your best "guesstimate" as to health care expenses that you are virtually certain to incur, such as maintenance prescription drugs, routine dental care, and routine eye care or any services for which you make multiple and foreseeable provider visits.

Only about one in five Federal employees are signing up each year for FSA accounts. This means that about four out of five employees are leaving money on the table each year. Almost everyone has at least a few hundred dollars in foreseeable out-of-pocket health care expenses. Those who don't sign up are throwing away a one-third discount on these costs. We recommend that ALL employees who are not in High Deductible plans establish an FSA if they have foreseeable expenses.

Health Savings Accounts

Both Health Reimbursement Arrangements (HRAs) and Health Savings Accounts (HSAs) provide significant tax advantages, beyond those available through Premium Conversion and FSAs. The simpler case involves HRAs, where your savings account can grow as long as you stay with the same plan (if you change plans the entire amount is lost), and you can also use an FSA to supplement the HRA amount set aside by the plan. For example, if you expect out of pocket drug and dental expenses of five hundred dollars next year, you could place that amount in an FSA in the expectation that the HRA amount paid through your premiums would remain available for unforeseen expenses next year or in future years. Unfortunately, retirees cannot use the FSA method of supplementing HRAs.

HSAs convey far larger advantages. First, you can add to your HSA account by advance planning, just as if it were an FSA. Second, while you can only establish an FSA account in advance, you can add to your HSA account at any time during the year. Thus, if you have unanticipated expenses late in the year of an extra thousand dollars, in most High Deductible plans you can have a thousand dollars transferred from your pay to your HSA, lower your taxable income by a thousand dollars, pay the bill through the HSA, and obtain what amounts to a one-third discount on your unplanned expenses. Or you can transfer the extra thousand dollars even if you don't have any unexpected expenses, saving one third in taxes, and build up your account for future years. Since you retain the HSA account for life, regardless of Open Season plan changes or retirement, and it can accumulate tax-free earnings, it can become a very substantial lifelong protection against health care expense.

This account augmentation advantage is dramatic if you consider the catastrophic guarantee provided by most FEHB plans. Consider a traditional plan, national or local, that holds self-only total out-of-pocket cost to $6,000, without significant loopholes. Compare that to a High Deductible plan, with a guarantee of $7,000 for a self-only enrollment, also without significant loopholes. The traditional plan seems better. However, under the High Deductible plan your plan-paid HSA account of $1,000 (a typical amount) can be used to defray large expenses, thereby reducing your potential loss to $6,000. Beyond that, you are allowed to make tax advantaged voluntary contributions of over

$2,000 and pay your bills through your augmented account. This lets you save approximately $700 through lower tax payments if you face catastrophic expense. Hence, your total cost exposure is only about $5,300, lower than that claimed by the traditional plan, and reversing the conclusion as to which plan has a better guarantee. Most HDHP plans, evaluated this way, offer catastrophic expense protection as good as or better than most traditional plans.

While retirees over the age of 65 cannot establish HSAs, those nearing retirement not only can take advantage of HSAs, but also are eligible for "catch up" contributions after age 55, until enrolled in Medicare. These contributions can reduce after-tax expenses by hundreds of dollars a year more, or simply be added to the growing HSA balance. After retirement, the HSA balance remains available for the rest of your life, and continues to earn tax-free returns.

Chapter 11

Key Tips and Final Plan Selection

The data we have presented should help you to quickly and easily narrow your choice to two or three of the plans, out of the dozens you are offered. At this point, compare the brochures of these carefully. Underline key points, or parts of the plans that confuse you, and compare these points among the plans. It is very easy to use our online Web site, or OPMs, to find copies of plan brochures for your area. Then you can search on a word such as "maternity," "surgery," or "chiropractor" in the brochure for each plan and find the benefit details in seconds. Probably the plans will be similar on most things, so concentrate on differences that are important to you.

When you have figured out the major differences among the best plans, you are ready to make your final decision. One way to do this is to write out the most important ways in which the plans differ. These differences may not be strictly financial. For example, suppose it turns out that your choice is between a national plan and an HMO. Let's say that our ratings show that the HMO costs $1,000 dollars a year less on average, and has slightly better coverage for a benefit you need. But you are unwilling to give up a particular doctor you have been using for years. This seems to be an impasse, but there are several possible ways to resolve it. Perhaps your doctor is affiliated with the HMO—why not ask? Or consider using part of the money you will save by joining the HMO to continue going to your doctor and paying out-of-pocket (using a Flexible Spending Account will cut this cost by a third). Or you may have more than one doctor you want to keep and conclude that the national plan is well worth the higher cost.

Throughout this *Guide* we have argued that your best strategy is to make the primary factor in your plan selection the predicted cost of the plan for families like yours. This takes into account that none of us can predict whether or not we may have a heart attack, a stroke, a cancer, or other costly condition that strikes unexpectedly. You should use your known, predictable routine expenses to calculate how much to put in a Flexible Spending Account, not to choose an insurance plan whose main purpose is to protect you against unexpected and high expenses. There is an important exception to this general strategy. If you know that you will need some particular service next year, and it is very expensive (for example, hip surgery or maternity) and likely to cost you tens of thousands of dollars, it makes sense to select the physician you would like to use (or several you are considering) and ask two simple questions: "What plan networks are you in?" and "In your experience, which Federal employee health plan or plans pay best for the care I need?" Sometimes the answer will be that all of them pay well. But sometimes the answer will be that only a few plans pay well. In that case, look first at these plans and choose one of them after you complete your detective work by reading the brochure section on your procedure, calling the plan, or checking with other people who have been in your situation. But do not forget that some other disease may strike, so factor in both known problems and overall ratings in choosing among these few plans.

Whatever your personal decision turns on, you may be overwhelmed by details and confused by the choices you face. So here are some concluding thoughts based on some of the most common questions we have heard. Try to focus your decision on several key questions. Are you willing to join an HMO or a High Deductible plan? Do you expect big bills for a particular event such as surgery? Do you really want to have a particular benefit, such as chiropractic or hearing aid? Do you really "have to have" doctor sawbones in the plan network? (Hint: in the DC metro area, we have a "doc find" feature that tells you which plan networks include doctor sawbones.) Perhaps you can afford a higher premium to get the benefits you want, or perhaps you cannot and must pick a plan that at least gives you good catastrophic protection.

Tips

Throughout the *Guide* we have provided vital tips. We repeat some here:

- **Getting "Free" Health Insurance**—Some Consumer-Driven and High Deductible FEHB plans provide you a savings account larger than your actual premium cost after taxes. You can end the year with more money than you started if your medical costs are low.
- **Avoid a Big Risk**—Many people who are covered by their spouse's insurance drop FEHB insurance. This saves premium costs. However, if you are not enrolled and die suddenly, your spouse cannot ever enroll again. Your best option is to carry an FEHB family policy and drop the spousal insurance.
- **Protect Your Retirement**—It is not expensive to enroll in an FEHB plan or plans for the five years before retirement. Several plans have annual premiums that are about $1,500. These plans cost about $1,000 after tax savings. Some plans give you savings accounts higher than the tax advantaged premium cost.
- **Be Sure to Elect a Survivor Annuity for Your Spouse**—If you die and your spouse receives no Federal pension, your spouse will lose FEHB health insurance coverage forever. If you die while enrolled as self-only, your spouse will also lose coverage.
- **Bargain with Out of Network Providers**—Most plans have very low payments for non-preferred providers. Negotiate with these doctors before any expensive procedure. One good tactic is to ask for their "preferred" or Medicare rate.
- **Check Your Brochure**—Do not stay in the same plan without reading at least "How We Change" for next year or join a new plan without checking any benefits of particular importance to your health care.
- **Flexible Spending Account**—You can only establish your FSA during Open Season. Be sure to consider carefully this important option to reduce your health costs. Almost all employees should set up an FSA.
- **Medicare Flexibility at a Low or High Price**—The best two arguments for paying the Medicare Part B premium are to preserve your choices over time, as both the FEHB and Medicare programs evolve, and to get you low costs for providers who are not in your plan network. This choice is costly in most but not all plans. Check out the plans we rate as lowest cost with Medicare Part B.
- **Huge Annuitant Cost Saving**—Annuitants with Medicare Parts A and B can suspend their FEHB enrollment, join a Medicare Advantage plan, and pay only the Medicare premium. They can reenroll in an FEHB plan in the future without penalty, and in the meantime, enjoy good catastrophic protection, have low copays, and save thousands in premium costs. In some plans they can enroll in both programs, but collect a reimbursement for most of the Part B premium while also enjoying good catastrophic protection and low copays, and saving the cost of a second premium.
- **Dealing with a Known High Expense**—There is an exception to our general advice about focusing on overall plan costs, not just one benefit category. If you know for sure that you will need an expensive service, you should look for the answer to "Which plans pay best?" If several plans pay equally well, then you can choose whichever of these is an overall better buy.

Questions and Answers

Here is a short list of frequent questions and their answers (we provide a far longer list in the online Guide):

- **What if I expect to have a baby?** What plan offers the best maternity benefits? Most plans offer low or no cost maternity coverage. Check brochures for this, and check network lists online to make sure you will have a good selection of obstetricians. Or select an obstetrician and then use her experience to steer you towards a few plans from which to choose.

- **What if I am going to have a major operation?** Pay particular attention to catastrophic limits. If you know for sure that you are going to face bills of $25,000 or more, then pick a plan with a tight limit on your costs. In comparing catastrophic expense limits, use *Guide* figures. Our estimates include the "for sure" premium expense and adjust for inconsistencies among stated catastrophic limits, such as failing to include deductibles in the stated limit. If you are not sure what plans will work best in your case, check brochures and consult your surgeon to discuss which plans work best. Be sure your surgeon is in your plan network or will give you a network rate.
- **My two doctors aren't preferred providers for any plan. What should I do?** Set up an FSA account for about half the amount you expect to spend on those doctors. Then pick one of the top ranked plans that includes a fee-for-service benefit, use that benefit for whatever it will pay (which will probably be about half), and use the FSA to cover the rest. Or change doctors.
- **I need over 30 psychiatric visits. What plan is best?** The mental health parity requirement—which theoretically allows unlimited visits at a low cost—might arguably make all plans meet your needs. But plans require using preferred providers to get network rates. First, talk to your provider and see if he or she is "preferred" under any plan. If so, this plan is likely to be your best choice. Alternatively, most plans will pay sixty or seventy percent of the "plan allowance" for out of network visits. Since that is well below what most providers charge, you will likely pay half or more of the cost of each visit. Try making an arithmetic calculation. Estimate the number of visits you are likely to make and how much each of several plans will pay for these visits. Then add the annual premium cost to the amount that you will pay the doctor under each of those plans. If one of them stands out, you have an answer. If they are all about the same, choose on some other basis (like our overall ratings). Finally, you are a perfect candidate for a Flexible Spending Account, and your FSA tax savings will reduce your cost by about a third.
- **I really like the service from plan X. But it is rated halfway down your cost table. Would I be a sucker to stay with it?** No. Differences of several hundred dollars in estimated costs can move a plan up or down the table a long way. Our methods of estimating average costs are only approximations. Differences of $100 or less are not significant, and a national plan even halfway down the table is a perfectly acceptable deal. Furthermore, staying with the same plan will eliminate the hassle of changing doctors and of dealing with a plan bureaucracy that may not be as customer friendly as the one you have now.
- **You rated the plan I am in highly last year, but this year it has moved way down. Why did this happen and should I switch?** Premium differences are the biggest factor in our cost rankings, and premiums can swing widely from year to year. That is probably why your plan moved so far—but check the brochure's change page for a benefit cutback that could have affected our ratings. Or other plans could have improved their benefits. One of the big change factors, for example, is the catastrophic limit promised to you by the plan: these often move up or down by thousands of dollars and are big factors in our ratings. You can stick with your plan if it has not become unreasonably costly and has given you good service. But consider the possible savings from the plans we rank higher.
- **I don't have much money and can't afford an expensive premium. Is it safe to join one of the plans with a really low premium?** All plans are reputable, and all will pay the benefits they promise. Every plan, not just the ones with the lowest premiums, has gaps or loopholes of one kind or another. But the lower-premium national plans generally expose you to higher copayments and deductibles, so they may not save you as much money as you think. Look at our ratings tables and several brochures carefully, and then decide. A lower premium does not mean a worse plan, or a higher premium a better plan. Our estimates of average costs are a far better guide to likely costs than premiums alone.
- **I'm not very healthy and could easily have expenses of many thousands of dollars next year. I don't think that your rankings based on average costs are what I should use. What should I do?** A good method is to skip the average column and look at the column for high expenses of $30,000. Within that column, choose among several plans that our comparisons indicate are relatively low-cost. Another approach is to compare catastrophic limits. But keep in mind that our "average" columns include some very expensive years. Most people, in most years, will be out-of-pocket far less.

- **I can't decide whether I should get Medicare Part B and join a plan that guarantees I won't pay anything at all for medical bills, or plan to drop Medicare Part B and save about $1,700 a year in premium cost.** If your doctors are mostly preferred providers, consider dropping Part B. You won't save the entire amount of the Part B premium, but you will save most of it in most years. The main two arguments for getting Part B is that you have complete flexibility to use any doctor who accepts new Medicare patients, even if he is not preferred, and in the many plans with wraparound benefits you will pay nothing for hospital or doctor costs. But these savings and this flexibility costs you close to or even more than a thousand dollars a year in most plans. Check out the plans we rate as costing you almost nothing, or even saving you money, when you are covered by Part B. Whatever you do, do not drop out of the FEHB program. If you decide to keep Part B, move to a low premium plan that waives cost sharing for those with Medicare Parts A and B, such as Aetna Direct, Blue Cross Basic, MHBP High Deductible, or in the DC area CareFirst High Deductible. Some plans not only provide a Medicare wraparound, but also pay part of the Part B premium.
- **My spouse has excellent family coverage from his or her employer and pays no premium. Is there any reason why I should not drop out of the Federal program?** If you are within five years of retirement, do not even consider dropping out. That private plan will go away sooner or later and you and your spouse will be stuck. You are not allowed to remain in the FEHB program after retirement without five years of continuous prior enrollment immediately preceding retirement (there are some narrow exceptions, such as layoffs). A good move would be to join a High Deductible plan, rely mainly on your spouse's coverage for medical care, and save the Health Savings Account money as your "IRA on steroids".
- **I read that High Deductible plans are bad buys for older and less healthy individuals.** Nonsense. These plans are among the best deals in the program. Taking into account their tax advantages and savings accounts, they rival or beat many other plans. If you know for sure that your routine physician and drug expenses, priced at retail, will be three or four thousand dollars next year, you will probably do better in an HMO or national plan with low copayments. But high expense, in and of itself, is not an argument against High Deductible plans. They have some of the best catastrophic limit guarantees.
- **Some expensive plans have higher quality scores than some less expensive plans. How much weight should I put on quality?** The quality scores are driven by survey results from enrollees in each plan. Our ratings also show some of the particular factors those enrollees most like or dislike. Only you can judge how important these are to you. It may help to consider two things: most enrollees in just about all plans rate the plans quite favorably; and ultimately it is the doctors you choose, not the plan, that drives the quality of medical care you get. That said, the anecdotal evidence we get tells us that these scores measure things that are important and real.
- **I have an expensive condition that I am not sure is covered by several plans that you rank high. What should I do?** The first step is to get those plan brochures and compare them side-by-side. OPM's policy for standard brochure formats and clear English is immensely helpful. If you read and compare the specific language you may find the answer. If you do not, call at least one plan, and preferably several plans, and call again to protect yourself against mistakes that plan representatives sometimes make. If you are still not sure, consult providers who deal with your condition, or other patients with your condition, or both. Sometimes there is no way around doing your homework.
- **Skip all the details. What is the best plan?** There is no one best plan. Every plan is best for at least some people. Our rankings give you a good starting point, but only a starting point. If you don't want to be bothered with details, then check out only one or two plans carefully. But whatever else you do, read the "how we change" pages of the brochure, along with the "summary of benefits" near the end of the brochure, before you stay in the plan you are in or sign up for a new plan.

Cost & Special Features of All Plans			Average yearly cost in dollars (premiums and out-of-pocket costs)					
			General Schedule			Annuitants 55 to 64		
Plan code	Plan name (primary service area)	Phone number	Self only	Self plus one	Family	Self only	Self plus one	Family of two
National Plans								
Z24-6	Aetna Advantage	888-238-6240	3000	6110	7060	4470	9250	9870
N61-3	Aetna Direct CDHP	888-238-6240	2130	4350	5170	3590	7380	7990
224-6	Aetna HealthFund HDHP	888-238-6240	2740	5710	5670	4540	9460	8740
474-6	APWU CDHP	800-222-2798	**1990**	**3960**	4660	3500	7060	7410
471-3	APWU-Hi	800-222-2798	2980	5510	6760	4390	8270	9790
111-3	Blue Cross Basic	800-411-2583	2230	4690	5150	3450	7280	7610
104-6	Blue Cross-Std	800-411-2583	3190	6730	7340	4760	10170	10680
131-3	FEP Blue Focus	800-411-2583	2180	4360	4870	**3250**	6710	7010
421-3	Compass Rose	888-438-9135	2480	5400	6010	3760	8190	8840
401-3	Foreign Service	202-833-4910	2060	4520	4700	**3110**	6810	**6780**
254-6	GEHA Elevate	800-821-6136	**1980**	**3850**	4570	**3100**	**6160**	**6770**
251-3	GEHA Elevate Plus	800-821-6136	2120	4400	4790	3300	6860	7120
311-3	GEHA-Hi	800-821-6136	2750	5830	7070	4190	8960	10470
314-6	GEHA-Std	800-821-6136	2220	4310	5060	3440	6810	7470
341-3	GEHA HDHP	800-821-6136	**1460**	**3020**	**3720**	**2600**	**5310**	**5900**
454-6	MHBP-Std	800-410-7778	2300	4570	4850	3450	6880	**6920**
414-6	MHBP Value Plan	800-410-7778	2480	5020	5440	3700	7620	7680
481-3	MHBP HDHP	800-694-9901	**1750**	**3590**	**4110**	**3080**	**6310**	**6500**
321-3	NALC-Hi	888-636-6252	2530	5420	5130	3790	8200	7430
KM1-3	NALC Value Plan	888-636-6252	2300	4660	5170	3510	7230	7340
324-6	NALC CDHP	888-636-6252	**1570**	**3450**	**4100**	**3000**	**6680**	**6810**
381-3	Rural Carrier	800-638-8432	3130	5380	5310	4710	8140	7690
441-3	SAMBA-Hi	800-638-6589	4290	9030	10000	6490	13690	14750
444-6	SAMBA-Std	800-638-6589	2670	5120	5540	4070	7880	8070
Local Plans								
Alaska								
JS1-3	Aetna HealthFund CDHP	888-238-6240	4680	10830	10730	7510	17300	16470
JS4-6	Aetna Value Plan	888-238-6240	5720	12920	12720	8670	19720	18910
Alabama								
F51-3	Aetna HealthFund CDHP	888-238-6240	3280	7680	7540	5410	12580	11700
F54-6	Aetna Value Plan	888-238-6240	3690	8230	8140	5630	12700	12040
DH1-3	QualChoice-Hi (Statewide) POS	800-235-7111	3050	4970	8530	4640	7600	12510

Lowest costs are in bold type. Note that in some plans, family costs are lower than self-plus-one costs.

Average yearly cost (continued)			Medicare wrap-around	Day limit in skilled nursing facility	Pays for...					
Annuitants 65 or older with Medicare Parts A & B										
Self only	Self plus one	Family			Routine dental	Chiro-practic	Acupunc-ture	Hearing aids	Adult vision care	Non network providers
4220	**8210**	8830	Yes	60	No	No	Little	No	Exam	Reduced
3820	**7470**	**8080**	Yes	60	No	No	Little	Yes	Exam	Reduced
6520	13370	12650	No	60	Some	No	Little	No	Exam	Reduced
5440	10950	11300	No	30	Yes	Yes	Yes	Some	Some	Reduced
5170	9990	11500	Yes	30	Yes	Some	Some	Some	No	Reduced
4540	9400	9730	Network only	0	Some	Some	Some	Yes	No	No
5750	11890	12400	Yes	30	Some	Some	Some	Yes	No	Reduced
3760	**7690**	**7990**	Network only	0	No	Some	Some	No	Exam	No
4670	9960	10610	Yes	90	Yes	Yes	Yes	Some	Exam	Reduced
4410	9240	9210	Yes	90	Some	Yes	Yes	Yes	No	Reduced
4900	9770	10380	No	0	Yes	Some	Yes	No	No	Reduced
4580	9230	9490	Yes	21	Yes	Some	Yes	Some	No	Reduced
5200	10880	12390	Yes	21	Yes	Some	Yes	Yes	No	Reduced
4580	8820	9480	Yes	21	Yes	Some	Yes	Yes	No	Reduced
4480	9010	9600	No	21	Yes	Some	Yes	No	Yes	Reduced
4410	8850	8890	Yes	40	No	Yes	Yes	Yes	No	Reduced
5700	11480	11540	No	40	No	Yes	Yes	Some	No	Reduced
3370	**6580**	**6770**	Yes	28	No	Yes	Yes	Some	No	Reduced
4830	10280	9510	Yes	0	Yes	Yes	Some	Some	No	Reduced
5410	11100	11210	No	0	Yes	Some	Some	Some	No	Reduced
4990	10800	10930	No	0	Yes	Some	Some	Some	No	Reduced
6040	10640	10180	Yes	60	Yes	Yes	Yes	Yes	No	Reduced
7490	15790	16850	Yes	45	No	Yes	Some	Some	No	Reduced
4950	9740	9930	Yes	30	No	Some	Some	Some	No	Reduced
9530	21340	20510	No	60	Some	Yes	Little	No	Exam	Reduced
10650	23660	22850	No	60	No	Yes	Little	No	Exam	Reduced
7430	16610	15730	No	60	Some	Yes	Little	No	Exam	Reduced
7610	16630	15970	No	60	No	Yes	Little	No	Exam	Reduced
6000	10310	15220	Yes	60	No	Some	No	Yes	Exam	Reduced

Cost & Special Features of All Plans			Average yearly cost in dollars (premiums and out-of-pocket costs)					
Plan code	Plan name (primary service area)	Phone number	General Schedule			Annuitants 55 to 64		
			Self only	Self plus one	Family	Self only	Self plus one	Family of two
DH4-6	QualChoice-Std (Statewide)	800-235-7111	2210	4050	5080	3410	**6230**	7400
KK1-3	United Choice Open Access	877-835-9861	2550	5200	6710	3900	8000	9900
AS1-3	United Choice Plus Primary	877-835-9861	2230	4300	4840	3480	6810	7150
Y81-3	United Choice Primary	877-835-9861	2190	4210	4750	3430	**6680**	7010
LS1-3	United HDHP	877-835-9861	**1720**	**3700**	**4250**	**2870**	**6220**	**6430**
Arizona								
G51-3	Aetna HealthFund CDHP	888-238-6240	3880	9050	8920	6310	14620	13770
G54-6	Aetna Value Plan	888-238-6240	2830	6300	6170	4340	9810	9100
WQ1-3	Aetna Open Access	800-537-9384	5970	14970	14660	9040	22630	21870
R61-3	Humana CoverageFirst CDHP (Ph'nix)	800-448-6262	2440	4730	4970	4160	8180	7940
R64-6	Humana Value Plan (Ph'nix)	800-448-6262	3010	5850	6400	4510	8910	9080
R91-3	Humana CoverageFirst CDHP (Tuc'n)	800-448-6262	2090	**3940**	**4460**	3630	6990	7180
R94-6	Humana Value Plan(Tuc'n)	800-448-6262	2910	5630	6170	4350	8580	8740
BF1-3	Humana Health-Hi (Ph'nix)	800-448-6262	8450	17750	18430	12770	26820	27430
BF4-6	Humana Health-Std (Ph'nix)	800-448-6262	6430	13390	13910	9770	20370	20650
C71-3	Humana Health-Hi (Tuc'n)	800-448-6262	5160	10670	11020	7830	16200	16320
C74-6	Humana Health-Std (Tuc'n)	800-448-6262	3470	7020	7250	5330	10820	10660
WF1-3	United Choice Plus Primary	877-835-9861	2220	4280	4820	3470	6790	7120
VD1-3	United Choice Primary	877-835-9861	2220	4280	4820	3470	6780	7120
KT1-3	United Choice Open Access	877-835-9861	2640	5390	6930	4030	8280	10220
LU1-3	United HDHP	877-835-9861	**1690**	**3660**	**4200**	**2840**	**6150**	**6350**
Arkansas								
F51-3	Aetna HealthFund CDHP	888-238-6240	3280	7680	7540	5410	12580	11700
F54-6	Aetna Value Plan	888-238-6240	3690	8230	8140	5630	12700	12040
DH1-3	QualChoice-Hi (Statewide) POS	800-235-7111	3050	4970	8530	4640	7600	12510
DH4-6	QualChoice-Std (Statewide)	800-235-7111	2210	4050	5080	3410	**6230**	7400
KK1-3	United Choice Open Access	877-835-9861	2550	5200	6710	3900	8000	9900
KK1-3	United Choice Open Access	877-835-9861	2550	5200	6710	3900	8000	9900
AS1-3	United Choice Plus Primary	877-835-9861	2230	4300	4840	3480	6810	7150
Y81-3	United Choice Primary	877-835-9861	2190	4210	4750	3430	**6680**	7010
LS1-3	United HDHP	877-835-9861	**1720**	**3700**	**4250**	**2870**	**6220**	**6430**

Lowest costs are in bold type. Note that in some plans, family costs are lower than self-plus-one costs.

Average yearly cost (continued) — Annuitants 65 or older with Medicare Parts A & B: Self only	Self plus one	Family	Medicare wrap-around	Day limit in skilled nursing facility	Pays for... Routine dental	Chiro-practic	Acupunc-ture	Hearing aids	Adult vision care	Non network providers
4680	8740	9910	Yes	60	No	Some	No	Yes	Exam	No
5780	11540	13440	No	60	Some	Some	Some	No	Exam	No
5290	10560	10890	No	60	Some	Some	Some	Yes	Exam	Reduced
5230	10430	10760	No	60	Some	Some	Some	Yes	Exam	No
4870	10150	10350	No	60	Some	Yes	Some	Yes	Exam	Reduced
8340	18660	17800	No	60	Some	Yes	Little	No	Exam	Reduced
6320	13750	13030	No	60	No	Yes	Little	No	Exam	Reduced
10990	26370	25610	No	60	Yes	Yes	Some	No	Yes	No
4350	8610	**8370**	Yes	60	No	Some	Some	No	No	Reduced
4540	8820	8990	Yes	60	No	Yes	Some	No	No	No
3820	**7420**	**7610**	Yes	60	No	Some	Some	No	No	Reduced
4390	**8500**	**8650**	Yes	60	No	Yes	Some	No	No	No
13870	28950	29560	Yes	100	No	Yes	Some	No	Exam	No
10570	21850	22130	Yes	100	No	Some	Some	No	Exam	No
8940	18330	18450	Yes	100	No	Yes	Some	No	Exam	No
6130	12290	12130	Yes	100	No	Some	Some	No	Exam	No
5280	10540	10870	No	60	Some	Some	Some	Yes	Exam	Reduced
5280	10530	10870	No	60	Some	Some	Some	Yes	Exam	No
5910	11820	13760	No	60	Some	Some	Some	No	Exam	No
4840	10080	10280	No	60	Some	Yes	Some	Yes	Exam	Reduced
7430	16610	15730	No	60	Some	Yes	Little	No	Exam	Reduced
7610	16630	15970	No	60	No	Yes	Little	No	Exam	Reduced
6000	10310	15220	Yes	60	No	Some	No	Yes	Exam	Reduced
4680	8740	9910	Yes	60	No	Some	No	Yes	Exam	No
5780	11540	13440	No	60	Some	Some	Some	No	Exam	No
5780	11540	13440	No	60	Some	Some	Some	No	Exam	No
5290	10560	10890	No	60	Some	Some	Some	Yes	Exam	Reduced
5230	10430	10760	No	60	Some	Some	Some	Yes	Exam	No
4870	10150	10350	No	60	Some	Yes	Some	Yes	Exam	Reduced

Cost & Special Features of All Plans			Average yearly cost in dollars (premiums and out-of-pocket costs)					
Plan code	Plan name (primary service area)	Phone number	General Schedule			Annuitants 55 to 64		
			Self only	Self plus one	Family	Self only	Self plus one	Family of two
California								
JS1-3	Aetna HealthFund CDHP	888-238-6240	4680	10830	10730	7510	17300	16470
2X1-3	Aetna Open Access (LA/Bakersfield)	800-537-9384	3720	8850	8640	5670	13460	12840
JS4-6	Aetna Value Plan	888-238-6240	5720	12920	12720	8670	19720	18910
B31-3	Anthem Blue Cross (Southern)	800-235-8631	3200	6530	7090	4730	9770	10200
SI1-3	Blue Shield Access-Hi (Southern)	800-880-8086	3370	7430	7570	5060	11230	11130
SI4-6	Blue Shield Access-Std (San Diego)	800-880-8086	2620	5790	5850	3940	8770	8550
T41-3	Health Net Basic (Northern)	800-522-0088	4120	8800	9770	6260	13410	14430
P61-3	Health Net Basic (Southern)	800-522-0088	**1800**	**3450**	**3870**	**2780**	**5380**	**5580**
LB1-3	Health Net-Hi (Northern)	800-522-0088	8890	19730	21280	13380	29690	31700
LP1-3	Health Net-Hi (Southern)	800-522-0088	5190	11240	12400	7830	16970	18380
LB4-6	Health Net-Std (Northern)	800-522-0088	7700	16860	18560	11590	25450	27570
LP4-6	Health Net-Std (Southern)	800-522-0088	5080	11100	12280	7660	16810	18150
KC1-3	Kaiser Basic (Northern)	800-464-4000	2620	5900	5800	3950	8960	8330
NZ1-3	Kaiser-Hi (Fresno)	800-464-4000	2760	6930	6380	4160	10470	9370
591-3	Kaiser-Hi (Northern)	800-464-4000	4550	11670	11130	6840	17580	16480
621-3	Kaiser-Hi (Southern/Bakersfield)	800-464-4000	2430	6160	5610	3660	9310	8210
NZ4-6	Kaiser-Std (Fresno)	800-464-4000	2040	4440	4710	**3080**	6790	**6790**
594-6	Kaiser-Std (Northern)	800-464-4000	3350	8350	7890	5010	12610	11510
624-6	Kaiser-Std (Southern/Bakersfield)	800-464-4000	**1820**	**3950**	**4210**	**2760**	**6060**	**6060**
Colorado								
G51-3	Aetna HealthFund CDHP	888-238-6240	3880	9050	8920	6310	14620	13770
G54-6	Aetna Value Plan	888-238-6240	2830	6300	6170	4340	9810	9100
WW1-3	BlueAdvantage (Denv/Boulder/CS)	833-611-6919	2220	4530	4970	3400	6890	7190
R21-3	Humana Health Basic (Col Springs)	800-448-6262	2470	4890	5400	3850	7740	7900
RZ1-3	Humana Health Basic (Denv/Boulder)	800-448-6262	2460	4850	5360	3820	7680	7830
NR1-3	Humana Health-Hi (Col Springs)	800-448-6262	3550	7230	7410	5420	11030	10910
NT1-3	Humana Health-Hi (Denv/Boulder)	800-448-6262	3090	6250	6390	4740	9570	9380
NR4-6	Humana Health-Std (Col Springs)	800-448-6262	2380	4640	5080	3700	7240	7410
NT4-6	Humana Health-Std (Denv/Boulder)	800-448-6262	2330	4520	4960	3610	7060	7230
N41-3	Kaiser Basic student POS (Most of St)	800-632-9700	2400	4590	4900	3580	7010	7010
651-3	Kaiser-Hi student POS (Most of St)	800-632-9700	2970	6940	6440	4560	10670	9570
654-6	Kaiser-Std student POS (Most of St)	800-632-9700	2370	5260	5170	3650	8130	7580

Lowest costs are in bold type. Note that in some plans, family costs are lower than self-plus-one costs.

Average yearly cost (continued)			Medicare wrap-around	Day limit in skilled nursing facility	Pays for...						
Annuitants 65 or older with Medicare Parts A & B											
Self only	Self plus one	Family			Routine dental	Chiro-practic	Acupunc-ture	Hearing aids	Adult vision care	Non network providers
9530	21340	20510	No	60	Some	Yes	Little	No	Exam	Reduced
7630	17200	16580	No	60	Yes	Yes	Some	No	Yes	No
10650	23660	22850	No	60	No	Yes	Little	No	Exam	Reduced
6310	12510	12940	Yes	100	No	Yes	Yes	Yes	Exam	No
6940	14990	14890	No	100	No	Yes	No	Some	Yes	No
5820	12520	12310	No	100	No	Yes	No	Some	Yes	No
7280	15290	16310	Yes	100	No	Yes	Yes	Some	Exam	No
3800	**7260**	**7450**	Yes	100	No	Yes	Yes	Some	Exam	No
15330	33430	35440	No	100	No	Yes	Yes	Some	Exam	No
9790	20710	22130	No	100	No	Yes	Yes	Some	Exam	No
13580	29400	31520	No	100	No	Yes	Yes	Some	Exam	No
9660	20760	22090	No	100	No	Yes	Yes	Some	Exam	No
4830	11110	10490	No	100	No	Yes	Yes	No	Exam	No
5850	13480	12380	Yes	100	No	Yes	Yes	No	Exam	No
8540	20660	19550	Yes	100	No	Yes	Yes	No	Exam	No
5350	12310	11210	Yes	100	No	Some	Yes	No	Exam	No
4490	9650	9650	Yes	100	No	Yes	Yes	No	Exam	No
6370	15360	14260	Yes	100	No	Yes	Yes	No	Exam	No
4170	8860	8860	Yes	100	No	Some	Yes	No	Exam	No
8340	18660	17800	No	60	Some	Yes	Little	No	Exam	Reduced
6320	13750	13030	No	60	No	Yes	Little	No	Exam	Reduced
5410	10690	11000	No	100	No	Yes	Yes	No	Exam	No
4440	8600	**8760**	Yes	100	No	Some	Some	No	Yes	No
4420	**8540**	**8690**	Yes	100	No	Some	Some	No	Yes	No
6580	13260	13150	Yes	100	No	Some	Some	No	Yes	No
5900	11800	11610	Yes	100	No	Some	Some	No	Yes	No
4560	8840	9020	Yes	100	No	Some	Some	No	Yes	No
4480	8670	8830	Yes	100	No	Some	Some	No	Yes	No
4750	9970	9970	Some	100	No	Some	Some	No	Exam	No
5990	13370	12270	Yes	100	No	Some	Some	No	Exam	No
4920	10780	10230	Yes	100	No	Some	Some	No	Exam	No

Cost & Special Features of All Plans

Plan code	Plan name (primary service area)	Phone number	Average yearly cost in dollars (premiums and out-of-pocket costs): General Schedule			Annuitants 55 to 64		
			Self only	Self plus one	Family	Self only	Self plus one	Family of two
KT1-3	United Choice Open Access	877-835-9861	2640	5390	6930	4030	8280	10220
LU1-3	United HDHP	877-835-9861	**1690**	**3660**	**4200**	**2840**	**6150**	**6350**
Connecticut								
EP1-3	Aetna HealthFund CDHP	888-238-6240	5260	12140	12050	8370	19260	18450
EP4-6	Aetna Value Plan	888-238-6240	3200	7150	7030	4900	11070	10380
Delaware								
EP1-3	Aetna HealthFund CDHP	888-238-6240	5260	12140	12050	8370	19260	18450
P34-6	Aetna Open Access Basic (Phil)	800-537-9384	7310	16790	16520	11100	25460	24720
P31-3	Aetna Open Access-Hi (Philadelphia)	800-537-9384	8370	20670	20430	12630	31190	30510
EP4-6	Aetna Value Plan	888-238-6240	3200	7150	7030	4900	11070	10380
District of Columbia								
F51-3	Aetna HealthFund CDHP	888-238-6240	3280	7680	7540	5410	12580	11700
JN4-6	Aetna Open Access Basic	800-537-9384	2650	5030	5640	4090	7820	8280
JN1-3	Aetna Open Access-Hi	800-537-9384	5650	12650	12290	8570	19140	18340
QQ4-6	Aetna Saver	800-537-9384	2970	5820	6470	4390	8810	9150
F54-6	Aetna Value Plan	888-238-6240	3690	8230	8140	5630	12700	12040
B64-6	CareFirst Blue Value Plus	888-789-9065	2430	4190	5520	3730	**6520**	8200
B61-3	CareFirst HDHP	888-789-9065	**1710**	**3310**	**4090**	**2960**	**5810**	**6450**
2G4-6	CareFirst-Std POS	888-789-9065	3130	5480	7410	4780	8420	11140
T71-3	Kaiser Basic	877-574-3337	**1740**	**3560**	**4000**	**2660**	**5560**	**5830**
E31-3	Kaiser-Hi	877-574-3337	2100	5310	4690	**3220**	8100	7000
E34-6	Kaiser-Std	877-574-3337	**1770**	**3790**	**4000**	**2740**	**5910**	**5930**
JP1-3	MD-IPA	877-835-9861	3740	6400	11850	5700	9800	17650
LR1-3	United Choice Open Access	877-835-9861	2560	5220	5990	3910	8030	8810
L91-3	United Choice Plus Advanced	877-835-9861	2140	4270	5430	**3110**	**6320**	7650
AS1-3	United Choice Plus Primary	877-835-9861	2230	4300	4840	3480	6810	7150
Y81-3	United Choice Primary	877-835-9861	2190	4210	4750	3430	**6680**	7010
V41-3	United HDHP	877-835-9861	**1780**	**3840**	**4390**	**2970**	**6430**	**6640**
Florida								
F51-3	Aetna HealthFund CDHP	888-238-6240	3280	7680	7540	5410	12580	11700
F54-6	Aetna Value Plan	888-238-6240	3690	8230	8140	5630	12700	12040
WZ1-3	AvMed HDHP (South)	800-882-8633	3180	5960	7600	5020	9500	11390
ML4-6	AvMed-Std (South)	800-882-8633	3010	5660	7130	4460	8470	10210

Lowest costs are in bold type. Note that in some plans, family costs are lower than self-plus-one costs.

Average yearly cost (continued)			Medicare wrap-around	Day limit in skilled nursing facility	Pays for...					
Annuitants 65 or older with Medicare Parts A & B										
Self only	Self plus one	Family			Routine dental	Chiro-practic	Acupunc-ture	Hearing aids	Adult vision care	Non network providers
5910	11820	13760	No	60	Some	Some	Some	No	Exam	No
4840	10080	10280	No	60	Some	Yes	Some	Yes	Exam	Reduced
10390	23290	22480	No	60	Some	Yes	Little	No	Exam	Reduced
6890	15010	14320	No	60	No	Yes	Little	No	Exam	Reduced
10390	23290	22480	No	60	Some	Yes	Little	No	Exam	Reduced
12690	28780	28040	No	60	Yes	Yes	Little	No	Yes	No
14530	34820	34140	No	60	Yes	Yes	Little	No	Yes	No
6890	15010	14320	No	60	No	Yes	Little	No	Exam	Reduced
7430	16610	15730	No	60	Some	Yes	Little	No	Exam	Reduced
6050	11570	12040	No	60	Yes	Some	Little	Some	Yes	No
10460	22780	21980	No	60	Yes	Some	Little	Some	Yes	No
6280	12620	12950	No	60	No	Some	Little	No	Yes	No
7610	16630	15970	No	60	No	Yes	Little	No	Exam	Reduced
4680	**8560**	10250	Yes	Unlim	Yes	Some	Some	Yes	Exam	Reduced
3710	**6760**	**7400**	Yes	Unlim	Yes	Some	Some	Yes	Exam	Reduced
6040	10960	13670	Yes	Unlim	Yes	Some	Some	Yes	Exam	Reduced
4420	8730	9010	Yes	100	No	Some	Some	No	Exam	No
4710	10980	9880	Yes	100	Yes	Yes	Yes	No	Exam	No
4290	8820	8840	Yes	100	Yes	Some	Some	No	Exam	No
6840	12050	19890	Yes	60	Yes	Some	Some	No	Yes	No
5790	11570	12350	No	60	Some	Some	Some	No	Exam	No
4960	10100	11440	No	60	Some	Some	Some	No	Exam	Reduced
5290	10560	10890	No	60	Some	Some	Some	Yes	Exam	Reduced
5230	10430	10760	No	60	Some	Some	Some	Yes	Exam	No
4970	10350	10570	No	60	Some	Yes	Some	Yes	Exam	Reduced
7430	16610	15730	No	60	Some	Yes	Little	No	Exam	Reduced
7610	16630	15970	No	60	No	Yes	Little	No	Exam	Reduced
6970	13310	15200	Yes	30	No	Yes	No	Yes	No	No
6510	12390	14140	Yes	30	No	Some	No	Yes	No	No

Cost & Special Features of All Plans			Average yearly cost in dollars (premiums and out-of-pocket costs)					
			General Schedule			Annuitants 55 to 64		
Plan code	Plan name (primary service area)	Phone number	Self only	Self plus one	Family	Self only	Self plus one	Family of two
EA1-3	Capital Health (Tallahassee)	850-383-3311	2370	4870	5080	3620	7400	7380
W91-3	Humana CoverageFirst CDHP (D'tona)	800-448-6262	**1990**	**3730**	**4240**	3480	**6660**	**6840**
X21-3	Humana CoverageFirst CDHP (Orl)	800-448-6262	**1940**	**3630**	**4130**	3410	**6510**	**6680**
QP1-3	Humana CoverageFirst CDHP (South)	800-448-6262	2490	4860	5100	4230	8370	8140
MJ1-3	Humana CoverageFirst CDHP (Tampa)	800-448-6262	4270	8680	9100	6910	14100	14130
EX1-3	Humana Medical-Hi (Daytona)	800-448-6262	4030	8290	8510	6130	12590	12560
E21-3	Humana Medical-Hi (Orlando)	800-448-6262	6500	13610	14070	9850	20570	20910
EE1-3	Humana Medical-Hi (South)	800-448-6262	5800	12100	12500	8790	18310	18550
LL1-3	Humana Medical-Hi (Tampa)	800-448-6262	10160	21460	22300	15320	32350	33240
EX4-6	Humana Medical-St (Daytona)	800-448-6262	3020	6040	6220	4650	9330	9110
E24-6	Humana Medical-Std (Orlando)	800-448-6262	2890	5760	5930	4450	8910	8670
EE4-6	Humana Medical-Std (South)	800-448-6262	5140	10600	10990	7820	16170	16260
LL4-6	Humana Medical-Std (Tampa)	800-448-6262	5760	11940	12390	8760	18170	18360
W94-6	Humana Value (Daytona)	800-448-6262	2890	5590	6130	4320	8510	8670
X24-6	Humana Value (Orlando)	800-448-6262	2850	5500	6040	4260	8380	8530
MJ4-6	Humana Value (Tampa)	800-448-6262	2900	5610	6160	4340	8550	8710
QP4-6	Humana Value Plan (South)	800-448-6262	2900	5610	6150	4340	8550	8710
KK1-3	United Choice Open Access	877-835-9861	2550	5200	6710	3900	8000	9900
LV1-3	United Choice Plus Advance	877-835-9861	2620	5620	9950	3830	8360	14410
AS1-3	United Choice Plus Primary	877-835-9861	2230	4300	4840	3480	6810	7150
Y81-3	United Choice Primary	877-835-9861	2190	4210	4750	3430	**6680**	7010
LS1-3	United HDHP	877-835-9861	**1720**	**3700**	**4250**	**2870**	**6220**	**6430**
Georgia								
F51-3	Aetna HealthFund CDHP	888-238-6240	3280	7680	7540	5410	12580	11700
2U1-3	Aetna Open Access (Atlanta/Athens)	800-537-9384	10550	24270	24050	15910	36580	35950
F54-6	Aetna Value Plan	888-238-6240	3690	8230	8140	5630	12700	12040
QM1-3	Blue Open Access POS (Atlanta/Ath)	844-423-9988	2180	4500	5640	3320	6890	8230
AD1-3	Humana CoverageFirst CDHP (Atl)	800-448-6262	4480	9130	9560	7210	14750	14820
S91-3	Humana CoverageFirst CDHP (Col)	800-448-6262	2230	4310	4620	3850	7520	7430
LM1-3	Humana CoverageFirst CDHP (Macon)	800-448-6262	2130	4070	4560	3700	7160	7330
Q71-3	Humana Employers Basic (Atlanta)	800-448-6262	3430	6990	7270	5280	10890	10700
RM1-3	Humana Employers Basic (Columbus)	800-448-6262	2710	5400	5930	4200	8500	8690
RJ1-3	Humana Employers Basic (Macon)	800-448-6262	2610	5180	5700	4050	8170	8350
DG1-3	Humana Employers-Hi (Atlanta)	800-448-6262	7550	15840	16430	11430	23940	24430

Lowest costs are in bold type. Note that in some plans, family costs are lower than self-plus-one costs.

Average yearly cost (continued)			Medicare wrap-around	Day limit in skilled nursing facility	Pays for...					
Annuitants 65 or older with Medicare Parts A & B										
Self only	Self plus one	Family			Routine dental	Chiro-practic	Acupunc-ture	Hearing aids	Adult vision care	Non network providers
5620	11230	11210	No	60	No	Some	No	No	Exam	No
3670	**7090**	**7270**	Yes	60	No	Some	Some	No	No	Reduced
3600	**6930**	**7110**	Yes	60	No	Some	Some	No	No	Reduced
4420	8800	**8570**	Yes	60	No	Some	Some	No	No	Reduced
7100	14530	14560	Yes	60	No	Some	Some	No	No	Reduced
7240	14760	14730	Yes	100	No	Yes	Some	No	No	No
10950	22740	23080	Yes	100	No	Yes	Some	No	No	No
9900	20480	20720	Yes	100	No	Yes	Some	No	No	No
16430	34520	35410	Yes	100	No	Yes	Some	No	No	No
5510	10960	10730	Yes	100	No	Yes	Some	No	No	No
5310	10540	10300	Yes	100	No	Yes	Some	No	No	No
8690	17790	17890	Yes	100	No	Yes	Some	No	No	No
9620	19800	19990	Yes	100	No	Yes	Some	No	No	No
4360	**8430**	**8580**	Yes	60	No	Yes	Some	No	No	No
4300	**8300**	**8450**	Yes	60	No	Yes	Some	No	No	No
4380	**8470**	**8620**	Yes	60	No	Yes	Some	No	No	No
4380	**8470**	**8620**	Yes	60	No	Yes	Some	No	No	No
5780	11540	13440	No	60	Some	Some	Some	No	Exam	No
5700	12170	18230	No	60	Some	Some	Some	No	Exam	Reduced
5290	10560	10890	No	60	Some	Some	Some	Yes	Exam	Reduced
5230	10430	10760	No	60	Some	Some	Some	Yes	Exam	No
4870	10150	10350	No	60	Some	Yes	Some	Yes	Exam	Reduced
7430	16610	15730	No	60	Some	Yes	Little	No	Exam	Reduced
17860	40310	39690	No	60	Yes	Yes	Some	No	Yes	No
7610	16630	15970	No	60	No	Yes	Little	No	Exam	Reduced
5270	10750	12090	No	60	No	Yes	No	No	No	Reduced
7400	15180	15250	Yes	60	No	Some	Some	No	No	Reduced
4040	**7950**	**7850**	Yes	60	No	Some	Some	No	No	Reduced
3890	**7590**	**7760**	Yes	60	No	Some	Some	No	No	Reduced
5870	11750	11560	Yes	100	No	Some	Some	No	Yes	No
4800	9360	9550	Yes	100	No	Some	Some	No	Yes	No
4640	9030	9210	Yes	100	No	Some	Some	No	Yes	No
12580	26170	26660	Yes	100	No	Yes	Some	No	No	No

Cost & Special Features of All Plans			Average yearly cost in dollars (premiums and out-of-pocket costs)					
			General Schedule			Annuitants 55 to 64		
Plan code	Plan name (primary service area)	Phone number	Self only	Self plus one	Family	Self only	Self plus one	Family of two
CB1-3	Humana Employers-Hi (Columbus)	800-448-6262	6160	12860	13300	9350	19470	19750
DN1-3	Humana Employers-Hi (Macon)	800-448-6262	3220	6520	6680	4930	9970	9810
DG4-6	Humana Employers-Std (Atlanta)	800-448-6262	6530	13620	14140	9920	20700	21000
CB4-6	Humana Employers-Std (Columbus)	800-448-6262	7160	14970	15560	10860	22730	23130
DN4-6	Humana Employers-Std (Macon)	800-448-6262	2970	5940	6120	4570	9200	8970
AD4-6	Humana Value Plan (Atlanta)	800-448-6262	3670	7330	7620	5500	11120	10910
S94-6	Humana Value Plan (Columbus)	800-448-6262	2960	5750	6300	4440	8760	8930
LM4-6	Humana Value Plan (Macon)	800-448-6262	3150	6140	6710	4710	9350	9540
LA1-3	Kaiser Basic (Most of St) student POS	888-865-5813	**1440**	**2910**	**3080**	**2220**	**4560**	**4560**
F81-3	Kaiser-Hi (Most of St) student POS	888-865-5813	2440	5650	5110	3760	8720	7610
F84-6	Kaiser-Std (Most of St) student POS	888-865-5813	**1970**	**3590**	**4270**	**3060**	**5650**	**6300**
LV1-3	United Choice Plus Advance	877-835-9861	2620	5620	9950	3830	8360	14410
AS1-3	United Choice Plus Primary	877-835-9861	2230	4300	4840	3480	6810	7150
Y81-3	United Choice Primary	877-835-9861	2190	4210	4750	3430	**6680**	7010
Guam								
B41-3	Calvo's Selectcare-Hi	671-477-9808	**1620**	**3030**	**3900**	**2540**	**4740**	**5770**
B44-6	Calvo's Selectcare-Std	671-477-9808	**1650**	**3080**	**4060**	**2600**	**4930**	**6040**
JK1-3	TakeCare-Hi	671-647-3526	**1570**	**2970**	**3530**	**2430**	**4590**	**5200**
JK4-6	TakeCare-Std	671-647-3526	**1530**	**2850**	**3710**	**2390**	**4430**	**5440**
KX1-3	TakeCare HDHP	671-647-3526	**1560**	**3380**	**3980**	**2590**	**5750**	**5850**
Hawaii								
JS1-3	Aetna HealthFund CDHP	888-238-6240	4680	10830	10730	7510	17300	16470
JS4-6	Aetna Value Plan	888-238-6240	5720	12920	12720	8670	19720	18910
871-3	HMSA POS	800-776-4672	**1850**	**3930**	**4180**	**2850**	**6050**	**6150**
874-6	HMSA Standard	800-776-4672	**1980**	4140	**4500**	**2990**	**6390**	**6460**
631-3	Kaiser-Hi student POS	808-432-5955	**1990**	4610	**4520**	**3050**	7120	**6670**
634-6	Kaiser-Std student POS	808-432-5955	**1670**	**3640**	**3880**	**2570**	**5670**	**5670**
Idaho								
9K4-6	Aetna Health/Altius HDHP	800-837-0977	**1940**	**3690**	**4080**	**3190**	**6130**	**6190**
9K1-3	Aetna Health/Altius-Hi	800-837-0977	4820	10440	10110	7300	15880	15040
DK4-6	Aetna Health/Altius-Std	800-837-0977	3190	6640	6320	4850	10140	9240
H41-3	Aetna HealthFund CDHP	888-238-6240	3280	7660	7520	5400	12550	11670
H44-6	Aetna Value Plan	888-238-6240	3580	8030	7930	5470	12400	11730

Lowest costs are in bold type. Note that in some plans, family costs are lower than self-plus-one costs.

Average yearly cost (continued)			Medicare wrap-around	Day limit in skilled nursing facility	Pays for...					
Annuitants 65 or older with Medicare Parts A & B					Routine dental	Chiro-practic	Acupunc-ture	Hearing aids	Adult vision care	Non network providers
Self only	Self plus one	Family								
10500	21700	21980	Yes	100	No	Yes	Some	No	No	No
6090	12210	12040	Yes	100	No	Yes	Some	No	No	No
10780	22300	22600	Yes	100	No	Yes	Some	No	No	No
11730	24330	24730	Yes	100	No	Yes	Some	No	No	No
5430	10800	10570	Yes	100	No	Yes	Some	No	No	No
5540	11040	10820	Yes	60	No	Yes	Some	No	No	No
4470	8680	8840	Yes	60	No	Yes	Some	No	No	No
4750	9260	9450	Yes	60	No	Yes	Some	No	No	No
3580	**7300**	**7300**	Yes	100	No	Some	No	No	Exam	No
5120	11410	10310	Yes	100	Some	Yes	No	No	Exam	No
4430	**8490**	9140	Yes	100	Some	Some	No	No	Exam	No
5700	12170	18230	No	60	Some	Some	Some	No	Exam	Reduced
5290	10560	10890	No	60	Some	Some	Some	Yes	Exam	Reduced
5230	10430	10760	No	60	Some	Some	Some	Yes	Exam	No
3950	**7510**	**8530**	Yes	100	Some	Some	Little	Some	Exam	No
3890	**7450**	**8560**	Yes	100	Some	Little	Little	Some	Exam	No
3910	**7410**	**8010**	Yes	100	Yes	Some	Little	Some	Yes	No
4340	**8160**	9170	No	60	Some	Some	Little	No	Yes	No
4620	9970	10070	No	100	Yes	Some	No	No	Yes	No
9530	21340	20510	No	60	Some	Yes	Little	No	Exam	Reduced
10650	23660	22850	No	60	No	Yes	Little	No	Exam	Reduced
4720	9730	9840	No	100	Yes	Some	No	Yes	No	Reduced
4950	10350	10420	Yes	100	No	Some	No	Yes	No	Reduced
4720	10080	9630	Yes	120	Some	No	No	Yes	Exam	No
4320	8970	8970	Yes	120	Some	No	No	Yes	Exam	No
4670	9160	9230	Yes	30	No	Some	No	Yes	Exam	Reduced
8470	18100	17270	Yes	30	Yes	Some	No	Yes	Exam	No
6020	12370	11460	Yes	30	No	Some	No	Yes	Exam	No
7430	16580	15710	No	60	Some	Yes	Little	No	Exam	Reduced
7460	16330	15670	No	60	No	Yes	Little	No	Exam	Reduced

Cost & Special Features of All Plans			Average yearly cost in dollars (premiums and out-of-pocket costs)					
			General Schedule			Annuitants 55 to 64		
Plan code	Plan name (primary service area)	Phone number	Self only	Self plus one	Family	Self only	Self plus one	Family of two
541-3	Kaiser Washington-Hi (WA/N ID)	888-901-4636	3590	7860	7350	5370	11830	10730
544-6	Kaiser Washington-Std (WA/N ID)	888-901-4636	2290	4600	4850	3480	6930	**6930**
Illinois								
H41-3	Aetna HealthFund CDHP	888-238-6240	3280	7660	7520	5400	12550	11670
H44-6	Aetna Value Plan	888-238-6240	3580	8030	7930	5470	12400	11730
9G1-3	Blue Preferred-Hi POS (St L/Other)	888-811-2092	3550	7040	7340	5390	10730	10800
9G4-6	Blue Preferred-Std (St L/Other)	888-811-2092	2330	5620	6490	3560	8630	9490
K84-6	Health Alliance (So IL/So IN/Cen IA)	800-851-3379	3020	6640	8320	4470	10010	11990
GB1-3	Humana CoverageFirst CDHP (Cent'l)	800-448-6262	6130	12690	13290	9700	20100	20410
MW1-3	Humana CoverageFirst CDHP (Chi)	800-448-6262	4020	8140	8520	6520	13270	13270
RW1-3	Humana Health Basic (Chicago)	800-448-6262	3140	6330	6520	4840	9770	9570
AB1-3	Humana Health Basic (Rockford/NW)	800-448-6262	3210	6470	6670	4940	9990	9790
751-3	Humana Health-Hi (Chicago)	888-393-6765	6890	14410	14930	10430	21800	22180
9F1-3	Humana Health-Hi (Rockford/NW)	888-393-6765	12480	26440	27530	18820	39840	41070
754-6	Humana Health-Std (Chicago)	888-393-6765	4770	9830	10180	7280	15020	15060
AB4-6	Humana Health-Std (Rockford/NW)	888-393-6765	6360	13230	13740	9650	20120	20400
GB4-6	Humana Value Plan (Central)	800-448-6262	3840	7680	7990	5750	11650	11460
MW4-6	Humana Value Plan (Chicago)	800-448-6262	3810	7630	7930	5710	11570	11380
EY1-3	MercyCare HMO-Hi (Rockford)	800-895-2421	3080	6170	8550	4650	9350	12580
EY4-6	MercyCare HMO-Std (Rockford)	800-895-2421	2710	6170	6190	4090	7910	8860
761-3	Union Health (Chicago)	312-423-4200	2760	6070	7400	4170	9140	10840
L91-3	United Choice Plus Advanced (Chicago)	877-835-9861	2140	4270	5430	**3110**	**6320**	7650
AS1-3	United Choice Plus Primary	877-835-9861	2230	4300	4840	3480	6810	7150
Y81-3	United Choice Primary	877-835-9861	2190	4210	4750	3430	**6680**	7010
Indiana								
JS1-3	Aetna HealthFund CDHP	888-238-6240	4680	10830	10730	7510	17300	16470
JS4-6	Aetna Value Plan	888-238-6240	5720	12920	12720	8670	19720	18910
K84-6	Health Alliance (So IL/So IN/Cen IA)	800-851-3379	3020	6640	8320	4470	10010	11990
TC1-3	Humana Cov'First CDHP (Louisville)	800-448-6262	2090	**3950**	**4470**	3640	7000	7200
MW1-3	Humana CoverageFirst CDHP (Chi)	800-448-6262	4020	8140	8520	6520	13270	13270
X31-3	Humana CoverageFirst CDHP (Cin'ati)	800-448-6262	3080	6140	6420	5120	10270	10120
RW1-3	Humana Health Basic (Chicago)	800-448-6262	3140	6330	6520	4840	9770	9570
W61-3	Humana Health Basic (Cincinnati)	800-448-6262	2680	5350	5880	4140	8420	8600

Lowest costs are in bold type. Note that in some plans, family costs are lower than self-plus-one costs.

Average yearly cost (continued)			Medicare wrap-around	Day limit in skilled nursing facility	Pays for...					
Annuitants 65 or older with Medicare Parts A & B					Routine dental	Chiro-practic	Acupunc-ture	Hearing aids	Adult vision care	Non network providers
Self only	Self plus one	Family								
6390	14110	13010	Yes	100	Some	Yes	Some	No	Exam	No
4170	9060	9060	Yes	100	No	Yes	Some	No	Exam	No
7430	16580	15710	No	60	Some	Yes	Little	No	Exam	Reduced
7460	16330	15670	No	60	No	Yes	Little	No	Exam	Reduced
7400	14560	14640	No	60	No	Some	No	No	Exam	No
5610	12580	13430	Yes	90	No	Some	No	No	Exam	No
4750	10470	12450	Yes	Unlim	No	Some	No	Some	Exam	No
9890	20520	20840	Yes	60	No	Some	Some	No	No	Reduced
6710	13700	13700	Yes	60	No	Some	Some	No	No	Reduced
5700	11370	11170	Yes	100	No	Some	Some	No	Yes	No
5800	11590	11390	Yes	100	No	Some	Some	No	Yes	No
11590	24030	24420	Yes	100	No	Some	Some	No	Yes	No
19980	42070	43300	Yes	100	No	Some	Some	No	Yes	No
8140	16620	16670	Yes	100	No	Some	Some	No	Yes	No
10510	21720	22000	Yes	100	No	Some	Some	No	Yes	No
5790	11570	11380	Yes	60	No	Yes	Some	No	No	No
5750	11490	11290	Yes	60	No	Yes	Some	No	No	No
6560	13000	16230	No	120	No	Some	Some	Some	Exam	No
5910	11640	12590	No	120	No	Some	Some	Some	Exam	No
5720	12180	13880	Yes	60	No	Yes	No	No	Some	No
4960	10100	11440	No	60	Some	Some	Some	No	Exam	Reduced
5290	10560	10890	No	60	Some	Some	Some	Yes	Exam	Reduced
5230	10430	10760	No	60	Some	Some	Some	Yes	Exam	No
9530	21340	20510	No	60	Some	Yes	Little	No	Exam	Reduced
10650	23660	22850	No	60	No	Yes	Little	No	Exam	Reduced
4750	10470	12450	Yes	Unlim	No	Some	No	Some	Exam	No
3830	**7430**	**7620**	Yes	60	No	Some	Some	No	No	Reduced
6710	13700	13700	Yes	60	No	Some	Some	No	No	Reduced
5310	10690	10550	Yes	60	No	Some	Some	No	No	Reduced
5700	11370	11170	Yes	100	No	Some	Some	No	Yes	No
4680	9100	9280	Yes	100	No	Some	Some	No	Exam	No

Cost & Special Features of All Plans			Average yearly cost in dollars (premiums and out-of-pocket costs)					
			General Schedule			Annuitants 55 to 64		
Plan code	Plan name (primary service area)	Phone number	Self only	Self plus one	Family	Self only	Self plus one	Family of two
751-3	Humana Health-Hi (Chicago)	888-393-6765	6890	14410	14930	10430	21800	22180
A61-3	Humana Health-Hi (Cincinnati)	800-448-6262	9040	19010	19750	13650	28690	29390
MH1-3	Humana Health-Hi (Louisville)	800-448-6262	5850	12170	12590	8880	18440	18670
754-6	Humana Health-Std (Chicago)	888-393-6765	4770	9830	10180	7280	15020	15060
A64-6	Humana Health-Std (Cincinnati)	800-448-6262	6610	13750	14290	10020	20910	21210
MH4-6	Humana Health-Std (Louisville)	800-448-6262	4080	8320	8610	6230	12770	12700
MW4-6	Humana Value Plan (Chicago)	800-448-6262	3810	7630	7930	5710	11570	11380
X34-6	Humana Value Plan (Cincinnati)	800-448-6262	3090	6020	6590	4630	9170	9350
761-3	Union Health (Chicago)	312-423-4200	2760	6070	7400	4170	9140	10840
L91-3	United Choice Plus Advanced (Chicago)	877-835-9861	2140	4270	5430	**3110**	**6320**	7650
Iowa								
H41-3	Aetna HealthFund CDHP	888-238-6240	3280	7660	7520	5400	12550	11670
H44-6	Aetna Value Plan	888-238-6240	3580	8030	7930	5470	12400	11730
K84-6	Health Alliance (So IL/So IN/Cen IA)	800-851-3379	3020	6640	8320	4470	10010	11990
V31-3	HealthPartners-Hi (Statewide)	800-883-2177	2320	5080	5840	3620	7890	8720
V34-6	HealthPartners-Std (Statewide)	952-883-5000	2350	4460	4960	3480	**6690**	7010
LJ1-3	United Choice Open Access	877-835-9861	2600	5310	6840	3970	8160	10090
AS1-3	United Choice Plus Primary	877-835-9861	2230	4300	4840	3480	6810	7150
Y81-3	United Choice Primary	877-835-9861	2190	4210	4750	3430	**6680**	7010
N71-3	United HDHP	877-835-9861	2030	4370	4960	3340	7220	7500
Kansas								
G51-3	Aetna HealthFund CDHP	888-238-6240	3880	9050	8920	6310	14620	13770
HA1-3	Aetna Open Access-Hi (Kansas City)	800-537-9384	6280	15110	14990	9370	22620	21830
HA4-6	Aetna Open Access-Std (Kansas City)	800-537-9384	3450	8580	8490	5130	12830	11930
G54-6	Aetna Value Plan	888-238-6240	2830	6300	6170	4340	9810	9100
PH1-3	Humana CoverageFirst CDHP (KS City)	800-448-6262	2410	4690	4900	4110	8090	7850
MS1-3	Humana Health-Hi (Kansas City)	800-448-6262	10800	22810	23720	16300	34390	35360
MS4-6	Humana Health-Std (Kansas City)	800-448-6262	5740	11890	12340	8720	18120	18300
PH4-6	Humana Value Plan (Kansas City)	800-448-6262	2830	5460	6000	4230	8320	8470
Kentucky								
H41-3	Aetna HealthFund CDHP	888-238-6240	3280	7660	7520	5400	12550	11670
H44-6	Aetna Value Plan	888-238-6240	3580	8030	7930	5470	12400	11730
TC1-3	Humana Cov'First CDHP (Louisville)	800-448-6262	2090	**3950**	**4470**	3640	7000	7200

Lowest costs are in bold type. Note that in some plans, family costs are lower than self-plus-one costs.

Average yearly cost (continued)			Medicare wrap-around	Day limit in skilled nursing facility	Pays for...					
Annuitants 65 or older with Medicare Parts A & B										
Self only	Self plus one	Family			Routine dental	Chiro-practic	Acupunc-ture	Hearing aids	Adult vision care	Non network providers
11590	24030	24420	Yes	100	No	Some	Some	No	Yes	No
14700	30740	31440	Yes	100	No	Some	Some	No	Exam	No
9980	20570	20800	Yes	100	No	Yes	Some	No	Exam	No
8140	16620	16670	Yes	100	No	Some	Some	No	Yes	No
10790	22310	22610	Yes	100	No	Some	Some	No	Exam	No
7040	14240	14170	Yes	100	No	Some	Some	No	Exam	No
5750	11490	11290	Yes	60	No	Yes	Some	No	No	No
4660	9080	9270	Yes	60	No	Yes	Some	No	No	No
5720	12180	13880	Yes	60	No	Yes	No	No	Some	No
4960	10100	11440	No	60	Some	Some	Some	No	Exam	Reduced
7430	16580	15710	No	60	Some	Yes	Little	No	Exam	Reduced
7460	16330	15670	No	60	No	Yes	Little	No	Exam	Reduced
4750	10470	12450	Yes	Unlim	No	Some	No	Some	Exam	No
4870	10260	11090	Yes	120	Some	Yes	Yes	Some	No	Nationwide
5250	10170	10480	No	120	No	Yes	Yes	No	No	Nationwide
5850	11700	13630	No	60	Some	Some	Some	No	Exam	No
5290	10560	10890	No	60	Some	Some	Some	Yes	Exam	Reduced
5230	10430	10760	No	60	Some	Some	Some	Yes	Exam	No
5340	11150	11430	No	60	Some	Yes	Some	Yes	Exam	Reduced
8340	18660	17800	No	60	Some	Yes	Little	No	Exam	Reduced
11290	26540	25740	No	60	Yes	Yes	No	Yes	Exam	No
7040	16890	15990	No	60	Yes	Yes	No	Yes	Exam	No
6320	13750	13030	No	60	No	Yes	Little	No	Exam	Reduced
4300	**8520**	**8270**	Yes	60	No	Some	Some	No	No	Reduced
17400	36520	37490	Yes	100	No	Yes	Some	No	Exam	No
9520	19590	19770	Yes	100	No	Some	Some	No	Exam	No
4270	**8240**	**8380**	Yes	60	No	Yes	Some	No	No	No
7430	16580	15710	No	60	Some	Yes	Little	No	Exam	Reduced
7460	16330	15670	No	60	No	Yes	Little	No	Exam	Reduced
3830	**7430**	**7620**	Yes	60	No	Some	Some	No	No	Reduced

Cost & Special Features of All Plans

Plan code	Plan name (primary service area)	Phone number	Average yearly cost in dollars (premiums and out-of-pocket costs): General Schedule			Annuitants 55 to 64		
			Self only	Self plus one	Family	Self only	Self plus one	Family of two
X31-3	Humana CoverageFirst CDHP (Cin'ati)	800-448-6262	3080	6140	6420	5120	10270	10120
6N1-3	Humana CoverageFirst CDHP (Lex)	800-448-6262	2820	5570	5830	4730	9420	9240
W61-3	Humana Health Basic (Cincinnati)	800-448-6262	2680	5350	5880	4140	8420	8600
A61-3	Humana Health-Hi (Cincinnati)	800-448-6262	9040	19010	19750	13650	28690	29390
MI1-3	Humana Health-Hi (Lex/Central)	800-448-6262	8070	16920	17570	12190	25580	26130
MH1-3	Humana Health-Hi (Louisville)	800-448-6262	5850	12170	12590	8880	18440	18670
A64-6	Humana Health-Std (Cincinnati)	800-448-6262	6610	13750	14290	10020	20910	21210
MI4-6	Humana Health-Std (Lex/Central)	800-448-6262	4280	8760	9070	6540	13420	13380
MH4-6	Humana Health-Std (Louisville)	800-448-6262	4080	8320	8610	6230	12770	12700
X34-6	Humana Value Plan (Cincinnati)	800-448-6262	3090	6020	6590	4630	9170	9350
LJ1-3	United Choice Open Access	877-835-9861	2600	5310	6840	3970	8160	10090
AS1-3	United Choice Plus Primary	877-835-9861	2230	4300	4840	3480	6810	7150
Y81-3	United Choice Primary	877-835-9861	2190	4210	4750	3430	**6680**	7010
N71-3	United HDHP	877-835-9861	2030	4370	4960	3340	7220	7500
Louisiana								
F51-3	Aetna HealthFund CDHP	888-238-6240	3280	7680	7540	5410	12580	11700
F54-6	Aetna Value Plan	888-238-6240	3690	8230	8140	5630	12700	12040
AE1-3	Humana Health-Hi (Baton Rouge)	800-448-6262	5550	11530	11910	8420	17480	17660
BC1-3	Humana Health-Hi (New Orleans)	800-448-6262	4180	8600	8850	6380	13090	13070
AE4-6	Humana Health-Std (Baton Rouge)	800-448-6262	3620	7350	7580	5550	11300	11170
BC4-6	Humana Health-Std (New Orleans)	800-448-6262	2590	5090	5550	4010	7920	8120
KK1-3	United Choice Open Access	877-835-9861	2550	5200	6710	3900	8000	9900
AS1-3	United Choice Plus Primary	877-835-9861	2230	4300	4840	3480	6810	7150
Y81-3	United Choice Primary	877-835-9861	2190	4210	4750	3430	**6680**	7010
LS1-3	United HDHP	877-835-9861	**1720**	**3700**	**4250**	**2870**	**6220**	**6430**
Maine								
EP1-3	Aetna HealthFund CDHP	888-238-6240	5260	12140	12050	8370	19260	18450
EP4-6	Aetna Value Plan	888-238-6240	3200	7150	7030	4900	11070	10380
Maryland								
F51-3	Aetna HealthFund CDHP	888-238-6240	3280	7680	7540	5410	12580	11700
JN4-6	Aetna Open Access Basic	800-537-9384	2650	5030	5640	4090	7820	8280
JN1-3	Aetna Open Access-Hi	800-537-9384	5650	12650	12290	8570	19140	18340
QQ4-6	Aetna Saver	800-537-9384	2970	5820	6470	4390	8810	9150

Lowest costs are in bold type. Note that in some plans, family costs are lower than self-plus-one costs.

Average yearly cost (continued) Annuitants 65 or older with Medicare Parts A & B: Self only	Self plus one	Family	Medicare wrap-around	Day limit in skilled nursing facility	Pays for... Routine dental	Chiro-practic	Acupunc-ture	Hearing aids	Adult vision care	Non network providers
5310	10690	10550	Yes	60	No	Some	Some	No	No	Reduced
4920	9850	9670	Yes	60	No	Some	Some	No	No	No
4680	9100	9280	Yes	100	No	Some	Some	No	Exam	No
14700	30740	31440	Yes	100	No	Some	Some	No	Exam	No
13300	27710	28260	Yes	100	No	Yes	Some	No	Exam	No
9980	20570	20800	Yes	100	No	Yes	Some	No	Exam	No
10790	22310	22610	Yes	100	No	Some	Some	No	Exam	No
7340	14900	14860	Yes	100	No	Some	Some	No	Exam	No
7040	14240	14170	Yes	100	No	Some	Some	No	Exam	No
4660	9080	9270	Yes	60	No	Yes	Some	No	No	No
5850	11700	13630	No	60	Some	Some	Some	No	Exam	No
5290	10560	10890	No	60	Some	Some	Some	Yes	Exam	Reduced
5230	10430	10760	No	60	Some	Some	Some	Yes	Exam	No
5340	11150	11430	No	60	Some	Yes	Some	Yes	Exam	Reduced
7430	16610	15730	No	60	Some	Yes	Little	No	Exam	Reduced
7610	16630	15970	No	60	No	Yes	Little	No	Exam	Reduced
9580	19710	19890	Yes	100	No	Some	Some	No	Exam	No
7540	15320	15300	Yes	100	No	Some	Some	No	Exam	No
6410	12900	12770	Yes	100	No	Some	Some	No	Exam	No
4870	9520	9720	Yes	100	No	Some	Some	No	Exam	No
5780	11540	13440	No	60	Some	Some	Some	No	Exam	No
5290	10560	10890	No	60	Some	Some	Some	Yes	Exam	Reduced
5230	10430	10760	No	60	Some	Some	Some	Yes	Exam	No
4870	10150	10350	No	60	Some	Yes	Some	Yes	Exam	Reduced
10390	23290	22480	No	60	Some	Yes	Little	No	Exam	Reduced
6890	15010	14320	No	60	No	Yes	Little	No	Exam	Reduced
7430	16610	15730	No	60	Some	Yes	Little	No	Exam	Reduced
6050	11570	12040	No	60	Yes	Some	Little	Some	Yes	No
10460	22780	21980	No	60	Yes	Some	Little	Some	Yes	No
6280	12620	12950	No	60	No	Some	Little	No	Yes	No

Cost & Special Features of All Plans			Average yearly cost in dollars (premiums and out-of-pocket costs)					
Plan code	Plan name (primary service area)	Phone number	General Schedule			Annuitants 55 to 64		
			Self only	Self plus one	Family	Self only	Self plus one	Family of two
F54-6	Aetna Value Plan	888-238-6240	3690	8230	8140	5630	12700	12040
B64-6	CareFirst Blue Value Plus	888-789-9065	2430	4190	5520	3730	**6520**	8200
B61-3	CareFirst HDHP	888-789-9065	**1710**	**3310**	**4090**	**2960**	**5810**	**6450**
2G4-6	CareFirst-Std POS	888-789-9065	3130	5480	7410	4780	8420	11140
T71-3	Kaiser Basic	877-574-3337	**1740**	**3560**	**4000**	**2660**	**5560**	**5830**
E31-3	Kaiser-Hi	877-574-3337	2100	5310	4690	**3220**	8100	7000
E34-6	Kaiser-Std	877-574-3337	**1770**	**3790**	**4000**	**2740**	**5910**	**5930**
JP1-3	MD-IPA	877-835-9861	3740	6400	11850	5700	9800	17650
LR1-3	United Choice Open Access	877-835-9861	2560	5220	5990	3910	8030	8810
L91-3	United Choice Plus Advanced	877-835-9861	2140	4270	5430	**3110**	**6320**	7650
AS1-3	United Choice Plus Primary	877-835-9861	2230	4300	4840	3480	6810	7150
Y81-3	United Choice Primary	877-835-9861	2190	4210	4750	3430	**6680**	7010
V41-3	United HDHP	877-835-9861	**1780**	**3840**	**4390**	**2970**	**6430**	**6640**
Massachusetts								
EP1-3	Aetna HealthFund CDHP	888-238-6240	5260	12140	12050	8370	19260	18450
EP4-6	Aetna Value Plan	888-238-6240	3200	7150	7030	4900	11070	10380
Michigan								
G51-3	Aetna HealthFund CDHP	888-238-6240	3880	9050	8920	6310	14620	13770
G54-6	Aetna Value Plan	888-238-6240	2830	6300	6170	4340	9810	9100
LX1-3	Blue Care Network (Detroit)	800-662-6667	2680	6280	6560	4070	9480	9630
K51-3	Blue Care Network (Flint/Sag)	800-662-6667	4400	10230	10760	6650	15410	15920
521-3	Health Alliance-Hi (Det/Flint/Sag)	800-556-9765	3110	7290	7650	4750	11060	11290
GY4-6	Health Alliance-Std (Det/Flint/Sag)	800-556-9765	2530	5120	5580	3740	7690	7950
Y41-3	Priority Health Value (Lower Peninsula)	800-446-5674	2730	5410	5950	4060	8060	8270
LE1-3	Priority Health-Hi (Lower Peninsula)	800-446-5674	4170	8960	9540	6340	13540	14090
LE4-6	Priority Health-Std (Lower Peninsula)	800-446-5674	2560	4930	5430	3850	7540	7780
Minnesota								
H41-3	Aetna HealthFund CDHP	888-238-6240	3280	7660	7520	5400	12550	11670
H44-6	Aetna Value Plan	888-238-6240	3580	8030	7930	5470	12400	11730
V31-3	HealthPartners-Hi	800-883-2177	2320	5080	5840	3620	7890	8720
V34-6	HealthPartners-Std	952-883-5000	2350	4460	4960	3480	**6690**	7010

Lowest costs are in bold type. Note that in some plans, family costs are lower than self-plus-one costs.

Average yearly cost (continued)			Medicare wrap-around	Day limit in skilled nursing facility	Pays for...					
Annuitants 65 or older with Medicare Parts A & B										
Self only	Self plus one	Family			Routine dental	Chiro-practic	Acupunc-ture	Hearing aids	Adult vision care	Non network providers
7610	16630	15970	No	60	No	Yes	Little	No	Exam	Reduced
4680	**8560**	10250	Yes	Unlim	Yes	Some	Some	Yes	Exam	Reduced
3710	**6760**	**7400**	Yes	Unlim	Yes	Some	Some	Yes	Exam	Reduced
6040	10960	13670	Yes	Unlim	Yes	Some	Some	Yes	Exam	Reduced
4420	8730	9010	Yes	100	No	Some	Some	No	Exam	No
4710	10980	9880	Yes	100	Yes	Yes	Yes	No	Exam	No
4290	8820	8840	Yes	100	Yes	Some	Some	No	Exam	No
6840	12050	19890	Yes	60	Yes	Some	Some	No	Yes	No
5790	11570	12350	No	60	Some	Some	Some	No	Exam	No
4960	10100	11440	No	60	Some	Some	Some	No	Exam	Reduced
5290	10560	10890	No	60	Some	Some	Some	Yes	Exam	Reduced
5230	10430	10760	No	60	Some	Some	Some	Yes	Exam	No
4970	10350	10570	No	60	Some	Yes	Some	Yes	Exam	Reduced
10390	23290	22480	No	60	Some	Yes	Little	No	Exam	Reduced
6890	15010	14320	No	60	No	Yes	Little	No	Exam	Reduced
8340	18660	17800	No	60	Some	Yes	Little	No	Exam	Reduced
6320	13750	13030	No	60	No	Yes	Little	No	Exam	Reduced
5990	13170	13310	No	Unlim	No	Some	No	Yes	Yes	No
8570	19100	19600	No	Unlim	No	Some	No	Yes	Yes	No
6720	14820	15040	Yes	Unlim	No	No	No	Yes	Exam	No
5670	11470	11730	Yes	100	No	No	No	Yes	Exam	No
4470	8650	8860	Yes	45	No	Yes	No	No	Exam	No
7780	16400	16960	Yes	45	No	Yes	No	No	Exam	No
4630	9020	9270	Yes	45	No	Yes	No	No	Exam	No
7430	16580	15710	No	60	Some	Yes	Little	No	Exam	Reduced
7460	16330	15670	No	60	No	Yes	Little	No	Exam	Reduced
4870	10260	11090	Yes	120	Some	Yes	Yes	Some	No	Nationwide
5250	10170	10480	No	120	No	Yes	Yes	No	No	Nationwide

Cost & Special Features of All Plans

Plan code	Plan name (primary service area)	Phone number	Average yearly cost in dollars (premiums and out-of-pocket costs)					
			General Schedule			Annuitants 55 to 64		
			Self only	Self plus one	Family	Self only	Self plus one	Family of two
Missouri								
G51-3	Aetna HealthFund CDHP	888-238-6240	3880	9050	8920	6310	14620	13770
HA1-3	Aetna Open Access-Hi (Kansas City)	800-537-9384	6280	15110	14990	9370	22620	21830
HA4-6	Aetna Open Access-Std (Kansas City)	800-537-9384	3450	8580	8490	5130	12830	11930
G54-6	Aetna Value Plan	888-238-6240	2830	6300	6170	4340	9810	9100
9G1-3	Blue Preferred-Hi POS (St L/Other)	888-811-2092	3550	7040	7340	5390	10730	10800
9G4-6	Blue Preferred-Std (St L/Other)	888-811-2092	2330	5620	6490	3560	8630	9490
PH1-3	Humana CoverageFirst CDHP (KS City)	800-448-6262	2410	4690	4900	4110	8090	7850
MS1-3	Humana Health-Hi (Kansas City)	800-448-6262	10800	22810	23720	16300	34390	35360
MS4-6	Humana Health-Std (Kansas City)	800-448-6262	5740	11890	12340	8720	18120	18300
PH4-6	Humana Value Plan (Kansas City)	800-448-6262	2830	5460	6000	4230	8320	8470
AS1-3	United Choice Plus Primary	877-835-9861	2230	4300	4840	3480	6810	7150
Y81-3	United Choice Primary	877-835-9861	2190	4210	4750	3430	**6680**	7010
Mississippi								
H41-3	Aetna HealthFund CDHP	888-238-6240	3280	7660	7520	5400	12550	11670
H44-6	Aetna Value Plan	888-238-6240	3580	8030	7930	5470	12400	11730
KK1-3	United Choice Open Access	877-835-9861	2550	5200	6710	3900	8000	9900
AS1-3	United Choice Plus Primary	877-835-9861	2230	4300	4840	3480	6810	7150
Y81-3	United Choice Primary	877-835-9861	2190	4210	4750	3430	**6680**	7010
LS1-3	United HDHP	877-835-9861	**1720**	**3700**	**4250**	**2870**	**6220**	**6430**
Montana								
H41-3	Aetna HealthFund CDHP	888-238-6240	3280	7660	7520	5400	12550	11670
H44-6	Aetna Value Plan	888-238-6240	3580	8030	7930	5470	12400	11730
Nebraska								
H41-3	Aetna HealthFund CDHP	888-238-6240	3280	7660	7520	5400	12550	11670
H44-6	Aetna Value Plan	888-238-6240	3580	8030	7930	5470	12400	11730
Nevada								
G51-3	Aetna HealthFund CDHP	888-238-6240	3880	9050	8920	6310	14620	13770
G54-6	Aetna Value Plan	888-238-6240	2830	6300	6170	4340	9810	9100
NM1-3	Health Plan of Nevada (Las Vegas)	877-545-7378	2360	4080	5510	3570	**6200**	8070
KT1-3	United Choice Open Access	877-835-9861	2640	5390	6930	4030	8280	10220
WF1-3	United Choice Plus Primary	877-835-9861	2220	4280	4820	3470	6790	7120

Lowest costs are in bold type. Note that in some plans, family costs are lower than self-plus-one costs.

Average yearly cost (continued)			Medicare wrap-around	Day limit in skilled nursing facility	Pays for...					
Annuitants 65 or older with Medicare Parts A & B										
Self only	Self plus one	Family			Routine dental	Chiro-practic	Acupunc-ture	Hearing aids	Adult vision care	Non network providers
8340	18660	17800	No	60	Some	Yes	Little	No	Exam	Reduced
11290	26540	25740	No	60	Yes	Yes	No	Yes	Exam	No
7040	16890	15990	No	60	Yes	Yes	No	Yes	Exam	No
6320	13750	13030	No	60	No	Yes	Little	No	Exam	Reduced
7400	14560	14640	No	60	No	Some	No	No	Exam	No
5610	12580	13430	Yes	90	No	Some	No	No	Exam	No
4300	**8520**	**8270**	Yes	60	No	Some	Some	No	No	Reduced
17400	36520	37490	Yes	100	No	Yes	Some	No	Exam	No
9520	19590	19770	Yes	100	No	Some	Some	No	Exam	No
4270	**8240**	**8380**	Yes	60	No	Yes	Some	No	No	No
5290	10560	10890	No	60	Some	Some	Some	Yes	Exam	Reduced
5230	10430	10760	No	60	Some	Some	Some	Yes	Exam	No
7430	16580	15710	No	60	Some	Yes	Little	No	Exam	Reduced
7460	16330	15670	No	60	No	Yes	Little	No	Exam	Reduced
5780	11540	13440	No	60	Some	Some	Some	No	Exam	No
5290	10560	10890	No	60	Some	Some	Some	Yes	Exam	Reduced
5230	10430	10760	No	60	Some	Some	Some	Yes	Exam	No
4870	10150	10350	No	60	Some	Yes	Some	Yes	Exam	Reduced
7430	16580	15710	No	60	Some	Yes	Little	No	Exam	Reduced
7460	16330	15670	No	60	No	Yes	Little	No	Exam	Reduced
7430	16580	15710	No	60	Some	Yes	Little	No	Exam	Reduced
7460	16330	15670	No	60	No	Yes	Little	No	Exam	Reduced
8340	18660	17800	No	60	Some	Yes	Little	No	Exam	Reduced
6320	13750	13030	No	60	No	Yes	Little	No	Exam	Reduced
5050	8950	10820	Yes	Unlim	No	Yes	No	Yes	Exam	No
5910	11820	13760	No	60	Some	Some	Some	No	Exam	No
5280	10540	10870	No	60	Some	Some	Some	Yes	Exam	Reduced

Cost & Special Features of All Plans			Average yearly cost in dollars (premiums and out-of-pocket costs)					
			General Schedule			Annuitants 55 to 64		
Plan code	Plan name (primary service area)	Phone number	Self only	Self plus one	Family	Self only	Self plus one	Family of two
VD1-3	United Choice Primary	877-835-9861	2220	4280	4820	3470	6780	7120
LU1-3	United HDHP	877-835-9861	**1690**	**3660**	**4200**	**2840**	**6150**	**6350**
New Hampshire								
EP1-3	Aetna HealthFund CDHP	888-238-6240	5260	12140	12050	8370	19260	18450
EP4-6	Aetna Value Plan	888-238-6240	3200	7150	7030	4900	11070	10380
New Jersey								
EP1-3	Aetna HealthFund CDHP	888-238-6240	5260	12140	12050	8370	19260	18450
JR4-6	Aetna Open Access Basic (Northern)	800-537-9384	7810	17910	17650	11860	27150	26420
P34-6	Aetna Open Access Basic (Phil)	800-537-9384	7310	16790	16520	11100	25460	24720
JR1-3	Aetna Open Access-Hi (Northern)	800-537-9384	9070	20960	20720	13690	31620	30950
P31-3	Aetna Open Access-Hi (Philadelphia)	800-537-9384	8370	20670	20430	12630	31190	30510
EP4-6	Aetna Value Plan	888-238-6240	3200	7150	7030	4900	11070	10380
811-3	GHI Health HDHP (NY State/N NJ)	212-501-4444	2320	4620	5110	3920	7820	7900
804-6	GHI Health-Std (NY State/N NJ)	212-501-4444	5200	12270	12690	7900	18720	18820
New Mexico								
G51-3	Aetna HealthFund CDHP	888-238-6240	3880	9050	8920	6310	14620	13770
G54-6	Aetna Value Plan	888-238-6240	2830	6300	6170	4340	9810	9100
PS1-3	Presbyterian Wellness (NM/El Paso)	800-356-2219	3260	6680	7270	4850	10080	10220
P21-3	Presbyterian-Hi (NM/El Paso)	800-356-2219	3640	8240	8280	5540	12500	12210
PS4-6	Presbyterian-Std (NM/El Paso)	800-356-2219	3170	7350	7510	4700	11200	10780
EL1-3	True Health-Hi (NM/El Paso)	844-508-4677	2250	4560	4950	3380	6880	7110
New York								
EP1-3	Aetna HealthFund CDHP	888-238-6240	5260	12140	12050	8370	19260	18450
JC4-6	Aetna Open Access Basic (NYC/Upst)	800-537-9384	5650	14000	13700	8610	21280	20500
JC1-3	Aetna Open Access-Hi (NYC/Upst)	800-537-9384	7280	18540	18280	11000	27990	27280
EP4-6	Aetna Value Plan	888-238-6240	3200	7150	7030	4900	11070	10380
SG1-3	CDPHP-Hi (Alb/Sch) student POS	877-269-2134	4810	9320	14990	7260	14040	22220
SG4-6	CDPHP-Std (Alb/Sch) student POS	877-269-2134	2380	4550	7040	3630	6930	10240
811-3	GHI Health HDHP (NY State/N NJ)	212-501-4444	2320	4620	5110	3920	7820	7900
804-6	GHI Health-Std (NY State/N NJ)	212-501-4444	5200	12270	12690	7900	18720	18820
511-3	HIP HMO-Hi (NYC/Southeast)	800-447-8255	5580	8670	17250	8420	13110	25610
YL4-6	HIP HMO-Std (NYC/Southeast)	800-447-8255	4410	6980	13650	6590	10590	19800
QA4-6	Independent Health HDHP (Buffalo)	800-501-3439	**1910**	4290	4920	3340	7350	7660

Lowest costs are in bold type. Note that in some plans, family costs are lower than self-plus-one costs.

Average yearly cost (continued)			Medicare wrap-around	Day limit in skilled nursing facility	Pays for...					
Annuitants 65 or older with Medicare Parts A & B										
Self only	Self plus one	Family			Routine dental	Chiro-practic	Acupunc-ture	Hearing aids	Adult vision care	Non network providers
5280	10530	10870	No	60	Some	Some	Some	Yes	Exam	No
4840	10080	10280	No	60	Some	Yes	Some	Yes	Exam	Reduced
10390	23290	22480	No	60	Some	Yes	Little	No	Exam	Reduced
6890	15010	14320	No	60	No	Yes	Little	No	Exam	Reduced
10390	23290	22480	No	60	Some	Yes	Little	No	Exam	Reduced
13440	30460	29740	No	60	Yes	Yes	Little	No	Yes	No
12690	28780	28040	No	60	Yes	Yes	Little	No	Yes	No
15590	35260	34580	No	60	Yes	Yes	Little	No	Yes	No
14530	34820	34140	No	60	Yes	Yes	Little	No	Yes	No
6890	15010	14320	No	60	No	Yes	Little	No	Exam	Reduced
6120	12430	12510	Yes	30	No	Some	Yes	No	Yes	Reduced
8740	20130	20230	Yes	30	Some	Some	Yes	Yes	Yes	Reduced
8340	18660	17800	No	60	Some	Yes	Little	No	Exam	Reduced
6320	13750	13030	No	60	No	Yes	Little	No	Exam	Reduced
6380	13000	13150	Yes	60	No	Some	Some	No	Child Exam	No
6800	14960	14660	Yes	60	No	Some	Some	No	Child Exam	No
5740	12470	12050	Yes	60	No	Some	Some	No	Child Exam	No
4720	9460	9690	No	60	No	Some	Some	No	Exam	No
10390	23290	22480	No	60	Some	Yes	Little	No	Exam	Reduced
10190	24600	23820	No	60	Yes	Yes	Little	No	Yes	No
12900	31620	30910	No	60	Yes	Yes	Little	No	Yes	No
6890	15010	14320	No	60	No	Yes	Little	No	Exam	Reduced
9240	17800	25980	No	90	No	Yes	Some	Some	Exam	No
5600	10750	14060	No	90	No	Yes	Some	Some	Exam	No
6120	12430	12510	Yes	30	No	Some	Yes	No	Yes	Reduced
8740	20130	20230	Yes	30	Some	Some	Yes	Yes	Yes	Reduced
10440	16940	29440	Yes	Unlim	Some	Some	No	Yes	Exam	No
8800	14990	24210	Yes	30	Some	Some	No	Yes	Exam	No
5470	11450	11760	No	45	Some	Yes	No	No	Some	Reduced

Cost & Special Features of All Plans

Plan code	Plan name (primary service area)	Phone number	Average yearly cost in dollars (premiums and out-of-pocket costs): General Schedule			Annuitants 55 to 64		
			Self only	Self plus one	Family	Self only	Self plus one	Family of two
QA1-3	Independent Health-Hi POS (Buffalo)	800-501-3439	3110	8720	9170	4770	13270	13540
C54-6	Independent Health-Std POS (Buff)	800-501-3439	2810	7890	8320	4330	12080	12260
North Carolina								
F51-3	Aetna HealthFund CDHP	888-238-6240	3280	7680	7540	5410	12580	11700
F54-6	Aetna Value Plan	888-238-6240	3690	8230	8140	5630	12700	12040
KK1-3	United Choice Open Access	877-835-9861	2550	5200	6710	3900	8000	9900
AS1-3	United Choice Plus Primary	877-835-9861	2230	4300	4840	3480	6810	7150
Y81-3	United Choice Primary	877-835-9861	2190	4210	4750	3430	**6680**	7010
LS1-3	United HDHP	877-835-9861	**1720**	**3700**	**4250**	**2870**	**6220**	**6430**
North Dakota								
H41-3	Aetna HealthFund CDHP	888-238-6240	3280	7660	7520	5400	12550	11670
H44-6	Aetna Value Plan	888-238-6240	3580	8030	7930	5470	12400	11730
V31-3	HealthPartners-Hi	800-883-2177	2320	5080	5840	3620	7890	8720
V34-6	HealthPartners-Std	952-883-5000	2350	4460	4960	3480	**6690**	7010
Ohio								
JS1-3	Aetna HealthFund CDHP	888-238-6240	4680	10830	10730	7510	17300	16470
JS4-6	Aetna Value Plan	888-238-6240	5720	12920	12720	8670	19720	18910
3A4-6	AultCare HDHP (Canton)	330-363-6360	**1570**	**3540**	5120	**2730**	**6030**	7740
3A1-3	AultCare-Hi (Canton)	330-363-6360	3280	6450	8350	4960	9760	12400
X31-3	Humana CoverageFirst CDHP (Cin'ati)	800-448-6262	3080	6140	6420	5120	10270	10120
W61-3	Humana Health Basic (Cincinnati)	800-448-6262	2680	5350	5880	4140	8420	8600
A61-3	Humana Health-Hi (Cincinnati)	800-448-6262	9040	19010	19750	13650	28690	29390
A64-6	Humana Health-Std (Cincinnati)	800-448-6262	6610	13750	14290	10020	20910	21210
X34-6	Humana Value Plan (Cincinnati)	800-448-6262	3090	6020	6590	4630	9170	9350
UX1-3	Medical Mutual Basic (Cleve/Akron)	800-315-3144	2590	5120	5690	3810	7710	7970
YF1-3	Medical Mutual Basic (Dayton)	800-315-3144	2590	5120	5690	3810	7710	7970
X61-3	Medical Mutual Basic (Toledo)	800-315-3144	2590	5120	5690	3810	7710	7970
644-6	Medical Mutual-Std (Cleve/Akron)	800-315-3144	5340	11500	12720	8080	17460	18830
YF4-6	Medical Mutual-Std (Dayton)	800-315-3144	4870	10460	11590	7370	15910	17130
X64-6	Medical Mutual-Std (Toledo)	800-315-3144	3910	8360	9290	5940	12750	13690
Oklahoma								
JS1-3	Aetna HealthFund CDHP	888-238-6240	4680	10830	10730	7510	17300	16470
JS4-6	Aetna Value Plan	888-238-6240	5720	12920	12720	8670	19720	18910

Lowest costs are in bold type. Note that in some plans, family costs are lower than self-plus-one costs.

Average yearly cost (continued)			Medicare wrap-around	Day limit in skilled nursing facility	Pays for...					
Annuitants 65 or older with Medicare Parts A & B										
Self only	Self plus one	Family			Routine dental	Chiro-practic	Acupunc-ture	Hearing aids	Adult vision care	Non network providers
6840	17180	17450	No	45	No	Yes	No	No	Some	Reduced
6450	16080	16260	No	30	No	Yes	No	No	Some	Reduced
7430	16610	15730	No	60	Some	Yes	Little	No	Exam	Reduced
7610	16630	15970	No	60	No	Yes	Little	No	Exam	Reduced
5780	11540	13440	No	60	Some	Some	Some	No	Exam	No
5290	10560	10890	No	60	Some	Some	Some	Yes	Exam	Reduced
5230	10430	10760	No	60	Some	Some	Some	Yes	Exam	No
4870	10150	10350	No	60	Some	Yes	Some	Yes	Exam	Reduced
7430	16580	15710	No	60	Some	Yes	Little	No	Exam	Reduced
7460	16330	15670	No	60	No	Yes	Little	No	Exam	Reduced
4870	10260	11090	Yes	120	Some	Yes	Yes	Some	No	Nationwide
5250	10170	10480	No	120	No	Yes	Yes	No	No	Nationwide
9530	21340	20510	No	60	Some	Yes	Little	No	Exam	Reduced
10650	23660	22850	No	60	No	Yes	Little	No	Exam	Reduced
4750	9890	11600	Yes	Unlim	No	Yes	No	Some	Yes	Reduced
6320	12510	15150	Yes	Unlim	Yes	Yes	No	Some	Yes	No
5310	10690	10550	Yes	60	No	Some	Some	No	No	Reduced
4680	9100	9280	Yes	100	No	Some	Some	No	Exam	No
14700	30740	31440	Yes	100	No	Some	Some	No	Exam	No
10790	22310	22610	Yes	100	No	Some	Some	No	Exam	No
4660	9080	9270	Yes	60	No	Yes	Some	No	No	No
5790	11640	11910	No	100	No	No	No	No	Exam	No
5790	11640	11910	No	100	No	No	No	No	Exam	No
5790	11640	11900	No	100	No	No	No	No	Exam	No
10160	21450	22820	No	100	No	Some	No	No	Exam	No
9450	19900	21130	No	100	No	Some	No	No	Exam	No
8020	16740	17680	No	100	No	Some	No	No	Exam	No
9530	21340	20510	No	60	Some	Yes	Little	No	Exam	Reduced
10650	23660	22850	No	60	No	Yes	Little	No	Exam	Reduced

Cost & Special Features of All Plans			Average yearly cost in dollars (premiums and out-of-pocket costs)					
Plan code	Plan name (primary service area)	Phone number	General Schedule			Annuitants 55 to 64		
			Self only	Self plus one	Family	Self only	Self plus one	Family of two
IM1-3	GlobalHealth-Hi (Statewide)	877-280-2989	2200	4140	5430	3360	**6320**	7930
IM4-6	GlobalHealth-Std (Statewide)	877-280-2989	2710	5080	6030	4020	7590	8520
Oregon								
H41-3	Aetna HealthFund CDHP	888-238-6240	3280	7660	7520	5400	12550	11670
H44-6	Aetna Value Plan	888-238-6240	3580	8030	7930	5470	12400	11730
571-3	Kaiser Northwest-Hi	800-813-2000	2600	5870	5350	3970	8980	7880
574-6	Kaiser Northwest-Std	800-813-2000	2490	5220	5300	3740	7930	7640
KT1-3	United Choice Open Access	877-835-9861	2640	5390	6930	4030	8280	10220
WF1-3	United Choice Plus Primary	877-835-9861	2220	4280	4820	3470	6790	7120
VD1-3	United Choice Primary	877-835-9861	2220	4280	4820	3470	6780	7120
LU1-3	United HDHP	877-835-9861	**1690**	**3660**	**4200**	**2840**	**6150**	**6350**
Panama								
431-3	Panama Canal	800-424-8196	**1900**	**3580**	**3830**	**2880**	**5380**	**5550**
Pennsylvania								
H41-3	Aetna HealthFund CDHP	888-238-6240	3280	7660	7520	5400	12550	11670
YE1-3	Aetna Open Access (Western)	800-537-9384	6400	16810	16520	9690	25390	24650
P34-6	Aetna Open Access Basic (Phil)	800-537-9384	7310	16790	16520	11100	25460	24720
P31-3	Aetna Open Access-Hi (Philadelphia)	800-537-9384	8370	20670	20430	12630	31190	30510
H44-6	Aetna Value Plan	888-238-6240	3580	8030	7930	5470	12400	11730
GG4-6	Geisinger-Std (Harr/York/Lanc/N'th)	800-447-4000	3970	8260	8720	5870	12410	12580
LR1-3	United Choice Open Access	877-835-9861	2560	5220	5990	3910	8030	8810
AS1-3	United Choice Plus Primary	877-835-9861	2230	4300	4840	3480	6810	7150
Y81-3	United Choice Primary	877-835-9861	2190	4210	4750	3430	**6680**	7010
V41-3	United HDHP	877-835-9861	**1780**	**3840**	**4390**	**2970**	**6430**	**6640**
8W4-6	UPMC HDHP (Western)	888-876-2756	2030	4230	4770	3500	7300	7460
YS4-6	UPMC HDHP Eastern)	888-876-2756	2930	6570	6820	4840	10790	10520
YS1-3	UPMC-Hi (Eastern)	877-648-9641	6300	14140	14620	9440	21310	21580
8W1-3	UPMC-Hi (Western)	877-648-9641	4650	10430	10750	6960	15750	15770
YT4-6	UPMC-Std (Eastern)	877-648-9641	4550	10140	10480	6840	15390	15360
UW4-6	UPMC-Std (Western)	877-648-9641	2750	5990	6150	4140	9170	8870
Puerto Rico								
ZJ1-3	Humana Health POS	800-314-3121	**1140**	**2310**	**2480**	**1750**	**3500**	**3620**
891-3	Triple-S Salud POS	800-981-3241	**1180**	**2460**	**2600**	**1830**	**3750**	**3810**

Lowest costs are in bold type. Note that in some plans, family costs are lower than self-plus-one costs.

Average yearly cost (continued)			Medicare wrap-around	Day limit in skilled nursing facility	Pays for...					
Annuitants 65 or older with Medicare Parts A & B					Routine dental	Chiro-practic	Acupunc-ture	Hearing aids	Adult vision care	Non network providers
Self only	Self plus one	Family								
5320	10080	11690	No	Unlim	No	Yes	No	No	Exam	No
6110	11620	12550	No	Unlim	No	Some	No	No	Exam	No
7430	16580	15710	No	60	Some	Yes	Little	No	Exam	Reduced
7460	16330	15670	No	60	No	Yes	Little	No	Exam	Reduced
4710	10930	9830	Yes	100	No	Yes	Yes	No	Yes	No
4160	9280	8990	Yes	100	No	Yes	Yes	No	Yes	No
5910	11820	13760	No	60	Some	Some	Some	No	Exam	No
5280	10540	10870	No	60	Some	Some	Some	Yes	Exam	Reduced
5280	10530	10870	No	60	Some	Some	Some	Yes	Exam	No
4840	10080	10280	No	60	Some	Yes	Some	Yes	Exam	Reduced
4590	8720	8890	Yes	60	Yes	Yes	Yes	Some	No	Reduced
7430	16580	15710	No	60	Some	Yes	Little	No	Exam	Reduced
11640	29130	28390	No	60	Yes	Yes	Some	No	Yes	No
12690	28780	28040	No	60	Yes	Yes	Little	No	Yes	No
14530	34820	34140	No	60	Yes	Yes	Little	No	Yes	No
7460	16330	15670	No	60	No	Yes	Little	No	Exam	Reduced
6850	13850	14020	Yes	60	No	Some	No	No	Exam	No
5790	11570	12350	No	60	Some	Some	Some	No	Exam	No
5290	10560	10890	No	60	Some	Some	Some	Yes	Exam	Reduced
5230	10430	10760	No	60	Some	Some	Some	Yes	Exam	No
4970	10350	10570	No	60	Some	Yes	Some	Yes	Exam	Reduced
5430	11120	11280	No	100	Yes	Yes	Some	Yes	Exam	No
6780	14620	14350	No	100	Yes	Yes	Some	Yes	Exam	No
11340	25060	25330	No	100	Yes	Yes	Some	Some	Exam	No
8870	19500	19520	No	100	Yes	Yes	Some	Some	Exam	No
8660	18630	18600	No	100	Yes	Yes	Some	Some	Exam	No
5960	12410	12110	No	100	Yes	Yes	Some	Some	Exam	No
3410	**6760**	**6880**	Yes	60	Yes	Some	No	No	Exam	Reduced
3440	**6930**	**6980**	Yes	Unlim	Yes	Yes	Some	Some	Yes	Reduced

Cost & Special Features of All Plans			Average yearly cost in dollars (premiums and out-of-pocket costs)					
Plan code	Plan name (primary service area)	Phone number	General Schedule			Annuitants 55 to 64		
			Self only	Self plus one	Family	Self only	Self plus one	Family of two
Rhode Island								
EP1-3	Aetna HealthFund CDHP	888-238-6240	5260	12140	12050	8370	19260	18450
EP4-6	Aetna Value Plan	888-238-6240	3200	7150	7030	4900	11070	10380
South Carolina								
JS1-3	Aetna HealthFund CDHP	888-238-6240	4680	10830	10730	7510	17300	16470
JS4-6	Aetna Value Plan	888-238-6240	5720	12920	12720	8670	19720	18910
South Dakota								
G51-3	Aetna HealthFund CDHP	888-238-6240	3880	9050	8920	6310	14620	13770
G54-6	Aetna Value Plan	888-238-6240	2830	6300	6170	4340	9810	9100
V31-3	HealthPartners-Hi	800-883-2177	2320	5080	5840	3620	7890	8720
V34-6	HealthPartners-Std	952-883-5000	2350	4460	4960	3480	**6690**	7010
Tennessee								
F51-3	Aetna HealthFund CDHP	888-238-6240	3280	7680	7540	5410	12580	11700
UB1-3	Aetna Open Access (Memphis)	800-537-9384	5170	14180	13860	7840	21450	20670
F54-6	Aetna Value Plan	888-238-6240	3690	8230	8140	5630	12700	12040
TT1-3	Humana CoverageFirst CDHP (Knox)	800-448-6262	2650	5190	5450	4470	8870	8660
GJ1-3	Humana Health-Hi (Knoxville)	800-448-6262	6420	13390	13860	9730	20270	20580
GJ4-6	Humana Health-Std (Knoxville)	800-448-6262	4160	8500	8800	6360	13040	12980
TT4-6	Humana Value Plan (Knoxville)	800-448-6262	3240	6390	6890	4850	9710	9810
KK1-3	United Choice Open Access	877-835-9861	2550	5200	6710	3900	8000	9900
AS1-3	United Choice Plus Primary	877-835-9861	2230	4300	4840	3480	6810	7150
Y81-3	United Choice Primary	877-835-9861	2190	4210	4750	3430	**6680**	7010
LS1-3	United HDHP	877-835-9861	**1720**	**3700**	**4250**	**2870**	**6220**	**6430**
Texas								
JS1-3	Aetna HealthFund CDHP	888-238-6240	4680	10830	10730	7510	17300	16470
JS4-6	Aetna Value Plan	888-238-6240	5720	12920	12720	8670	19720	18910
TV1-3	Humana CoverageFirst CDHP (Austin)	800-448-6262	3420	6870	7190	5630	11360	11270
TP1-3	Humana CoverageFirst CDHP (C Ch)	800-448-6262	2460	4800	5020	4190	8260	8020
T31-3	Humana CoverageFirst CDHP (H'ston)	800-448-6262	2760	5420	5690	4630	9210	9020
TU1-3	Humana CoverageFirst CDHP (S Ant)	800-448-6262	2070	**3900**	**4410**	3600	6910	7110
QY1-3	Humana Health Basic (Austin)	800-448-6262	3460	7080	7370	5310	11020	10830
Q21-3	Humana Health Basic (Corpus Christi)	800-448-6262	3250	6630	6900	5000	10350	10130

Lowest costs are in bold type. Note that in some plans, family costs are lower than self-plus-one costs.

Average yearly cost (continued)			Medicare wrap-around	Day limit in skilled nursing facility	Pays for...					
Annuitants 65 or older with Medicare Parts A & B					Routine dental	Chiro-practic	Acupunc-ture	Hearing aids	Adult vision care	Non network providers
Self only	Self plus one	Family								
10390	23290	22480	No	60	Some	Yes	Little	No	Exam	Reduced
6890	15010	14320	No	60	No	Yes	Little	No	Exam	Reduced
9530	21340	20510	No	60	Some	Yes	Little	No	Exam	Reduced
10650	23660	22850	No	60	No	Yes	Little	No	Exam	Reduced
8340	18660	17800	No	60	Some	Yes	Little	No	Exam	Reduced
6320	13750	13030	No	60	No	Yes	Little	No	Exam	Reduced
4870	10260	11090	Yes	120	Some	Yes	Yes	Some	No	Nationwide
5250	10170	10480	No	120	No	Yes	Yes	No	No	Nationwide
7430	16610	15730	No	60	Some	Yes	Little	No	Exam	Reduced
9790	25190	24410	No	60	Yes	Yes	Some	No	Yes	No
7610	16630	15970	No	60	No	Yes	Little	No	Exam	Reduced
4660	9290	9090	Yes	60	No	Some	Some	No	No	Reduced
10830	22400	22710	Yes	100	No	Yes	Some	No	Exam	No
7160	14510	14460	Yes	100	No	Some	Some	No	Exam	No
4880	9630	9730	Yes	60	No	Yes	Some	No	No	No
5780	11540	13440	No	60	Some	Some	Some	No	Exam	No
5290	10560	10890	No	60	Some	Some	Some	Yes	Exam	Reduced
5230	10430	10760	No	60	Some	Some	Some	Yes	Exam	No
4870	10150	10350	No	60	Some	Yes	Some	Yes	Exam	Reduced
9530	21340	20510	No	60	Some	Yes	Little	No	Exam	Reduced
10650	23660	22850	No	60	No	Yes	Little	No	Exam	Reduced
5820	11790	11700	Yes	60	No	Some	Some	No	No	Reduced
4380	8680	**8450**	Yes	60	No	Some	Some	No	No	Reduced
4830	9640	9450	Yes	60	No	Some	Some	No	No	Reduced
3790	**7340**	**7530**	Yes	60	No	Some	Some	No	No	Reduced
5850	11700	11510	Yes	100	No	Some	Some	No	Exam	No
5540	11030	10810	Yes	100	No	Some	Some	No	Exam	No

Cost & Special Features of All Plans			Average yearly cost in dollars (premiums and out-of-pocket costs)					
Plan code	Plan name (primary service area)	Phone number	General Schedule			Annuitants 55 to 64		
			Self only	Self plus one	Family	Self only	Self plus one	Family of two
Q61-3	Humana Health Basic (Houston)	800-448-6262	2710	5420	5950	4180	8520	8710
QX1-3	Humana Health Basic (San Antonio)	800-448-6262	3370	6880	7160	5170	10720	10510
UU1-3	Humana Health-Hi (Austin)	800-448-6262	9330	19670	20440	14100	29690	30440
UC1-3	Humana Health-Hi (Corpus Christi)	800-448-6262	5740	11940	12340	8710	18090	18310
EW1-3	Humana Health-Hi (Houston)	800-448-6262	6030	12570	13010	9150	19040	19300
UR1-3	Humana Health-Hi (San Antonio)	800-448-6262	8030	16880	17510	12150	25500	26050
UU4-6	Humana Health-Std (Austin)	800-448-6262	10520	22160	23090	15880	33510	34410
UC4-6	Humana Health-Std (Corpus Christi)	800-448-6262	3950	8030	8310	6030	12330	12240
EW4-6	Humana Health-Std (Houston)	800-448-6262	3920	7960	8240	5980	12230	12140
UR4-6	Humana Health-Std (San Antonio)	800-448-6262	5070	10440	10830	7710	15950	16030
TV4-6	Humana Value Plan (Austin)	800-448-6262	3190	6240	6810	4780	9500	9700
TP4-6	Humana Value Plan (Corpus Christi)	800-448-6262	2710	5200	5720	4050	7930	8060
T34-6	Humana Value Plan (Houston)	800-448-6262	2920	5650	6190	4370	8610	8770
TU4-6	Humana Value Plan (San Antonio)	800-448-6262	2920	5650	6190	4360	8610	8760
PS1-3	Presbyterian Wellness (NM/El Paso)	800-356-2219	3260	6680	7270	4850	10080	10220
P21-3	Presbyterian-Hi (NM/El Paso)	800-356-2219	3640	8240	8280	5540	12500	12210
PS4-6	Presbyterian-Std (NM/El Paso)	800-356-2219	3170	7350	7510	4700	11200	10780
A81-3	Scott & White Basic (Austin/Central)	800-321-7947	2970	6180	6780	4480	9390	9630
P81-3	Scott & White Basic (Dallas/Ft W)	800-321-7947	3010	6540	6950	4540	9930	9890
A84-6	Scott & White-Std (Austin/Central)	800-321-7947	3530	7580	7960	5270	11430	11550
P84-6	Scott & White-Std (Dallas/Ft W)	800-321-7947	3850	8280	8710	5740	12480	12670
EL1-3	True Health-Hi (NM/El Paso)	844-508-4677	2250	4560	4950	3380	6880	7110
L91-3	United Choice Plus Advanced (S Ant)	877-835-9861	2140	4270	5430	**3110**	**6320**	7650
AS1-3	United Choice Plus Primary	877-835-9861	2230	4300	4840	3480	6810	7150
Y81-3	United Choice Primary	877-835-9861	2190	4210	4750	3430	**6680**	7010
Utah								
9K4-6	Aetna Health/Altius HDHP	800-837-0977	**1940**	**3690**	**4080**	**3190**	**6130**	**6190**
9K1-3	Aetna Health/Altius-Hi	800-837-0977	4820	10440	10110	7300	15880	15040
DK4-6	Aetna Health/Altius-Std	800-837-0977	3190	6640	6320	4850	10140	9240
G51-3	Aetna HealthFund CDHP	888-238-6240	3880	9050	8920	6310	14620	13770
G54-6	Aetna Value Plan	888-238-6240	2830	6300	6170	4340	9810	9100
WX1-3	SelectHealth HDHP student POS	844-345-3342	**1630**	**3450**	**3780**	**2810**	**5900**	**5900**
SF4-6	SelectHealth-Std	844-345-3342	2290	4510	4750	3470	6900	**6900**

Lowest costs are in bold type. Note that in some plans, family costs are lower than self-plus-one costs.

Average yearly cost (continued)			Medicare wrap-around	Day limit in skilled nursing facility	Pays for...					
Annuitants 65 or older with Medicare Parts A & B										
Self only	Self plus one	Family			Routine dental	Chiro-practic	Acupunc-ture	Hearing aids	Adult vision care	Non network providers
4720	9200	9390	Yes	100	No	Some	Some	No	Exam	No
5710	11400	11190	Yes	100	No	Some	Some	No	Exam	No
15260	31920	32670	Yes	100	No	Some	Some	No	Some	No
9860	20320	20540	Yes	100	No	Some	Some	No	Some	No
10300	21270	21530	Yes	100	No	Some	Some	No	Some	No
13310	27730	28290	Yes	100	No	Some	Some	No	Some	No
16650	34910	35810	Yes	100	No	Some	Some	No	Some	No
6800	13730	13640	Yes	100	No	Some	Some	No	Some	No
6750	13630	13530	Yes	100	No	Some	Some	No	Some	No
8480	17350	17420	Yes	100	No	Some	Some	No	Some	No
4820	9410	9610	Yes	60	No	Yes	Some	No	No	No
4090	**7840**	**7970**	Yes	60	No	Yes	Some	No	No	No
4400	**8520**	**8680**	Yes	60	No	Yes	Some	No	No	No
4400	**8520**	**8680**	Yes	60	No	Yes	Some	No	No	No
6380	13000	13150	Yes	60	No	Some	Some	No	Child Exam	No
6800	14960	14660	Yes	60	No	Some	Some	No	Child Exam	No
5740	12470	12050	Yes	60	No	Some	Some	No	Child Exam	No
4970	9810	10040	Yes	Unlim	No	Some	Little	No	Exam	No
5030	10350	10300	Yes	Unlim	No	Some	Little	No	Exam	No
6250	13150	13270	Yes	Unlim	No	Some	Little	No	Exam	No
6730	14200	14380	Yes	Unlim	No	Some	Little	No	Exam	No
4720	9460	9690	No	60	No	Some	Some	No	Exam	No
4960	10100	11440	No	60	Some	Some	Some	No	Exam	Reduced
5290	10560	10890	No	60	Some	Some	Some	Yes	Exam	Reduced
5230	10430	10760	No	60	Some	Some	Some	Yes	Exam	No
4670	9160	9230	Yes	30	No	Some	No	Yes	Exam	Reduced
8470	18100	17270	Yes	30	Yes	Some	No	Yes	Exam	No
6020	12370	11460	Yes	30	No	Some	No	Yes	Exam	No
8340	18660	17800	No	60	Some	Yes	Little	No	Exam	Reduced
6320	13750	13030	No	60	No	Yes	Little	No	Exam	Reduced
4810	9740	9740	No	30	No	Some	No	Yes	Exam	No
5220	10410	10410	No	30	No	Some	No	Yes	Exam	No

Cost & Special Features of All Plans

Plan code	Plan name (primary service area)	Phone number	Average yearly cost in dollars (premiums and out-of-pocket costs): General Schedule			Annuitants 55 to 64		
			Self only	Self plus one	Family	Self only	Self plus one	Family of two
Vermont								
EP1-3	Aetna HealthFund CDHP	888-238-6240	5260	12140	12050	8370	19260	18450
EP4-6	Aetna Value Plan	888-238-6240	3200	7150	7030	4900	11070	10380
Virgin Islands								
851-3	Triple-S Salud POS	800-981-3241	**1760**	4170	**3920**	**2690**	**6310**	**5790**
Virginia								
JN4-6	Aetna Open Access Basic	800-537-9384	2650	5030	5640	4090	7820	8280
JN1-3	Aetna Open Access-Hi	800-537-9384	5650	12650	12290	8570	19140	18340
QQ4-6	Aetna Saver	800-537-9384	2970	5820	6470	4390	8810	9150
B64-6	CareFirst Blue Value Plus	888-789-9065	2430	4190	5520	3730	**6520**	8200
B61-3	CareFirst HDHP	888-789-9065	**1710**	**3310**	**4090**	**2960**	**5810**	**6450**
2G4-6	CareFirst-Std POS	888-789-9065	3130	5480	7410	4780	8420	11140
T71-3	Kaiser Basic	877-574-3337	**1740**	**3560**	**4000**	**2660**	**5560**	**5830**
E31-3	Kaiser-Hi	877-574-3337	2100	5310	4690	**3220**	8100	7000
E34-6	Kaiser-Std	877-574-3337	**1770**	**3790**	**4000**	**2740**	**5910**	**5930**
JP1-3	MD-IPA	877-835-9861	3740	6400	11850	5700	9800	17650
PG4-6	Optima Health HDHP (Hampton Roads)	800-206-1060	2520	4950	5470	4160	8250	8330
PG1-3	Optima Health-Hi (Hampton Roads)	800-206-1060	3140	7550	7170	4660	11380	10280
LR1-3	United Choice Open Access	877-835-9861	2560	5220	5990	3910	8030	8810
L91-3	United Choice Plus Advanced	877-835-9861	2140	4270	5430	**3110**	**6320**	7650
AS1-3	United Choice Plus Primary	877-835-9861	2230	4300	4840	3480	6810	7150
Y81-3	United Choice Primary	877-835-9861	2190	4210	4750	3430	**6680**	7010
V41-3	United HDHP	877-835-9861	**1780**	**3840**	**4390**	**2970**	**6430**	**6640**
Washington								
G51-3	Aetna HealthFund CDHP	888-238-6240	3880	9050	8920	6310	14620	13770
G54-6	Aetna Value Plan	888-238-6240	2830	6300	6170	4340	9810	9100
571-3	Kaiser Northwest-Hi	800-813-2000	2600	5870	5350	3970	8980	7880
574-6	Kaiser Northwest-Std	800-813-2000	2490	5220	5300	3740	7930	7640
L14-6	Kaiser Washington Options HDHP POS	888-901-4636	2270	4770	5180	3690	7820	7820
L11-3	Kaiser Washington Options-Std POS	888-901-4636	2990	6510	6070	4450	9840	8740
541-3	Kaiser Washington-Hi (WA/N ID)	888-901-4636	3590	7860	7350	5370	11830	10730
544-6	Kaiser Washington-Std (WA/N ID)	888-901-4636	2290	4600	4850	3480	6930	**6930**
KT1-3	United Choice Open Access	877-835-9861	2640	5390	6930	4030	8280	10220

Lowest costs are in bold type. Note that in some plans, family costs are lower than self-plus-one costs.

Average yearly cost (continued)			Medicare wrap-around	Day limit in skilled nursing facility	Pays for...					
Annuitants 65 or older with Medicare Parts A & B					Routine dental	Chiro-practic	Acupunc-ture	Hearing aids	Adult vision care	Non network providers
Self only	Self plus one	Family								
10390	23290	22480	No	60	Some	Yes	Little	No	Exam	Reduced
6890	15010	14320	No	60	No	Yes	Little	No	Exam	Reduced
4310	9490	8970	Yes	Unlim	Yes	Yes	Some	Some	Yes	Reduced
6050	11570	12040	No	60	Yes	Some	Little	Some	Yes	No
10460	22780	21980	No	60	Yes	Some	Little	Some	Yes	No
6280	12620	12950	No	60	No	Some	Little	No	Yes	No
4680	**8560**	10250	Yes	Unlim	Yes	Some	Some	Yes	Exam	Reduced
3710	**6760**	**7400**	Yes	Unlim	Yes	Some	Some	Yes	Exam	Reduced
6040	10960	13670	Yes	Unlim	Yes	Some	Some	Yes	Exam	Reduced
4420	8730	9010	Yes	100	No	Some	Some	No	Exam	No
4710	10980	9880	Yes	100	Yes	Yes	Yes	No	Exam	No
4290	8820	8840	Yes	100	Yes	Some	Some	No	Exam	No
6840	12050	19890	Yes	60	Yes	Some	Some	No	Yes	No
5580	11190	11270	No	100	No	No	No	No	Exam	No
5570	13350	12250	Yes	100	No	No	No	No	Exam	No
5790	11570	12350	No	60	Some	Some	Some	No	Exam	No
4960	10100	11440	No	60	Some	Some	Some	No	Exam	Reduced
5290	10560	10890	No	60	Some	Some	Some	Yes	Exam	Reduced
5230	10430	10760	No	60	Some	Some	Some	Yes	Exam	No
4970	10350	10570	No	60	Some	Yes	Some	Yes	Exam	Reduced
8340	18660	17800	No	60	Some	Yes	Little	No	Exam	Reduced
6320	13750	13030	No	60	No	Yes	Little	No	Exam	Reduced
4710	10930	9830	Yes	100	No	Yes	Yes	No	Yes	No
4160	9280	8990	Yes	100	No	Yes	Yes	No	Yes	No
5610	11590	11590	No	Unlim	Some	Some	Some	Some	Exam	Reduced
5430	11450	10350	Yes	Unlim	Some	Some	Some	Some	Exam	Reduced
6390	14110	13010	Yes	100	Some	Yes	Some	No	Exam	No
4170	9060	9060	Yes	100	No	Yes	Some	No	Exam	No
5910	11820	13760	No	60	Some	Some	Some	No	Exam	No

Cost & Special Features of All Plans

Plan code	Plan name (primary service area)	Phone number	Average yearly cost in dollars (premiums and out-of-pocket costs): General Schedule			Annuitants 55 to 64		
			Self only	Self plus one	Family	Self only	Self plus one	Family of two
WF1-3	United Choice Plus Primary	877-835-9861	2220	4280	4820	3470	6790	7120
VD1-3	United Choice Primary	877-835-9861	2220	4280	4820	3470	6780	7120
LU1-3	United HDHP	877-835-9861	**1690**	**3660**	**4200**	**2840**	**6150**	**6350**
West Virginia								
F51-3	Aetna HealthFund CDHP	888-238-6240	3280	7680	7540	5410	12580	11700
F54-6	Aetna Value Plan	888-238-6240	3690	8230	8140	5630	12700	12040
Wisconsin								
JS1-3	Aetna HealthFund CDHP	888-238-6240	4680	10830	10730	7510	17300	16470
JS4-6	Aetna Value Plan	888-238-6240	5720	12920	12720	8670	19720	18910
WD1-3	Dean Health-Hi	800-279-1301	6150	12470	13850	9280	18880	20530
WD4-6	Dean Health-Std	800-279-1301	2560	5460	6130	3860	8340	8880
WJ1-3	Group Health Coop	608-828-4853	3310	7260	9400	5000	10910	13920
V31-3	HealthPartners-Hi	800-883-2177	2320	5080	5840	3620	7890	8720
V34-6	HealthPartners-Std	952-883-5000	2350	4460	4960	3480	**6690**	7010
EY1-3	MercyCare HMO-Hi (Rockford)	800-895-2421	3080	6170	8550	4650	9350	12580
EY4-6	MercyCare HMO-Std (Rockford)	800-895-2421	2710	6170	6190	4090	7910	8860
TF1-3	Quartz-Hi	800-362-3310	4830	10870	11550	7320	16410	17130
TF4-6	Quartz-Std	800-362-3310	2950	5710	6340	4420	8660	9030
Wyoming								
9K4-6	Aetna Health/Altius HDHP	800-837-0977	**1940**	**3690**	**4080**	**3190**	**6130**	**6190**
9K1-3	Aetna Health/Altius-Hi	800-837-0977	4820	10440	10110	7300	15880	15040
DK4-6	Aetna Health/Altius-Std	800-837-0977	3190	6640	6320	4850	10140	9240
H41-3	Aetna HealthFund CDHP	888-238-6240	3280	7660	7520	5400	12550	11670
H44-6	Aetna Value Plan	888-238-6240	3580	8030	7930	5470	12400	11730

Lowest costs are in bold type. Note that in some plans, family costs are lower than self-plus-one costs.

Average yearly cost (continued)			Medicare wrap-around	Day limit in skilled nursing facility	Pays for...					
Annuitants 65 or older with Medicare Parts A & B										
Self only	Self plus one	Family			Routine dental	Chiro-practic	Acupunc-ture	Hearing aids	Adult vision care	Non network providers
5280	10540	10870	No	60	Some	Some	Some	Yes	Exam	Reduced
5280	10530	10870	No	60	Some	Some	Some	Yes	Exam	No
4840	10080	10280	No	60	Some	Yes	Some	Yes	Exam	Reduced
7430	16610	15730	No	60	Some	Yes	Little	No	Exam	Reduced
7610	16630	15970	No	60	No	Yes	Little	No	Exam	Reduced
9530	21340	20510	No	60	Some	Yes	Little	No	Exam	Reduced
10650	23660	22850	No	60	No	Yes	Little	No	Exam	Reduced
11220	22480	24130	No	120	No	Yes	Some	Yes	Exam	No
5820	12220	12760	No	120	No	Yes	Some	Yes	Exam	No
6820	14410	17430	No	30	Some	Yes	Yes	No	Exam	No
4870	10260	11090	Yes	120	Some	Yes	Yes	Some	No	Nationwide
5250	10170	10480	No	120	No	Yes	Yes	No	No	Nationwide
6560	13000	16230	No	120	No	Some	Some	Some	Exam	No
5910	11640	12590	No	120	No	Some	Some	Some	Exam	No
8550	18850	19570	Yes	90	No	Yes	Some	Some	Exam	No
4430	8810	9180	Yes	90	No	Some	Some	Some	Exam	No
4670	9160	9230	Yes	30	No	Some	No	Yes	Exam	Reduced
8470	18100	17270	Yes	30	Yes	Some	No	Yes	Exam	No
6020	12370	11460	Yes	30	No	Some	No	Yes	Exam	No
7430	16580	15710	No	60	Some	Yes	Little	No	Exam	Reduced
7460	16330	15670	No	60	No	Yes	Little	No	Exam	Reduced

Appendix

Our Methods and Data Sources

We compare plans in terms of their likely dollar cost to you, including both the "for sure" expense of the premium and the out-of-pocket (OOP) expenses you face for costs the plan does not pay. We estimate OOP expenses using actuarial methods to evaluate the cost-sharing details of each plan for various categories of costs. All FEHB plans cover 80 percent or more of most types of expenses whenever your costs are high, and provide a reasonably solid catastrophic limit guarantee. Therefore, the premium covers not only true insurance for rare, high-cost situations, but also pre-payment of routine expenses. When your medical costs are zero the premium is the only expense, but when your medical costs run into the tens of thousands the catastrophic limit (which in most plans is between $6,000 and $12,000 a year) comes into play. Most of the analysis underlying the *Guide* is aimed at quantifying, and expressing in terms of annual costs, the various risks you face and the reimbursement provided by each plan at each level of risk. We calculate costs assuming that you use only preferred providers, or providers who will agree to network fees, both because sensible consumers will avoid leaving the network if they can, and also because there is no realistic way to estimate the many unknown rates that individual providers may charge.

We calculate likely out-of-pocket costs, taking into account the probabilities of families of various sizes and ages incurring relatively low, medium, or high levels of expense (we actually use eight different expense levels, but do not present detailed results for all of these). The low-cost situations are most common but, when weighted for dollar amounts, accounts for a relatively small portion of likely spending. In statistical terms, health care expenses are a highly "skewed" distribution, and the average (or "mean") is far higher than the typical (or "median") spending level.

Although most persons do not know whether they will incur large expenses or not—heart attacks, serious accidents, and most other costly scenarios are relatively unpredictable—some persons do have a pretty good idea of some future costs. For example, they may be planning major surgery for a congenital problem. We present data for both groups: persons with and without good information on next year's expenses and, for those with good prior information, estimated out-of-pocket expenses at several expense levels for each plan. We caution users, however, to beware of attempting to estimate the costs of "known usage" expenses for anything much beyond maintenance drugs. The problem is few are likely to know, and few to have access to, information on such simple questions as the number of visits involved in dealing with a pinched nerve, or with the mix among hospital, surgical, and rehabilitation costs for a condition such as a knee or hip replacement. No one is likely to know if he or she will have a heart attack, a stroke, or a case of Lyme disease next year. Our methods do not force you to make guesses over such matters, or to pretend that the worst will not happen.

Most of the data used in the *Guide* come from the plan brochures themselves. Plans have several different benefit levels: one for most enrollees when using preferred providers, one for enrollees with Medicare, and one for enrollees when using out-of-plan providers (for most HMOs, reimbursement is zero in this last case, except in emergencies). When analyzed carefully, taking into account the exact wording of benefit descriptions, the brochures tell a clear story.

The premiums tell another clear story. However, more is needed to compare the plans usefully and completely.

The estimates of annual expenses we use in the cost tables are based on information taken from a number of sources. The most important of these is the Medical Expenditure Panel Survey (MEPS) of the Agency for Healthcare Research and Quality. This valuable survey produces information for researchers, health plans, and consumer advisors like us on what proportions of the population incur expenses of what kinds and at what dollar levels. We adjust MEPS data slightly to "smooth" the estimates and to cover persons most likely to approximate current FEHB plans' spending levels. Our cost tables also use rounded estimates to make them easier to read, and the cost headings represent ranges. For example, the entries for expenses of $3,000 represent a range from about $2,000 to $4,500.

Because some plans impose different deductibles and coinsurance for different services, the distribution of costs between hospital and other expenses can affect significantly the amount that a plan will require you to pay for a particular expense total. We model our comparisons closely to average experience. Though few persons or families will have exactly the same cost profile as used in our tables, most situations will be at least close. Our profile, when weighted for probability, corresponds closely to projected expenses of the employed and retired American population as a whole, both in total and in category of expense. Some of the details are shown in the table "Profile of Expenses Used for Cost Tables."

Our cost comparisons make several other simplifications. First, in analyzing most plans we have to make assumptions about the number of doctor visits and prescriptions to calculate the patient's share of expenses.

Second, we assume that all bills are for amounts negotiated between plans and preferred providers. Many doctors who are not in the plan network charge more than the plan allows, and all plans do not have the same "profiles" for calculating their maximums. Absent any basis for adjustment, we simply assume what is generally true: all preferred doctors have agreed to limit their charges to plan allowances, and some others will agree to meet that level (or will do so if you tell them what plan you have and explain your cost concerns). There are instances in which some plans' schedules for some procedures are well below those used by other plans. Unfortunately, there is no way to adjust for this in our tables, though you can protect yourself in the real world by using preferred

Profile of Expenses Used for Cost Tables (Approximate)

Level of expense	$0	$1,000	$3,000	$6,000	$12,000	$30,000	$60,000	$130,000
Components of Total Expense:								
Hospital	$0	$0	$0	$0	$5,000	$10,000	$29,000	$86,000
Surgical & Outpatient Facility	0	0	0	0	0	3,000	8,000	8,000
Primary & Specialist Physician	0	500	1,500	3,000	3,000	8,000	10,000	20,000
Prescription Drugs & Other	0	500	1,000	2,500	3,000	7,000	11,000	14,000
Dental	0	0	500	500	1,000	2,000	2,000	2,000
Risk of expense at each level:								
Self under age 55	12.0%	49%	15%	11%	8%	5%	1%	0.30%
Family of two under age 55	1.0%	35%	18%	16%	16%	12%	1%	1.00%
Self age 55 to 64	5.0%	33%	20%	19%	12%	9%	1%	1.00%
Family of two age 55 to 64	0.3%	12%	14%	17%	27%	24%	3%	3.00%
Self age 65 and older	4.0%	24%	20%	21%	16%	13%	2%	1.00%
Family of two age 65 and older	0.1%	6%	9%	14%	28%	34%	5%	3.00%

providers or by getting your provider to promise to stay within your plan's payment level before getting any expensive service.

Third, we assume that you take advantage of the best cost-sharing rate in each plan. Specifically, we assume that you get network rates by using network providers rather than providers who are not preferred with that plan. For drugs, we assume you use those in the plan formulary.

Fourth, we make assumptions about how many family members incur expenses at each total cost level in a year to calculate deductibles. For example, we assume that in a year with $1,000 in expenses, a family of five will have expenses for three members, and in a year with $130,000 in expenses, for all family members. In the real world, no one's actual set of yearly expenses will exactly match our assumptions. For plans whose coinsurance rates and deductibles are low or the same for most services, a different mix of expenses would have little or no effect on the cost estimates we present. For other plans, such as those with 100 percent coverage of hospitalization and limited coverage of prescription drugs, a different mix of expenses could change the estimates considerably. However, a different mix would not likely change any cost entry at $3,000 by more than two or three hundred dollars, or any entry for the $30,000 column by more than one or two thousand dollars. (Highly expensive specialty prescription drugs, such as some AIDS, hemophilia, growth hormone, chemotherapy, and osteo-arthritis drugs are the most important potential exceptions.)

We apply our methodology consistently across plans, so that any estimating problem is likely to be small in its effects on the comparative information in the tables.

Acknowledgements

The Guide is dedicated to the memory of David F. Lawton, a dedicated civil servant who worked hard and well at creating and improving the Federal Employees Health Benefits Program during its formative years. Special thanks to many OPM and plan staff who graciously provided information, assistance, and answers at short notice.

About the Authors

Walton Francis is a self-employed economist and policy analyst, expert in the analysis and evaluation of public programs. He has written on a wide range of subjects including program evaluation, statistical analysis, managed health care, and retirement benefits. His education includes Master's degrees from Yale and Harvard universities. He is a member of the National Academy of Social Insurance. He developed regulatory, budgetary, and legislative reforms for many policies and programs while working at the Office of Management and Budget and in the Office of the Secretary at the Department of Health and Human Services. He pioneered the systematic comparison of health insurance plans from a consumer perspective, starting with the 1979 edition of this guide. He has published articles and testified several times before Congress on the Federal Employees Health Benefits and Medicare programs. He evaluated both programs' performance in *Putting Medicare Consumers in Charge: Lessons from the FEHBP.*

Checkbook is a magazine and website produced by the nonprofit Center for the Study of Services. Checkbook rates the quality and prices of consumer services, ranging from auto repair shops to home improvement services to health-care providers in seven metropolitan areas: Washington, Boston, Chicago, Philadelphia, San Francisco, Seattle, and Minneapolis-St. Paul. In the health care field, Checkbook rates doctors, hospitals, dentists, and health insurance plans. The Center has a health care survey research arm that, in addition to conducting surveys for the Center's own publications and website, routinely conducts surveys under contract for government agencies, employer coalitions, and health plans, including many of the health plans evaluated in this book. The Center also produces national guides that evaluate surgeons and hospitals and provides comparison tools for several states' marketplace exchanges that help consumers choose health plans.